D0349277

Timothy O'Grady / Steve Pyke

Ich lese den Himmel

Roman

Mit einem Vorwort von
John Berger

Aus dem Englischen von
Uda Strätling

S. Fischer

Die englische Originalausgabe erschien 1997
unter dem Titel ›I Could Read The Sky‹
bei The Harvill Press, London
Copyright Text © Timothy O'Grady 1997
Copyright Fotos © Steve Pyke 1997
Copyright Vorwort © John Berger 1997
Deutsche Ausgabe:
© S. Fischer Verlag, Frankfurt am Main 2000
Gesamtherstellung: Clausen & Bosse, Leck
Printed in Germany 2000
ISBN 3-10-055210-5

Ich flüsterte: Erinnerung schmerzt
bei der kleinsten Berührung.
Giorgos Seferis

Das Vergessen verlängert das Exil,
und das Geheimnis der Erlösung heißt Erinnerung.
Baal Schem Tow /
Holocaust Memorial, San Francisco

EXIL ist kein Wort
Es ist ein Geräusch
Das Reißen der Haut
Eine volle Faust Lehm zuletzt auf dem Sarg
Exil ist kein Wort
Es ist dass du dich vor
Fotos rasierst anstatt Spiegeln
Exil ist kein Wort
Es ist frommes Falten der Hände
In der Leere der Kirche
Ist Verfassen der eigenen Hagiographie
Ist nicht endendes Unrecht
Der Sieg der Erinnerung über die Topographie
Exil ist kein Wort
Exil ist kein Wort

Peter Woods

Ich darf mich nicht zu tief in dieses Buch hineinbegeben, sonst bleibe ich für immer und kehre nicht wieder. Und dann könnte ich nicht jetzt, hier, auf dieser Seite stehen, auf dieser Seite vor dem Anfang des Buchs.

Ist es ein Buch? Dumme Frage. Wozu, wenn nicht zu einem Buch, schreibt man ein Vorwort? Aber ein Bastard ist dieses Buch. Im Dunkeln gemacht, wie Fotos in der Dunkelkammer entstehen. Man sollte es mit geschlossenen Augen betrachten, nicht beim ersten Mal, natürlich, später, wann immer man darin blättert.

Natürlich gleicht kein Buch dem anderen, so wenig wie ein Bergfink dem anderen. Und natürlich hört man beim Lesen hinter der Stimme, die spricht, einen ganzen Stimmenchor: O'Sullivan und Behan, O'Casey und Synge, Joyce und Jack Yeats (samt donnerndem Hufschlag vieler Pferde), Beckett und O'Flaherty, alle sind sie hier, im Dunkeln, schützen die neue Stimme mit ihrer Kunst, entreißen sie dem Vergessen, wie sie ihr auch Gesellschaft geleistet haben, als sie allein war und auf Wanderschaft.

Was haben wir hier also für einen Bastard?

Jeder Witzbold weiß, dass Lacher eine Frage des Timings sind. Es ist viel einfacher, die Leute zum Weinen zu bringen, denn Kummer wächst, während Lachen einen überkommt. Immer überrascht. Mit etwas Glück ist es im nächsten Leben umgekehrt.

Timing ist der kunstvolle Einsatz des Schweigens, seine geschickte Platzierung, ein Versteckspiel zur Freude und Überraschung des Zuhörers – so ähnlich, wie die Russen zu Ostern für die Kinder bemalte Eier verstecken. Und was besagt Schweigen in einer Geschichte? Das Ungesagte, oder?

In diesem Buch findet sich dauernd Ungesagtes. Am Anfang der Seite, bevor die Zeilen beginnen. Unten, wo sie aufhören. Und auch zwischen den Zeilen, zwischen den Sätzen. Oder, o Wunder, im Satz selbst. »Wenn ich abends im Bett liege, denke ich immerfort an Geld und Kate Creevy.« Am Ungesagten liegt es, dass einem dieser Satz lange im Kopf herumgeht. Nur das Ungesagte vermag mit einem Satz zu tanzen, und hier, im Dunkeln, tanzen die Sätze allezeit.

Das Schweigen des Ungesagten tut sich heimlich mit einem anderen Schweigen zusammen, nämlich dem Schweigen des Unsagbaren.

Was einmal ungesagt bleibt, kann ein andermal gesagt werden. Nur das Unsagbare, das kann nicht gesagt werden – es sei denn, beim Beten; aber das mag der liebe Gott wissen, ich weiß es nicht.

Vor dem Unsagbaren sind wir allein. Und eben deshalb werden, glaube ich jedenfalls, Geschichten erzählt. Alle Geschichten sind Wege, die an Klippen enden. Manchmal ragen sie vor uns auf, manchmal fallen sie steil vor unseren Füßen ab. Wenn uns aber eine Geschichte zum Unsagbaren führt, befinden wir uns in Gesellschaft. Darin, und nur darin, liegt der Trost.

Im Ungesagten und Unsagbaren.

Und nun lasst uns die Bilder anschauen. Schwarzweißfotografien. Weshalb arbeiten Fotografen – darunter einige der besten – immer noch hartnäckig in Schwarzweiß, wo doch Farbbilder so verführerisch, so einfach und so billig sind? Treibt sie ein Hang zum Nostalgischen? Zum Asketischen? Zur Moral? Schwarzweiß, das ist mächtig moralisch.

Ich denke, der Grund ist woanders zu suchen. Was tut denn die Malerei, egal welcher Stilrichtung? Sie lädt das, was nicht da ist, ein, sichtbar zu werden. Das beginnt mit dem, was nicht zu sehen ist. Da kann man jeden guten Maler fragen. Maler untersuchen den äußeren Schein, um an das zu kommen, was dahinter liegt. Visuelle Kunst ist die Jagd nach dem Unsichtbaren.

Der Vorteil von Schwarzweißfotografien ist, dass sie von der Suche nach dem zeugen, was nicht zu sehen ist, nach dem, was fehlt; nie geben sie vor, fertig zu sein, im Gegensatz zu Farbfotografien. Es gibt Farbfotografien, die sind »praller« als das Leben selbst!

Das Schwarzweißporträt eines Mannes in Kerry hingegen (S. 24) gesteht, dass es nie fertig sein kann, und das Gesicht des Mannes von Inishmaan (S. 93) wird von einem Meer des Unsichtbaren umtost.

Sie tun sich also zusammen, die geschriebenen Zeilen und die Fotografien, aber sie sagen nicht dasselbe. Sie wissen nicht dasselbe; darin besteht das Geheimnis des Zusammenlebens.

Die Fotos rufen uns all das in Erinnerung, was sich mit Worten nicht ausdrücken lässt. Das fängt schon beim ersten Bild von den Bretterplanken an, bei ihrer Maserung, dem Nagel und dem Vorhängeschloss.

Und die Worte rufen hervor, was eine Fotografie niemals zeigen kann. Hört nur:

Dann sagt er mir, dass er von der Musik gehört hat, die ich dem Akkordeon entlocke, und ich möchte so gern für ihn spielen, damit er bleibt. Er wird immer wieder schwächer, wie ein Radio bei schlechtem Empfang. Er lässt mir die Pralinen am Bett, dann steht er auf. Er legt mir eine große, warme Hand auf die Stirn und macht das Kreuzzeichen wie der Priester an Aschermittwoch mit der Asche.

»Du kannst denen daheim, denen, die sich an mich erinnern, sagen, ich hätte mich nach ihnen erkundigt. Wir gleichen uns, du und ich. Sag ihnen, dass wir ihnen vergeben und sie uns vergeben mögen.«

Dann geht er, das gallige Lachen, das mir gilt, reißt auf und schließt sich hinter ihm wieder wie ein Rauchkringel.

Hier, im Dunkeln, stoßen wir auf die Verbindung von Unsagbarem und Unsichtbarem. Das klingt kompliziert, nicht wahr, kompliziert und vage. Ist es aber nicht. Weil alles der Vorstellungskraft eintätowiert ist, Punkt für Punkt, mit der Nadel der Sehnsucht.

Oder wenn wir nicht an ein Buch denken, sondern an Lieder? Das Unsagbare, das Unsichtbare, die Wehmut der Musik, alles da. Um sie dreht sich die Musik. Wir haben hier ein Liederbuch ohne Noten. Auch deshalb ist dieses Buch ein Bastard und geht einem zu Herzen.

Lieder aus dem kümmerlichen Zimmer eines prachtvollen Lebens. *Prachtvoll* weder im ironischen noch überzogenen Sinne. Vielmehr kehrt das Wort nach Reisen um die halbe Welt an seinen schlichten Ursprung zurück: der ganzen Pracht.

Ich bleibe hier auf der Seite. Geht ruhig hinein ins Zimmer ...

Ich lese den Himmel

1

Es ist ganz dunkel hier im Zimmer, so dunkel, wie es
nur werden kann – im Winter vor Anbruch der Däm-
merung. Die Geräusche und Bilder sind da, aber ehe ich
sie richtig zu fassen kriege, flirrt und kracht alles durcheinander. Das Bettzeug ist klamm. Die Schmerzen im
Nacken sind wieder schlimm. Ich halte mich an mir
selbst fest, als Anker.

Dann regt sich etwas, ein Lüftchen. Ein Hauch nur, kaum mehr als der Flügelschlag einer Lerche, aber die Schwaden verziehen sich, und da sehe ich es – das Haus, das so goldrichtig am grünen Hang sitzt. Die Fuchsien rings ums Fenster sind rot, und das Stroh ist so hell, als würde es im Dach brennen. Ich bin meinem Bruder Joe auf den Rücken geklettert und male die Tür nach Norden raus mit den Händen an. Die Farbe haben wir, aber keinen Pinsel. Grüne Farbe läuft mir zwischen den kleinen Härchen an den Armen herab und unter den Pulloverärmeln bis auf die Brust. Ich merke es nicht. Ich bin vier, Joe ist sieben. Meine Hände schmieren wilde Kreise über die Tür. Ich sehe grüne Farbkleckse auf Joes Hemd und in seinem Nacken. Ich schaue in den Wirbel brauner Haare an meinem Hinterkopf, auf meinen schwarzen Pullover, meine Hose, meine schwarz verdreckten Füße. Bei dem Gesicht, das ich mache, könnte man meinen, es gibt auf der ganzen Welt nichts als diese Tür. Ich möchte so gern hinter das Gesicht kommen, aber das geht nicht. Ich horche angestrengt, ob ich mehr von der Melodie aus der Küche hören kann. Ich stemme mich gegen die Tür. Ich umklammere mich noch fester.

Das hier bin ich. Ich habe einen runden, kahlen Kopf. Meine Augen sind blau und wässrig und meine Finger vom Tabak ganz gelb. Ich bin allein hier, mit einem schwarzen Hund. Ich schlafe schlecht.

Der Stations-Day ist ein besonderer Tag. Am Abend kommt der Pfarrer und liest in der Küche die Messe, und wir erwarten Nachbarn und Verwandte. Die Brote haben wir längst fertig. Wir haben die Hühner im Topf. Wir haben Whiskey und Porter und Sherry.

Nur die Tür, die haben wir vergessen.

2

Joe am Stephen's Day im Dezember als Vogelscheuche. Das Stroh guckt ihm aus Ärmeln und Hemdkragen, er hat einen spitzigen Hut auf. Sein Gesicht ist blau angemalt. Er hat das erste Mal mit den anderen herumziehen und singen dürfen, und er hat bei den Nachbarn zehn Shilling zusammengebracht. Mary, Bernadette, Martin, Dermot, Vincent – alle waren sie unterwegs. Ich bin zu Hause, weil ich zu klein bin. Eileen ist auch zu Hause geblieben. Sie findet sich zu erwachsen, um mit den *wren boys* herumzuziehen.

Durchs Fenster sehe ich meinen Vater das Fahrrad an
die Wand lehnen. Seit er letzten Herbst bei der Kartof-
felernte in Lincolnshire gestürzt ist, hat er einen schlimmen Fuß. Er braucht einen Stock zum Gehen. Er hat die
rechte Pedale am Fahrrad gelöst, damit sie sich nicht
mitdreht, wenn er die linke tritt. Neuerdings sagt er, er
wird alt und lacht, aber das Fahrrad hat er heute am Stephen's Day die zwölf Meilen ganz bis Ballyconnor
geschoben und zurück. Eine Kraft hat der Mann. Er
kann ein Ruder über die Deckenbalken legen und sich
am linken wie am rechten Arm zehnmal hochziehen.
Wenn der Fuß bis April nicht in Ordnung ist, kommt
nächstes Jahr kein Geld rein.

Er tritt durch die Tür, Grinsen von Ohr zu Ohr und in der Hand einen Beutel. Wie einer dieser Säcke zum Füttern von Vieh. Auf seinen schwarzen Locken und den Schultern liegt Schnee. Sein Gesicht funkelt wie Wasser, wenn die Sonne ganz hell scheint. Wenn ich ihn humpeln sehe, könnte ich immerzu weinen.

Er zieht Joe mit zum Stuhl rüber und nimmt ihm den Hut ab. Aus seinem Beutel kommt ein Kasten zum Vorschein, und aus dem Kasten hebt er ein Akkordeon, eine einreihige Hohner. Wie die glänzt. Rot perlmuttschimmernd mit goldenen Sternchen und goldenem Zierkeder. Mit diesem hell strahlenden Gesicht beugt er sich über das Akkordeon, hält es wie ein Baby in den großen Händen – Tagelöhnerhänden, zerschunden, vernarbt, mit eingerissenen Nägeln und einem in einer Maschine zerquetschten Finger. Das Akkordeon hat so viel gekostet wie der halbe Marktpreis, den in dem Jahr eine Färse gebracht hätte.

Noch Jahre später habe ich bei meinen Besuchen daheim unter dem Bett und auf dem Boden nach dem Akkordeon gesucht. Ich habe es nie gefunden. Ich wusste ja nicht, dass es mit einem Neffen nach Amerika ausgewandert war, der gar nicht spielen konnte. Noch wusste ich damals am Morgen des Stephen's Day, wie die Weiden vor Binsen starren und Mauern einsinken können. Ich wusste nichts von Schnellstraßen und Maschinen und Tunneln und Baugerüsten. Es war ein heller Tag mit weiß leuchtendem Schnee.

Joe nimmt von Da strahlend das Akkordeon entgegen. Aber spielen konnte er nie. Die Musik ist auf mich gekommen, und nicht Joe.

3

Ich wage mich ja kaum noch vor die Tür wegen diesem blöden Kane aus Mulrany. Wenn ich das Fahrrad nehme, springt er hinter der Hecke hervor. Wenn ich zum Tanz will, springt er auf den Karren und quetscht sich neben mich auf den Bock. ›Entweder ich darf mit‹, sagt er, ›oder ich brenn euch das Haus nieder.‹ Der Mann ist sechzig!«

Eileen und Maura Fogarty an einem Sommerabend unter meinem Fenster. Ich höre sie lachen, hoch und hell ist der Klang, wie kleine Glocken. Vielleicht Altarschellen. Maura ist nicht mehr Kindermädchen in England. Sie trägt ein Kleid mit kleinen Rosen darauf, und sie spricht furchtbar schnell. Ich liege hellwach im Bett, und ich höre ihnen zu gern zu.

Jetzt kommt Matt Doran am Stock, mit seinem roten Hund.

»Maura erzählt mir von der großen Stadt, Matt«, erklärt Eileen.

»In der Stadt geben sie dir nicht mal einen Lehmklumpen umsonst«, meint er.

Er blinzelt in die untergehende Sonne und zieht weiter.

»Was ist mit Jim?«, fragt Maura.

»Fort. Sein Bruder hat ihm das Geld für die Überfahrt geschickt. Er hat jetzt Arbeit in einer Gerberei in Massatuchetts.« Wie sie bei den Wörtern manchmal die Buchstaben verdrehte. So wie Dermot mit dem Schielauge. Oder wie der Stummelfinger von Da. So kleine Sachen können dir nachts plötzlich zusetzen, wenn du allein

bist. »Kaum war er fort, ist Kane mit seinem Karren vorgefahren, um mit Da zu sprechen. Speichen verdreckt. Stiefel verdreckt. Nimmt seinen Hut in die Hand und fragt Da, kann er mich heiraten. Stell dir vor, den Rest deines Lebens mit so einer Kreatur verbringen zu müssen. Der mit seiner roten Nase und dem Glatzkopf. Er ist *dreckig*, Maura.«

»Und was hat dein Da gemeint?«

Ich sehe Eileen vor mir, wie sie die Brauen über die Nase runterrunzelt. Zwei katzbuckelnde Raupen. Kratzt sich mit nur einem Finger hinten am Kopf, genau wie es Da tut. »›Eine recht ordentliche Farm, Mädchen‹, sagt er, ›mit viel Vieh.‹ Aber er konnte mir dabei nicht in die

Augen sehen. Er weiß, dass ich weglaufen würde, wenn er mich zwingt.«

Eileen. Wenn ich erst mal nur an die Stimme denke, kann ich sie festhalten, aber ich finde ihr Gesicht nicht, mit achtzehn. Alle sagen, dass sie wunderschön war, mit dem rabenschwarzen Haar bis ganz über den Rücken, das Da sie nicht abschneiden lassen wollte. Das war immer das Letzte, was er sagte, am Tag bevor er nach Lincolnshire aufbrach – »Und schneide dir bitte die Haare nicht ab, während ich fort bin, Eileen.« Und weil er dich so hungrig angesehen hat, wenn er fort musste, hast du ihm sowieso nichts ausschlagen können.

Noch im September hat sie sich das Haar abgeschnitten. Im November ist sie in Dienst gegangen, zu reichen Leuten im Süden an einem Lough. Zwei Jahre darauf war sie in London.

4

Abend für Abend, eine ganze Winterwoche lang, wartete ich an der Tür, dann komme ich endlich rein. Die frische grüne Farbe sieht im Abendlicht Wunder wie schön aus. Hier im Zimmer ist die Luft neutral, wie Wasser in der Wanne, dort im Haus ist sie warm und satt. Eierbecher mit Whiskey. Torf. Der milde Schein der Lampe. Hühnerknochen, schwitzende Tänzer, die heiligen Messsachen, die der Priester einpackt. Dann Da auf der Flöte, so silbern und rein.

Danach drückt sich mein Uncle Eamon vom Stuhl hoch. Alles an ihm glänzt. Die Schuhe, der Ring, die Zähne, das weiße Hemd, seine Haut. Auch sein schwar-

zes Haar glänzt. Er steht direkt neben mir, und er legt
mir eine Hand auf die Schulter, um sich zu stützen. Seine Finger sind genau wie die von Da von der Arbeit in
England zerquetscht und zerschunden, aber alle sehen
immer nur den Anzug und wie er glänzt. Er zieht einen
roten Schein aus der Tasche und steckt ihn mir zu.

»Ich gebe hiermit bekannt, dass ich künftig einen
neuen Namen zu führen gedenke«, sagt er. »In Birmingham hat mir einer einen ungemein prachtvollen Hut ver-
kauft, ein Mann namens *Ros-coe.*« Er legte großes Gewicht in das Wort. »Das ist ein Name nach meinem
Geschmack, wie gemacht für jemand, nach dem sich die
Leute auch in der Stadt noch umdrehen. Roscoe.«

Im nächsten Augenblick ballt er die Hände zu Fäus-
ten, brüllt einmal laut und setzt aus dem Stand glatt über
den Tisch weg. Nicht ein Glas, nicht eine Flasche oder
Scheibe Brot regt sich.

Er geht neben Eileen in die Hocke. »Einen halben
Pint Whiskey her!«, ruft er. Er nimmt Eileens Hände
hoch und kurbelt an ihrem Arm, damit sie singt. »Na los,
Mädchen«, sagt er, »heraus mit der Stimme.«

Die vielen Stimmen. Matt Dorans Gänseschrei. Der
Schneider feierlich tief, wie fernes Donnergrollen. Da
und Ma beim Tanz. Ma mit ihren geschmierten Broten.
Der Lehrer mit einem Vers über Undank. Heaney, der
Straßenbauinspektor aus Dublin, der hat Mundharmo-

nika gespielt und getanzt, dass ihm Münzen und Tabak
aus den Taschen flogen. Uncle Roscoe ist auf den Händen einmal ums ganze Zimmer gelaufen und zur Tür
hinaus, während jeder, an dem er vorbeigekommen ist,
seinem neuen Namen alle Ehre antat. »Guten Abend,
Roscoe«, sagten sie. Eileen, die mit geschlossenen
Augen, Kopf im Nacken, »Róisín Dubh« gesungen hat.
Joe machte es nachher in der Ecke tuschelnd nach.

Ein Abend, den man nie vergisst.

Eileen holt mich gerade zu einem Reel, als sich wieder die schwere Luft über alles zu legen beginnt, und
während sie mich herumwirbelt und ich hochsehe, ist es
so, als drehte sich über mir die ganze Milchstraße.

5

Ich bin auf einem spitzen Fels oben hinter dem Haus in Labasheeda. Im Rücken nichts als die Kuppe des Hügels. Der Himmel sieht aus wie das Meer im Winter. Dann färbt er sich rot, wird klarer, und das ganze Tal unter mir füllt sich mit goldgelbem Licht. Ich drehe mich langsam auf meinem Fels.

Ganz außen links biegt die Straße nach Rathangan in die Eichen. Drei Milchkannen auf der Mauer neben

Matt mit seiner Pfeife, dem Stock und dem roten Hund. Unter seinen Füßen beginnt der Tullaherin seinen langsamen Anstieg. Murrans Feld, Lallys Feld. Das Feldstück, wo Joe Roddy der Schlag traf. Die Grube zum Wetten beim *pigeon toss*. Violette Streifen im Moor. Manche sagen, da liegen noch Knochen von der Hungersnot drin. Der Wasserfall lacht gurgelnd. Ma mit ihren Hühnern, ihr Schatten ein langer Strich auf dem Kalkstein. Ballinaclash. Ardnageeha. Killycolpy. Überall ziehen sich Steinmauern übers Land wie die Adern auf meinem Handrücken. John Hall mit seiner zahmen Gans baut

noch eine neue Mauer nach nirgendwo, weil er nichts
Besseres zu tun hat. Der Schneider hinter seinem Fens-
ter, der am Webstuhl einen weichen Stoff webt. Joe
Connor, der unter der Giebelwand mit seinem Sohn
Streit hat. Knocksouna. Glenanaar. Was hat Matt noch
gemeint, was das heißt? Schlucht der blutigen Schlacht.

Ich öffne die Augen in Kentish Town. Immer diese
neutrale Luft. Etwas graues Licht scheint herein, aber es
hat nichts vom klaren Stahlgrau der winterlichen See,
das ich vom Felsen aus sah. Neben dem Bett ein Stuhl.
Tabletten. Ein Hemd mit kleinen blauen Karos und ver-
wetztem Kragen. Eine Flasche Guinness dort, und eine
zweite auf dem Fensterbrett. Maggies Rosenkranz mit

den Glasperlen. Die Zeitung von daheim. Der schwarze Kasten mit dem Akkordeon. Eine Schale mit einem Löffel voll Suppe. Ein Schrank, den Menschen gemacht haben, die ich nicht kenne. Das graue Licht kriecht über die Hautflecken auf meinen Händen. Ich höre den Hund im Zimmer nebenan träumen. Ergibt das alles eine Summe? Ich warte.

Ich schaffe es zurück. Dunnamanagh. Cush. Fenit, der wüste Ort. Die rußschwarzen Mauern, wo die Black and Tans die O'Rourkes ausgeräuchert haben. Dunleaveys Feld, wo sie den Verräter hingeschleift haben und erschossen. Kennedys Hund, der nach Kühen schnappt. Baby schiebt ihren leeren Kinderwagen hinterm Tullaherin raus, an ihrem Hals an der Schnur blinken im milden Licht die Schlüssel, und Matt legt den Finger an die Kappe, als Baby vorbeigeht. »Wenn sie dir mal verloren vorkommen sollte«, hat er mir gesagt, »dann führ sie heim. Denn die Irren sind womöglich gesegnet.« Der Brunnen auf dem langen Feld. Matt sagt, in der Tiefe lebt ein Fisch, der dir verrät, wie es um die Verwandten in Amerika steht. Das goldene Licht scheint zwischen den Hecken auf Kate Creevy, des Schneiders Tochter. Brombeeren. Die MacDonaghs, gebeugt auf Stühlen in der Küche, beten den Rosenkranz. Ich sehe Dermot und Vincent am Forellenbach angeln. Das kupfrige Schimmern der flachen Felsen im Abendlicht. Capparoe. Ellistrin. Mullaghareirk. Oola. Dromdorry. Suil.

Labasheeda, das seidene Bett.

Ich drehe mich langsam auf meinem Fels.

Das bin ich.

6

Seit dem frühen Morgen knallt die Flinte. Ma meint nur, bis zum Abend wird Martin im ganzen Weiler alles erlegt haben, was kreucht und fleucht. Sie kann das Geräusch nicht leiden. »Ich muss dabei an die Angriffe denken«, erklärt sie. Aber sagen will sie nichts. Soll er doch seinen letzten Tag in Irland damit verbringen, mit der Schrotflinte von Da wild um sich zu töten.

Ich gehe zu Matt hinüber. Seine Frau sitzt mit einem Brief am Feuer. Matts Brille rutscht ihr von der Nase. Er steht am Tisch und schiebt ein Paket aus Amerika darauf herum. So, wie er mit spitzen Fingern daran herumzupft, würde man meinen, er hat ein krankes Huhn vor sich.

»Was hast du da, Matt?«, frage ich.

»Das hat uns Tom aus Chicago geschickt. Ingenieur muss man sein, um das aufzukriegen.«

Martin knallt zweimal mit der Flinte.

»Martin fährt morgen«, sage ich ihm.

»Martin. Ein junges Mädchen aus Killycolpy. John und Patrick, die beiden Jungen vom Schneider. Alle morgen früh mit der Bahn. Da bleiben nur der Schneider selbst und Kate übrig. Ob einer von denen so weit kommt wie Tom in Chicago?«

Die Schnur hat er jetzt ab, dann das Papier. Drinnen ist eine Holzkiste. Er hebelt sie mit dem Messer auf und späht hinein. Er schiebt die Hände an den Innenseiten hinunter und hebt was heraus. Ein viereckiges blankes schwarzes Ding mit einer schönen Schlussleiste oben drauf. Drahtgeflecht vorne über heugelbem Stoff und

dem geschriebenen Wort »Comet«. Zwei Drehknöpfe
groß wie Eulenaugen. Ein Radio ganz aus Amerika.

Matt dreht einen Knopf, dass es klickt. Da geht innen
ein Licht an, und wir hören eine Stimme, ganz leise.
Matt sieht von seinem Schoß hoch und zwinkert mir zu.

»Hör mal, Maire«, ruft er. »Tom hat uns aus Chicago
einen schwarzen Kasten mit einem kleinen Mann geschickt. Der redet davon, dass es oben in Dublin regnet.
Was meinst du, spricht er wie ein Yank?«

Matt dreht noch mal am Knopf, und die Stimme
knistert und jault. Wie wenn jemand seine Geige
stimmt.

Matt beugt sich herab, legt eine Hand ans Ohr und sagt: »Wie meinen, Sir?«

Maire Doran verdreht die Augen und kehrt zu ihrem Brief zurück, aber weil ihr Rücken bebt, weiß ich, dass sie lacht.

»Und du, steh nicht unnütz herum«, sagt Matt und reicht mir eine Flöte. So habe ich Matt in Erinnerung. Wie er die Brille aufsetzt und aus der Zeitung von General Franco vorliest. Ein paar Zeilen, uns dann über den Rand der Gläser ansieht, neu ansetzt, die Stimme hebt. Bis sein Gesicht die Farbe von Erdbeeren hat. Er kam nie bis zum Ende. »Und wenn ich hingehe und den Schurken mit bloßen Händen umbringe!«, rief er, und die Zeitung wurde zerknüllt in den Staub geschleudert. Ich erinnere mich, wie er zwei Jahre und tausend Körbe Sand brauchte, um sein Stück Feld zu bauen. Ich erinnere mich an Matt am Sarg seiner Tochter, und wie seine blauen Augen, die in dich drangen wie Speere, sich umwölkten, dieser starke Mann: gebrochen. Am Abend brüllte er empor in den Himmel. Ich spiele »The Pipe and the Hob« für ihn, dann gehe ich wieder.

Als ich am Morgen aufwache, muss ich daran denken, dass am Abend im Bett mehr Platz sein wird als sonst. Martin stolziert in der Küche schon in seinen neuen Schuhen und dem Mantel herum. Alle kommen zusammen, um Lebewohl zu sagen. Die beiden Gänse schnattern in der Hühnerlade von der Kommode. Ma kann nicht stillhalten. Vincent macht ein Gesicht, als wäre er böse, dass Martin geht und nicht er. Da erntet Rüben in England. Eileen gibt Martin eine Aufnahme von Ma und Da in einem ovalen Holzrahmen mit. Ma gibt ihm einen Rosenkranz und Brote. Wir geben ihm die Hand, Dermot, Vincent, Joe, ich und dann die Mädchen. Brid ist beim Hund vorm Feuer. Sie trägt ein gelbes Kleidchen, keine Schuhe. Ihre Füße sind ganz weiß von der Torfasche. Ma holt sie, damit sie sich von Martin verabschiedet. »Gib deinem Bruder Martin die Hand, Brid«, sagt sie. Damals war Brid kaum so lang wie sein Bein. Er beugt sich mit ausgestreckter Hand zu ihr runter, und sie sieht hoch. Sie hebt die Hand, dann hört sie auf. Sie sieht an ihm vorbei zum Fenster an der Tür nach Norden raus. Ihr Gesicht wird völlig reglos, bis es sich zusammenballt wie zur Faust, als sie anfängt zu heulen. »Häschen«, sagt sie. Wir schauen alle zum Fenster. Davor baumeln kopfüber vier tote Hasen, die Läufe mit Angelschnur zusammengebunden. Ihre Bäuche sind offen, weil Martin sie ausgenommen hat, das Fell blutig verschmiert. Ihre Mäuler sperrangelweit offen. Ihre toten Augen sind wie kleine Kohlestückchen. »Nun sag deinem Bruder Lebwohl, Brid«, sagt Ma. »Nein!«, schreit sie. Mir gellt die Spitze von ihrem Schrei in den Ohren. Sie reißt die Hände vor die Brust und schaut weg. Sie wird ihn nie wieder ansehen noch berühren.

Martin in New York. Manchmal versuche ich mir die breiten Avenues vorzustellen, die wie Bohrer glatt durch die Gebäude durchgehen. Dicke Fäuste voller Dollars für Martin. Eines Tages ist er in einen Ofen gefallen und war tot.

7

Eine Flasche zerspringt an der Mauer, es fallen Scherben. Dann kreischt eine Frau wie eine wild gewordene Katze, direkt unter meinem Fenster. Das geht weiter und weiter, bis sie keine Puste mehr hat, dann trollt sie sich endlich. Ich sehe sie vor mir: fett, lange Haare, schmuddelige rosa Strickjacke, verrutschte weiße Söckchen und Augen wie eine Ratte. Dabei habe ich gerade so schön geschlafen.

Ich mache Licht. Die Blase in der Tapete fast an der Zimmerdecke, und da der Fleck, wo ich mein Stout umgekippt habe. Maggie ist nicht da.

Ich fische in der Schublade nach den Fotos und hole sie vor. Obenauf Da vorm Haus mit schräg ins Gesicht gezogenem Strohhut und einem Grinsen, als hätte er gerade beim Kartenspiel gewonnen. Ich versuche, ganz in ihn reinzusehen. Brid mit den beiden alten Pferden und dann später in Florida mit einem großen Fisch. Ein Marlin, hat sie hinten draufgeschrieben. Das ist mir vorher nie aufgefallen. Dermots Junge in Kellneruniform vorm Hotel. Maggie hebt das Glas, das Kleid mit den Glockenblumen. Maggie kann ich nicht lange ansehen.

Dann komme ich zu mir in der Jacke, die Ma mir damals auf dem Markt in der Stadt gekauft hat. Hinten ins Futter war ein Name geschrieben, das weiß ich noch. J. Brady. Ich sehe ganz geradeaus, Falten in der Stirn und um den Mund, wo sich ein Lächeln breit macht, als würde ich einen Witz hören, von dem ich weiß, wie er ausgeht. Lippen glänzen so ein bisschen. Augen klar wie Quellwasser. Ma meint, die hohen Backen und die hellen Augen sind das Inselerbe von ihrer Seite her. Dieses schmale Gesicht von Backen bis Kinn. Was ich damals nicht alles konnte. Wie bin ich bloß zu einem Schädel gekommen, der die Form eines Fernsehers hat?

Aufzucken und Knall vom Licht beim Fotografen in dem kleinen Zimmer über dem Tabakwarenladen. Ma sieht zu. Ich sehe nichts, nur weißes Licht, aber ich merke, dass er mich raus haben will. Er muss mich am Arm führen. An den Wänden lauter Bräute. Die rothaarige Alice Curran aus Slieverue, die Martin abends mal vom Tanz heimbringen durfte. Eine Nonne ganz in Weiß. Der Teppich ist blau, nur an der Tür schon grau getreten. Stadtzimmer riechen immer so tot.

Ich lösche das Licht.

Nach dem Fotografieren ziehe ich mit Ma durch den Ort. Herrliche Körbe voll Eier und Stroh. Tragen mit frischer Butter in Kohlblättern. Kuchen. Heringe. Makrelen. Rotalgen. Männer rauchen, mit dem Rücken zur Wand. Hat denn im ganzen Ort niemand etwas zu tun? Das Wanderkino. Da drüben steht Lord Masboroughs Packard. Das heißt, dass alle Pächter südlich vom Fluss vierzehn Tage lang aus Hecken und Fluren Vögel scheuchen dürfen. Ma bleibt vor einem kleinen Mann mit dünnem Hals hinter einer Reihe Teekisten stehen. »Farm- und Hausgeräte aller Art«. Die Kleidertische der fliegenden Händler, wo Ma die Jacke für mich gekauft hat. Jetzt treibt Dermot mit leichten Stockschlägen gegen die Flanke die Banshee an uns vorbei. Die Ärmste,

ihre Augen sind weit aufgerissen. Pferde, Esel und Rinder ziehen durch die Straße. Aus Gänse- und Entensteigen krakeelt es. Die Säue tragen die Köpfe tief. Heute gehört der Ort den Tieren. Ich muss an ein Bild denken, das ich mal gesehen habe, vom englischen König an Coronation Day, und hinterdrein folgte eine Schar Männer in ihren Umhängen und Federbüschen und kurzen Hosen.

Peter Egan karrt eine Ladung Puter herbei. Sein Hemd starrt vor Ruß, weil er den lieben langen Tag vorm Kamin sitzt. Mein Vetter Joe Brennan steht im Eingang zum Pub.

»Wie kommt ein Tagedieb wie der zu dem vielen Geflügel?«, meint er zu mir.

Und da verrate ich ihm, dass Peter Egan eben nur eine Art von Arbeit kennt, nämlich wild angeln und Federvieh stehlen. Ich bin selig, mit Joe ein paar Worte wechseln zu können. Insbesondre, erkläre ich ihm, hat sich Peter Egan auf Truthühner verlegt. Und weil er einen Sohn in meinem Alter hat, weiß ich aus erster Hand, wie der alte Peter auf den Farmen ringsum verbreitet, zweimal hintereinander hätte er jetzt nachts ein Automobil mit voll aufgeblendeten Scheinwerfern aus dem Moor geradewegs in die Luft brausen sehen, mit Toten darin, die um Hilfe riefen, und dem Leibhaftigen am Steuer. Als sich darauf niemand mehr im Dunkeln vor die Tür traute, brauchte er die Puter nur noch einzusammeln. »Du musst sie am Schnabel packen«, hatte er seinem Jungen gesagt. »Dann können sie keinen Krach schlagen.«

Joe lacht. »Damit hast du dir deinen Zug Stout redlich verdient«, meint er und reicht mir sein Glas. Ich koste, erst das zweite Mal, seit Uncle Roscoe mich von seinem trinken ließ.

»Wo soll's denn noch hingehen?«, frage ich.

»Ein Stück weiter.«

Wir gehen neben den Tieren her. Ich halte Ausschau nach Ma und Dermont, und als ich sie nirgends sehe, komme ich mir komisch vor. Daheim wissen alle immer, wo alle sind. Die Sonne scheint, aber wegen der hohen Häuser reicht sie nicht bis zur Straße. Nur manchmal blendet sie wie die Lampe beim Fotografen, wenn sie eines der oberen Fenster trifft. Neben mir geht eine Färse, hinter mir eine dicke Sau. Die Pferde drumherum müssen am Zügel geführt werden. In der Luft hängt der Geruch von allen zusammen. Kate Creevy mit ihrer

Tante auf eine Tasse Tee beim Bäcker. Jedes Mal, wenn ich sie sehe, ist es wie ein Hieb vor die Brust.

»Und wann feiert Dermot Hochzeit?«, fragt Joe.

»Im Februar.«

»Vielleicht finden wir weiter vorn was für dich.«

Ich weiß nicht, was er meint. Aber ich bin doch wer, mit einem so harten Mann wie Joe durch den Ort zu ziehen. Die Stadtrüpel lungern an den Mauern herum. »Welches ist wohl das wahre Rindvieh, der Hornochse oder der Heuochse?«, meint einer. Ich kenn die Schimpfnamen noch alle, die sie mir in Ipswich und Barnstaple und Luton gegeben haben. Wenn er wollte, könnte sich Joe links und rechts so einen Flegel schnappen und gleich zwei auf einmal in den Fluss befördern. Ich weiß ja, was sie hier im Ort den lieben langen Tag treiben. Stehen rum, damit die Mauern nicht umkippen.

Dermot und die Banshee drehen jetzt links ab auf den Marktplatz. Wenn sie von da weggebracht wird, sehe ich sie nie wieder. Drei Jahre lang habe ich ihr den Stall ausgemistet und ihre Milch in die Molkerei getragen. Drüben unter den Bäumen warten die Bieter, und die Farmer führen ihr Vieh vor. Ihre Mienen sind so feierlich, dass man meinen könnte, es geht um eine Prozession in der Kirche.

Joe will weiter. Vor Neesons Pub am Ende des Weilers stehen neun junge Burschen und drei Mädchen vier Farmern in Jacken und Kappen gegenüber. Dann fährt noch ein fünfter vor und gesellt sich dazu. Jerry Blake sehe ich, Patsy O'Hagen, Dan O'Driscoll. Mary und Philomena Sweeney aus Tobermoney. Die anderen kenne ich nicht. Ich stelle mich mit Joe auch zu ihnen. Drüben vom Platz höre ich die Gebote der Käufer. Farmer gaffen von nah und fern zu uns her. Ich frage mich, was die Banshee wohl einbringt und wer sie nehmen wird. Joe schlendert zu dem Farmer hinüber, der eben mit Pferd und Wagen vorgefahren ist. Ich recke den Hals nach Dermot, ob er vom Platz kommt. Als ich mich wieder umdrehe, steht vor mir ein Mann. Schmallippig, und in den Mundwinkeln Spuren vom Porter. Unrasiert ist er, sein Kinn voll rötlicher Stoppeln. Sein Gesicht ist so feist, dass die Augen darin fast versinken. Ma hält nichts von Männern, die sich nicht rasieren.

»Kannst du mit Pferden und Rindern umgehen?«, fragt er.

»Kann ich.«

»Kannst du Torf stechen?«

»Kann ich.«

»Kannst du mit Maschinen umgehen?«

»Kann ich.«

»Bist du mit zehn Schilling, Kost und Logis einverstanden?«

»Wär ich wohl.«

»Also gut«, sagt er. »Warte morgen in der Früh hier auf mich.«

Er reicht mir einen alten Umschlag mit Namen und Adresse. Mit dem Umschlag in der Hand stehe ich auf der Straße. Joe steigt zu dem Mann auf den Wagenbock. Alles verläuft sich. Dermot ist wohl immer noch auf dem Platz und versucht dort, die Banshee loszuschlagen. Ich hoffe, jetzt wo sie ihm gehört, macht er aus der Farm richtig was, denn ich hätte sie gar zu gern selber gehabt.

8

Es tropft vom Dach in das Steinbecken an der Wand draußen. Der Klang von Wasser auf Wasser hält sich lange unter dem Blech, das er über das Becken gelegt hat. Ein ähnliches Geräusch habe ich heute Nachmittag im Gloucester Arms von so einem elektronischen Auto-

maten gehört. Irgendwo müssen sie die Geräusche ja her haben. Die Wand ist feucht, der Boden ist feucht. Ohne Schuhe kann man darauf nicht gehen.

Eine Kerze hat sie mir gegeben, aber keine Lampe. An der Wand ein Herz-Jesu-Bild mit Sprung. Ein Stuhl. Der ist auch nicht mehr heil. Eine Papiertüte mit dem Hemd zum Wechseln. Die Jacke, die Ma mir gekauft hat, die bewahrt Mrs. Casey drinnen extra in einem Schrank auf. Was war hier wohl vor mir drin, Hühner oder Schweine?

Die Arbeit ist stur, weil keiner spricht. Für den Tee werden sieben Tassen Wasser abgemessen und jeder kriegt zwei dünne Scheiben Brot. Am Abend erhalte ich zum Essen drei Kartoffeln und keine Butter. Es gibt für alles ein Maß, und es ist immer klein. Essen muss ich in der Scheune. Er hat fast 180 Morgen und drei Leute zusätzlich zu seinen drei Söhnen. Hinterher, als ich bei ihm angefangen hatte, sagte Joe, ich hätte einem kleineren Farmer zusagen sollen.

Es gibt hinten einen Ort, an den man zu Fuß nicht hinkonnte, den Totenteich. Dort ist einem Doktor Schlimmes zugestoßen, deshalb machen alle einen großen Bogen darum. Ich kenne hier die Namen der Orte nicht. Das Mädchen, das bei Mrs. Casey im Haus arbeitet, sieht mich nicht einmal an, wenn sie mit mir redet.

Wenn ich abends im Bett liege, denke ich immerfort an Geld und Kate Creevy. Wie weit ist es zwischen ihr und mir? Ich sehe sie in der Stadt vor mir hergehen. Sie hat einen Henkelkorb am Arm und einen Hut auf. Einen Hut! Dabei ist nicht mal Sonntag. Sie hat einen langen Schritt, aber leicht. Unter dem Rock zeichnet sich ihr

Bein ab. Manchmal knickt sie auf einem Stein um, der
im Weg liegt, und dann kippelt sie. Aber ich wäre da und
würde sie auffangen, bevor sie zu Fall kommt. Sie trägt
Handschuhe, grau wie die Brustfedern einer Taube. Das
Haar hochgesteckt, über dem Ohr hat es so einen schö-
nen Schwung, dann der schlanke Hals. Das Herz schlägt
mir bis in die Schläfe. Ich hole die Blechdose unter dem
Bett hervor. £1 2s.6d. Ein Pfund habe ich Sonntag beim
Wetten verloren. Ich zähle. Vier Shilling können jede
Woche für die Dose beiseite. Mal vier. Sechzehn Shil-
ling. Mal zwölf. Macht £9 12s im Jahr. Ich gebe den
Ziffern der Reihe nach Namen. Ferkel. Messer. Gutes
Geschirr. Pferd. Mantel aus schwarzem Fries, damit sie

es warm hat. Tünche. Fass Porter. Bett. Wie weit ist es zwischen ihr und mir? Sie bleibt stehen und sieht auf ihre Füße hinab. Schwarzer Senkel ein Krickel im Staub. Sie setzt den Fuß auf eine Mauerkante und rafft den Rock hoch. Rafft ihn so, dass der Saum auf ihrem Knie ruht. Die Haut an ihrem Bein hat die Farbe eines Pfirsichs. Ich sehe die Bewegung der zarten Knochen, während sie ihr Gleichgewicht hält. Ihr Mund ist leicht geöffnet. Der schlanke Hals. Die Finger, die an dem Schnürsenkel ziehen. Kleine Knöchelchen wie Hühnerknochen bewegen sich in ihren Händen. Sie spielten keine Rolle, die langen Jahre mit Maggie. Damals doch

nicht. In Gedanken Kate Creevy. Mit Daumen und Mittelfinger hätte ich ihre Fessel umschließen können. Als ich sie an der Mauer einhole, lässt sie den gerafften Rock immer noch auf ihrem Knie. Sie blickt hoch. Das Grün ihrer Augen. Mit Gold gefleckt. Wie soll ich nur einen Ton hervorbringen? Im Kopf kehren sich die Worte von innen nach außen. So weit. Ich begleite sie ein Stück Weges. Ich atme die ganze Luft um sie ein. Mein Brustkorb brennt lichterloh. Ob ich so nett wäre, sie in Caseys Karren zum Bahnhof zu fahren, damit sie ihre Schwester in Dublin besuchen kann? Ihr Vater will nicht. Schließer müsste der richtig heißen, sagt sie, und nicht Schneider.

Wär ich, natürlich, sage ich. Bist ein guter Kerl, sagt sie.
So weit zwischen ihr und mir. Ich schüttele die Blech-
dose. Kein Pferd darin, kein Ferkel, kein Bett. So weit.
Wäre nicht auch ein Hund ein guter Kerl?

9

Was ich konnte.
Ich konnte Netze flicken. Ein Strohdach decken.
Eine Treppe bauen. Aus Binsen einen Korb flechten. Einer Kuh das Bein schienen. Torf stechen. Eine Steinmauer bauen. Mit Joe drei Runden im Ring durchstehen, den Da in der Scheune gebaut hat. Sets tanzen. Den Himmel lesen. Ein Makrelenfass bauen. Straßen ausbessern. Ein Boot bauen. Einen Sattel aufpolstern. Ein Karrenrad aufziehen. Geschäfte machen. Ein Feld bauen. Mit Wendepflug, Wiesenschleppe und Drescher arbeiten. Das Meer lesen. Schießen und treffen. Schuhe machen. Schafe scheren. Gedichte behalten. Kartoffeln setzen. Pflügen und eggen. Den Wind lesen. Bienen halten. Hocken binden. Einen Sarg zimmern. Einen Schluck vertragen. Geschichten erzählen zum Fürchten. Beim Melken das richtige Lied vorsingen. Und auf dem Akkordeon siebenundzwanzig Lieder.

10

Ich schlage die Rinderhaut vom Spalt in der Bretterwand zurück. Der Spalt ist kaum mehr als faustgroß, aber es fällt Licht auf das Schwein. Es sieht Aug in Aug aus dem Dreck zu mir hoch. Das Auge vom Schwein blickt wie das Auge des Priesters. Seelenruhig und so sicher. Für mich ist gar nichts mehr sicher. Sieht man in so ein Schweinsauge mit blonden Wimpern, würde man meinen, das Kopfrechnen fällt ihm leichter als einem selbst. Beim Pferdeauge wird dir warm. Ein Kuhauge macht dich traurig. Ein Schafsauge gibt dir schnell das Gefühl, du wirst schon vom Hinschauen blöd.

Ich trete in den Fahrweg hinaus und sehe mich um. Tom Connors neue Frau spannt Laken auf die Leine. Wie kommt der bloß zu so einem prachtvollen Mädchen? Er hält Schweine im zusammengestauchten Wrack eines Automobils. Der Postbote segelt auf seinem Fahrrad heran. Er hat was für die Connors, für uns und für Matt, den Schneider lässt er aus. Der Schneider steht in der Wäsche an der Tür. Er hat nichts an den Füßen, und sein Haar steht vom Kopf ab. Er macht aus dem trüben Haus zwei Schritte in den Hof. Geweißt hat er nicht mehr, seit Kate fort ist. Er droht dem Rücken des Postboten mit der erhobenen Faust. »Ich scheiß auf dich!«, ruft er. »Ich scheiß auf dich und ich scheiß auf dein Fahrrad!« Ein Spuckefaden klebt ihm am Kinn. Er geht in sein Haus zurück. Matt sagt, dass er in der Küche auf dem Stuhl unter Zeitungspapier schläft.

Jetzt überquert Matt den Fahrweg mit seinem langen Messer, und wir gehen zurück auf den Hof. Matt meint, er hat den Überblick verloren, wo ich jetzt gerade bin. Ich sage, bei einer Familie namens Keenan an der Straße nach Ballyconnor. »Wenn die vielen Morgen Land, die du beackert hast, dir gehörten«, meint er, »wärst du reich wie Lord Masborough.« Ma schrubbt mitten auf dem Hof den Tisch ab. Mary füllt den Kessel, den Joe Connor und sein Bruder gebracht haben, mit Wasser und Salz. Dermot tritt vor die Tür, dann Da. Der hat eine Flasche Whiskey dabei. Er zwinkert Matt zu und stellt sie auf dem Fensterbrett ab. Brid ist draußen auf den Feldern, denn als sie das letzte Mal im Torfhaus die weißen Schweineseiten hängen sah, hat sie gedacht, sie sieht Gespenster.

Dermot treibt das Schwein in den Lauf. Sein Auge blickt jetzt nicht mehr so sicher, wo es uns alle sieht. Da stürzt sich darauf und landet im Dreck. Er rappelt sich mühsam hoch, während alle nach dem Schwein grabschen. In den Lungen von Da ist ein Rasseln. Er reibt sich die Schulter, auf die er gefallen ist. Er sieht sich um und lacht, aber an seinem Auge merke ich, dass er sich verloren vorkommt. Er hat ein rotes Hemd an, die Ärmel hochgekrempelt. Die Kraft in diesen Armen. Das Grinsen auf dem Foto mit Strohhut. Ein Lachen so breit, als gehörte ihm die ganze Welt und als würde er alles verschenken. Warum habe ich ihm nicht aufgeholfen? Warum habe ich ihn nicht gefragt, wer er ist?

Ich habe das Schwein um die Mitte gepackt. Früher hat es sich hingelegt wie ein Hund, wenn ich ihm über die Flanke strich. Sein Herz geht in der massigen Brust hoch wie kleine Bomben. Matt hat es jetzt bei den Ohren, Joe Conner beim Schwanz. Dermot legt ihm die Drahtschlinge um den Rüssel und zieht zu. Da schiebt von hinten. Wir wuchten es rücklings auf den Tisch, Da und Dermot packen die Hinterbeine, Joe Conner und sein Bruder Tom die vorderen, ich drücke den Kopf nach hinten. Das Schwein macht mehr Lärm als eine ganze Stadt. Matt blickt mit dem Messer in der Hand in die Runde und sagt, was er immer sagt, nämlich dass das Schwein als einziges Tier den Wind sieht. Dann schneidet er dem Schwein das Kreuzzeichen in die Kehle. »Also«, sagt er zu mir. »Wenn du alle Noten von ›Lord Gordon's Reel‹ triffst, triffst du sicherlich auch die Schlagader vom Schwein.« Er reicht mir das Messer.

Der Tag, als ich Joe auf dem Schlachthof in Ipswich fand. Männer mit weißen Hüten, die nach Schweinen traten und ihnen Papiernummern auf die Rücken pinnten. An den weißen Kacheln überall Blut. Ich musste mir die Finger in die Ohren stopfen, so schrien die Schweine, von denen manche schon am Boden waren und am Ende, während andere in den Pferchen über sie wegrannten. Die Luft vom Todesgeruch dick wie Klumpen. Einer treibt die Schweine mit Stockschlägen in den Tod. Einer bohrt ihnen Haken in die Hinterfüße, damit man sie kopfüber aufhängen kann. Einer schickt ihnen Strom durchs Gehirn. Wo ist Joe? Con hatte sagen hören, Joe würde im Hyde Park unter Büschen schlafen. Jemand anders meinte, er wäre mit der Handelsmarine aus Glasgow ausgelaufen. Jemand drittes, er hätte Familie in Birmingham. Pat Creevy war derjenige, der vom Schlachthof sprach. Ich gehe durch den weißen Raum voller Blut. Das Brummen der Stromschläge. Das siedende Wasser. Das Geräusch der Säge, die die Schweine durchtrennt. In einer Kabine am Ende des Raums steht Joe, mit blutgetränkten Tüchern behangen, breitbeinig über einem Abfluss, in der Hand ein langes Messer. Die hängenden Schweine fahren an einer Kette durch die Luft, und wenn sie vor ihm halten, sticht er sie ab. Dann wartet er, bis sie in den Abfluss leerlaufen. Er schneidet ihnen keine Kreuzzeichen in die Kehle. Abends gibt es bei ihm auf der Bude Schweinsfüße und ein paar Flaschen Stout, aber als ich vier Wochen später nach ihm frage, ist er weg.

Joe Connor singt für uns »The Rocks of Bawn«, Ma brät Rippenstücke und die Schweineleber in Butter. Die Flasche Whiskey ist halb leer. In Joes Stimme ist mehr als nur eine Lage. Es gibt das tiefe Brummen wie von Dudelsäcken, aber es liegt noch ein reiner heller Klang darüber. Bis er ihn singt, kannst du nie wissen, wo der nächste Ton herkommt. Ein Stein, in den Brunnen geworfen. Felsen, die unter der Erde kalben. Wie weiß Joe vom Schmerz dieses Mannes mit Land, das sich beim besten Willen nicht pflügen lässt? Wenn ich Akkordeon spiele, kenne ich so einen Klang, der mein eigen ist, nur erreiche ich ihn noch nicht. Irgendwie rot und gold und voll Licht. Schnell und sicher.

Wir essen das Schweinefleisch. Ich muss an die strampelnden Hinterfüße denken, als wollte das Schwein weglaufen, während aber doch schon das Blut aus der Wunde, die ich ihm zugefügt hatte, in die Schüssel schwallte. Als wir fertig gegessen haben, verlangt Matt wieder Musik. Da spielt Flöte, ich dann Akkordeon. Ein paar

Reels spielen wir gemeinsam. Dann soll ich für Matt
»The Moving Cloud« spielen. Ich habe Whiskey im
Leib. Irgendwas ist an der Art, wie Matt den Takt mit
dem Fuß klopft und den Kopf etwas schief legt, der Art,
wie er die Musik an diesem Abend zu sich hinzieht. Er
gleicht einem Mann mit dem Teller voll Stew nach
einem langen Tag auf den Feldern. Kaum habe ich die
ersten Noten angespielt, schwingen sich meine Hände
auf wie zwei Vögel. Ich spüre, wie sich das Lied in mir
Bahn bricht. Ich sehe die ganzen Töne vor mir wie kleine bunte Strandkiesel. Ich kann sie von allen Seiten
betrachten und finde genau den richtigen Platz für sie.
Und zwischendrin jedes Mal seelenruhig zum Brunnen

spazieren und zurück. Ma setzt sich ans Feuer. Mary lässt den Teller, den sie gerade spült. Brid kommt vom Hof herein. Wo ich bin, bin ich noch nie zuvor gewesen, aber ich kenne den Ort in- und auswendig. Da sieht auf meine Hände. Ich könnte sie noch wochenlang fliegen lassen. Ich beende das Lied und setze das Akkordeon auf den Boden. Die Küche klingt nach, als würde sich die Melodie nur langsam verabschieden. Dann ist es still. »So hast du noch nie gespielt«, sagt Matt. »Und wer weiß, ob du je wieder so spielen wirst.« Da tritt an den Tisch, schenkt sich und mir einen Whiskey ein und reicht die Flasche dann Joe Connor weiter. Er bringt mir mein Glas. Er macht ein Gesicht, als wäre ihm noch ein Kind geschenkt worden. »Jetzt bist du mir über«, sagt er. »Deine Zeit war gekommen.«

11

In der Küche regt sich etwas, ich werde davon wach. Es klingt wie Scharren von einem Tischbein auf dem Boden. Die ganze Nacht habe ich abwechselnd zehn Minuten geschlafen und eine Stunde wachgelegen. Ist die Fahrkarte für die Bahn in meiner Tasche oder in der Schublade? Unter der Tür fällt Licht aus der Küche. Ich erkenne ein Paar Schuhe und den Rand meines Koffers.

Ich gehe in die Küche. Dort liegt Da vorm Feuer auf dem Fußboden, die Arme um ein dösendes Kalb geschlungen. Er schaut hoch.

»Was ist?«, frage ich ihn.

»Nabelentzündung«, sagt er.

Und bettet den Kopf wieder neben sein Kalb.

12

Ich öffne ein Auge. Als Erstes ist da ein trockenes Gefühl. Im Mund lässt sich nichts bewegen, alles klebt. Dann Schmerz. Als würde in meinem Kopf ein kleines Tier mit Feuerpfoten herumrennen. Dann das Gefühl von Verderben und Schande. Ich betrachte das graue Kissen, das müde Rosa der Tagesdecke. Maggie mochte die Farbe an manchen Dingen. Heute Morgen wird in diesem Bett kein Trost zu finden sein.

Gestern Abend war ich, ich muss eben nachrechnen, fünf Stunden im Gloucester Arms. Um fünf bin ich hin und um zehn gegangen. Was soll ich sonst machen nach

der Runde mit dem Hund? Ich muss dem Griechen beim Dominospiel was gesagt haben; als er ging, hat er kein Wort mit mir geredet. Ich war schon draußen und fast an der Ecke, als mir einfiel, dass ich doch den Hund ans Stuhlbein gebunden hatte. Neun Pints habe ich getrunken und ein Käsesandwich gegessen. Einen komischen weißen Käse, den ich noch nie gegessen hatte. Ich vertrage nicht mehr so viel wie früher.

Am ersten Tag dachte ich, England würde nur aus grauen, nasstriefenden Mauern bestehen.

Als das Boot in den Hafen einläuft, verstauen wir unsere Instrumente und klappen die Sitze weg. Die großen Eisentüren, die sie aufgelassen haben, damit wir Luft kriegen, schließen sich, graues Wasser brodelt. Der Himmel sieht aus wie verdorbenes Schweinefleisch. Der Maschinenlärm bricht in den Frachtraum. Die Lastwagen stehen dort still und dunkel wie Kühe, die auf Regen warten. Zu sechst haben wir gespielt, als wären wir unter einem Dach groß geworden, und ungefähr dreißig Mann haben zugehört. Wir gehen an Deck, um einen Blick auf England zu werfen, und ich schmecke noch den ekligen Tee, den sie an Bord ausgeschenkt hatten. Wo eben beim Spielen die Gesichter noch strahlten, sieht man jetzt nichts mehr. Nur ein Warten. Wie bei Menschen, die im Krankenhaus warten.

Still gleiten wir in die Hafeneinfahrt. Rost. Die Wände zerschrammt und mit grünem Striemen verschmiert, das Wasser läuft nur so herunter. Vor uns öffnen sich die Schleusentore, und dann steigen wir an den Wänden hinauf. Die Schleuse ist für mich das reinste Wunder, aber ich begreife nicht, wozu sie da ist. Wir stehen. Die Schleuse ist wie ein Grab. Ein Mädchen mit schwar-

zem Haar, einem blauen Regenmantel und sehr weißem
Gesicht klammert sich an die Reling. Sie hat sich den
Koffer zwischen die Beine geklemmt. Ihre Augen sind
groß vor Angst, und sie ringt nach Luft. Als würde sie
ertrinken. Das ist das Einzige, was wir hören, während
wir dort im Wasser warten. Sie scheint nicht zu wissen,
wie ihr geschieht. Ich möchte gern zu ihr hingehen, aber
ich tue es nicht. Als das Schiff in der Schleuse weiter
steigt, fängt sie sich wieder.

Es geht zu den Schleusentoren hinaus zum Anleger.
Im Wasser schwimmen eine Zeitung, eine Puppe im rosa
Kleidchen und ein Automobilreifen. Der Puppe fehlt ein

Arm. Wir marschieren alle mit unseren Koffern hinaus auf den Kai. Wem jetzt doch noch Zweifel kommen, lässt es sich nicht anmerken. Ich halte ohne Grund Ausschau, ob mich jemand abholt. Es bläst ein ordentlicher Wind, und das überrascht mich. Ich habe es mir immer vollkommen windstill vorgestellt. Und ich muss an einen Wind daheim denken, der so stürmisch war, dass er eine Katze über die Mauer schleuderte. Alles verläuft sich, nur der junge John Joe, der Mundharmonika gespielt hat, muss wie ich zur Bahn. Ein langer Tunnel, wo dunkle Wände ölig aussehendes Wasser schwitzen. Dann die tiefen Schächte, als wir aus der Stadt rollen. Dunkle Ziegel, Moos und rinnendes Wasser. Ich bin in England.

Ich wälze mich herum. Die Schranktür steht offen. Dort hängt Maggies Kleid mit den Glockenblumen. Das Einzige, was ich nicht weggeben mag. Was ich dabeihatte, als ich auf dem Kai stand? Einen Koffer mit Kleidern. Mein Akkordeon. Den Zettel von Da, damit ich weiß, wo ich hin muss. £4 6s. an Erspartem und £2 von Ma, macht £6 6s. Wie viel habe ich jetzt? Ich suche meine Hose. Sie liegt noch genauso auf dem Boden, wie ich gestern aus ihr herausgestiegen bin. Ich muss hier wirklich mal Ordnung schaffen. In der Tasche £1.27. Und die Rentenzahlung kommt Donnerstag erst. Was mache ich heute? Ich bleibe im Bett liegen und denke an die grauen Mauern in Liverpool, an denen das Wasser herabbrann.

Am Tag, als ich fortging, ist Da in aller Frühe mit dem kranken Kalb raus und hat einen Bogen ums Haus gemacht. Ma brät mir zwei herrliche am Morgen frisch gelegte Eier. Sie gibt mir einen Rosenkranz mit und Brote. Sie geht zum Wandkasten hinüber, holt eine Schachtel hervor und reicht mir £2. Es ist eine prächtige Schachtel aus Kiefernholz, in der lauter Zigarren waren, als Martin sie Da aus New York geschickt hat. In dem Winter konnten sich die Männer, wenn sie abends vorbeischauten, rücklings vors Herdfeuer auf die Steine legen, Füße zur Glut, und Zigarren rauchen statt Pfeife.

Das letzte Brot habe ich gegessen, als ich an der North Wall darauf wartete, aufs Schiff gehen zu können. Die £2 habe ich aufbewahrt, bis ich vergessen hatte, welche es waren. Den Rosenkranz habe ich Ma in den Sarg gelegt.

Ich trete aus der Tür und sehe nach Da. Er trägt ein Schaf huckepack vom Haus weg am Brunnen vorbei. Genau wie Matt zieht er vor Baby, die sich mit ihrem Kinderwagen einen kleinen Hang hochkämpft, den Hut.

»Ein Glück, dass sie in Labasheeda sein kann«, hat er immer gesagt, »die Stadt würde sie erdrücken.« Ich hoffe, dass ihm das Schaf nicht zu schwer wird. Als Ma die Brote in meinen Koffer packen will, springt das Schnappschloss auf und die Kleider purzeln heraus. Sie bindet eine Schnur drumherum. Dermot holt den Karren, und wir biegen auf den Fahrweg. Die Sonne bricht durch die Wolken und bringt den ganzen Weiler zum Leuchten. Alle Farben in Mas Schal, wo sie an der weißen Wand lehnt. Ihre Haare, die rot sind, hier und da weiß, die Finger auch rot von der vielen Arbeit. Die Fuchsien und das neue Strohdach, die smaragdgrünen grau beringten Felder. Als wir anfahren, zieht es sich wieder zu. Ein Foto.

Ich stehe auf dem Karren und halte Ausschau nach Da, kann ihn aber nirgends entdecken. Möglich, dass er hinter der Hecke steht und zusieht. Was habe ich alles auf dieser Straße gemacht? Vieh getrieben. Mich vorm Lehrer versteckt. Zur Flöte getanzt. Gewartet, dass Da aus Lincolnshire heimkommt. Eines Tages wird sie mich in einem nagelneuen Anzug vollgestopft mit Geldscheinen heimkehren sehen.

Dermot lädt mich am Bahnhof ab wie einen Sack Getreide und wendet den Karren. Ich sehe ihm nach, aber er schaut nicht zurück. Er schlägt mit der Kappe nach einer Schmeißfliege, und an seinem Hinterkopf sehe ich einen zweishillingstückgroßen Kreis blanke Haut. Zum ersten Mal sehe ich den. Und fürchte um mein eigenes Haupthaar. Ich fahre mit der Hand hindurch, es scheint alles in Ordnung. Ob ich in den Tanzhallen in England ein Prachtmädchen finde, ehe mich mein Haar ganz im Stich lässt?

Am Bahnsteig steht Cornelius Breen mit seiner Ma und seinem Da und seiner Schwester Agnes. Vom anderen Bruder Paul bekommt seine Ma jeden Monat aus Philadelphia dreißig Dollar, und dazu um die sechs Pfund von Declan, der in England Straßen baut. Sie hat einen Mantel mit Pelz oben am Kragen, den sie extra aus Dublin hat kommen lassen. Sie haben das Haus verbreitert, jetzt gibt es ein Wohnzimmer, und der Priester kommt zum Nachmittagstee. Das ganze Jahr schon liegt sie Cornelius in den Ohren, dass er hinter dem Ofen hervor soll und hinaus in die Welt, Geld verdienen, aber er hat nicht mit sich reden lassen. Matt nennt ihn die Kartoffel, die zu lange gekocht worden ist, weil er weich im Hirn ist. Seine Ma hat ihm einen Koffer gekauft. Dann einen Anzug. Gute Anlage, hat sie sich wohl gesagt, aber es geschah nichts. Schließlich hat sie ihm zwölf Pfund und das Fahrgeld dazu versprochen, und da war er einverstanden. Sein Da steht mit der Kappe in der Hand und Leichenbittermiene da wie am offenen Grab. Ich sehe den Zug dampfen. Ich sehe zu der Bank hinüber, auf der ich einmal mit Kate Creevy gewartet habe. Cornelius' Ma beginnt zu weinen. »Ach, geh nicht fort, Sohn«, sagt sie und macht die Arme breit. Wahrscheinlich hat sie gedacht, das muss sie. Der Zug kommt. »Geh nicht, Cornelius«, sagt sie noch einmal. »Ist gut, Ma«, sagt Cornelius, »was soll ich da sagen«, marschiert zum Karren zurück, wirft seinen Koffer hinein und steigt auf. Von Ma hörte ich dann in einem Brief, dass er das ganze Geld innerhalb von drei Tagen in den Pubs gelassen hat.

Das Rattern der Räder auf den Schienen. Es klingt anders in England. Schwerer vielleicht. Warrington. Manchester. Stockport. Lange Zeilen aneinander gefüg-

ter klitzekleiner Häuser. Dahinter Schuppen mit Fahrrädern und Matratzen und Koffern bis unter die Dächer. John Joe redet die ganze Zeit von den Liedern aus Leitrim und dem Onkel, der sie alle auf der Geige spielen konnte. Ich sehe eine Frau Fisch in der Pfanne braten. Ihr Haar sieht aus, als wäre es aus Holz. Die Eile, die alle auf den Bahnhöfen treibt. Wie sie sich wohl anhören? Wie soll ich bloß mit ihnen reden?

Ich hole das Stück Papier hervor, das mir Da gegeben hat. »The Duke of Cumberland, Lincoln«, steht darauf. Es ist schon ganz zerrieben, so oft habe ich es hervorgezogen, seit ich fort bin. Ich falte es wieder zusammen und schiebe es in die Tasche. Was Da wohl jetzt macht?

Vielleicht weit ins Land sehen, die Sonne im Gesicht. Das blasse schwarzhaarige Mädchen, dem an Bord nicht wohl war, sitzt John Joe und mir gegenüber am Fenster und sieht wieder Wunder wie elend aus. Sie hält sich ein Taschentuch an die Lippen. Unter ihrem Sitz sehe ich eine kleine Pfütze, Tee hauptsächlich, wo sie erbrochen hat. Es ist niemand bei ihr. Da betritt ein riesengroßer Mann in einer Eisenbahnuniform den Waggon. Er hat einen roten Bart, eine Nase wie eine kleine Tomate und Augen so rot wie innen im Mund. Seine Mütze sitzt so weit hinten am Kopf, dass man das ganze Gesicht sieht. Er bleibt stehen, als er das Erbrochene auf dem Fußboden bemerkt. Er sieht sich um, rechts, links. Er sieht das Mädchen an. »Wer war das?«, fragt er. Seine Stimme wie ein Paukenschlag und schepperig. Alle im Wagen gucken schweigend zu. Das Mädchen zittert. Sie hält sich den Mund, als müsste sie wieder spucken. Er funkelt sie weiter an. Da wirft John Joe seinen Mantel hinter sich über die Rücklehne und schiebt die Ärmel seines Pullovers ganz weit hoch. Himmel, hat der Arme! Die könnten einen Bullen niederringen. »Ich war das«, sagt John Joe. Der Kerl fährt herum. John Joe sieht ihm direkt in die Augen, die baumdicken Arme vor der Brust verschränkt. Ich sehe ihm auch ins Auge, muss aber bald aufgeben, weil der Anblick so schlimm ist wie der von verdorbenem Fleisch. Bei John Joe ist an Kiefer, Hals und Armen alles in Bewegung. Sein rechtes Bein tanzt auf und ab, als würde es im Takt zu einem Reel wippen. Er sieht den Kerl unverwandt an, breit grinsend. Nur antippen, und er ginge hoch wie eine Mine. Es ist, als wäre die Luft aus Glas; John Joe und der Kerl sich Aug in Aug gegenüber. »Dass mir das nicht wieder vorkommt«, sagt der Bahngesellschaftsmann und zieht geschlagen ab. Die Waggontür kracht hinter ihm ins Schloss. John Joe zwinkert dem Mädchen zu. Sie lacht hellauf. Sie lacht in einer Weise, mit der sie wahrscheinlich selbst nicht gerechnet hat.

Ich bin bis Chester mit John Joe zusammengeblieben, dann musste ich in einen anderen Zug nach Sheffield umsteigen. Mit den Namen habe ich mich nie recht anfreunden können. Es steckt wenig Leben in ihnen, und an beiden Enden ist Schluss. Sie erinnern mich an Eisen. John Joe hatte auch keine Ahnung, wo er hinfährt, so wenig wie ich. »Wo hast du bloß die Arme her?«, frage ich ihn, bevor ich aussteige. »Ich bin Gipser«, sagt er, »die kriegst du vom ewigen Mörtelbretthalten.«

Im Duke of Cumberland sitzt Matts Neffe P. J. Doran auf einem hohen Hocker am Tresen, brennende Zigarette in der Hand, vor sich ein Pint und die Zeitung von daheim. Sein Haar ist geölt und gestriegelt. Christy Mangan, Dick Lally, Conor Dowd und sein Bruder Peter, Jimmy Burke und Dan Ryan hocken in einer trüben Ecke beieinander und spielen Karten. Dan habe ich zuletzt gesehen, da kam er mit zwei Hummerkörben vom Anleger hoch und der Wind wollte ihn glatt ins Meer zurückwerfen. Ein Kerryman – Florrie Clifford, ich erkenne ihn von einem Foto, das mir Da mal gezeigt hat – hält auf den Tresen zu. Zwei Stunden bin ich durch die Straßen von Lincoln, bis ich hergefunden habe. Ich mochte nichts reden, weil mich vielleicht jemand auslacht. Am Koffergriff habe ich mir die Hand wund gerieben. Als ich die Jungs sehe, falle ich fast über sie her.

Und dort, im Duke of Cumberland, bringe ich das Geld durcheinander, das mir Ma mitgegeben hat. Sie schieben dauernd Pints nach, aber es gibt nichts zu essen. Es gibt immer neue Runden Bitter mit einem Schuss dunklem Ale. Ich spiele für sie »The Good-Natured Man«, »The Whistler from Rosslea« und »The Humours of Tulla«. Das Geld rinnt mir aus der Tasche. Als ich vom Abort komme, stolpere ich über eine Schwelle vor der Tür und schlage mir das Gesicht direkt über der Nase auf. Vorm Spiegel stille ich das Blut. In meinem Kopf läuft ein Reel. Ich muss mich am Waschbecken festhalten. Ich kann kaum glauben, dass ich es bin, der mich da anschaut.

Dann bin ich in einem Auto. Am Steuer sitzt ein Engländer, den ich noch nie gesehen habe. Vom vielen Bier atmen die Männer wie Kühe. Sie reden von einem aus

Tyrone, älter schon, der nicht mehr die Kraft hat, Kartoffeln zu ernten, den wollen sie auf den Traktor setzen, während ich seinen Platz in der Kolonne einnehme. Ich habe keine Ahnung, was mit mir werden soll, aber ich stelle keine Fragen. Wir fahren aus der Stadt hinaus über die dunklen Landstraßen von Lincolnshire, bei der Geschwindigkeit werden Häuser und Hecken und Bäume in einem fort zurückgeschleudert, der Himmel knurrt wie ein Hund, dem missfällt, was er sieht. P. J. pfeift »James Connolly«. Wir steigen aus, und ich folge den anderen im Schlamm einen Pfad hinab zu einem dunklen Etwas. Peter Dowd schlittert auf dem Hosenboden den Hang hinunter. Wieso habe ich mich gar nicht

gefragt, was mit mir wird? Das Bier vielleicht. Und noch mehr die Angst vor einer Schande.

Wir kommen an eine Tür zu einem Gebäude aus Stein. Die Tür ist schwarz, abblätternde Farbe, und sie wird von einer Schnur zwischen zwei Nägeln zugehalten. Wir stehen vor einer Art Nebengebäude auf einer Farm. Mir wird kalt, während wir darauf warten, dass P. J. die Schnur abkriegt und uns hereinlässt. Dann geht die Tür auf, und wir zwängen uns nacheinander hinein. Wo sind wir? Irgendwo, wo Wärme ist und Bewegung und eine von irgendetwas belebte dickere Luft. P. J. entzündet eine Laterne, die an einem Nagel an der Wand hängt. So weit ich sehen kann Schweine. Der ganze Raum ist von einem Ende bis zum anderen voll mit Schweinen. Die Männer halten auf eine kurze Holztreppe zu, die aus dem Staub am Boden zu einer Luke führt. Die Schweine sehen zu, wie wir hinaufsteigen.

Oben gibt es auf dem Boden zu beiden Seiten an der Wand zwölf Schlafstellen aus Stroh und unter einem winzigen Fenster am Giebelende einen Waschtisch mit Waschschüssel. P. J. hängt die Laterne an einen Nagel und deutet auf den Strohsack, auf dem ich schlafen soll. Die Männer machen sich zum Schlafen bereit, ich stehe wie angewurzelt oben an der Treppe. Ich schmecke Salz von den Tränen, die mir in den Mund laufen. Mein Atem geht schwer, und das Blut schießt mit einer Geschwindigkeit in mir herum, dass ich denke, es wirft mich zu Boden. Aber ich lasse mir nichts anmerken. Unten rumoren die Schweine. Ich stehe über ihnen und atme ihren Atem. Ich wühle in meinen Taschen. Ich frage mich, ob ich genug Geld für die Heimfahrt habe und ob ich den Weg finden würde. Ich denke an das Bett, das ich in

Labasheeda zurückgelassen habe. Draußen ist es dunkel, und die Straße voller Kehren, die ich nicht kenne. Es gibt kein Zurück. Ich soll Kartoffeln ernten und mich nachts hier auf diesen Boden betten. Ich muss in England sein und unter Schweinen leben.

13

Für mich sind die Kartoffeln wie aus Lehm. Oder Wachs. Oder fauligen Laubklumpen. Wenn ich von der Erde hochblicke, aus der ich sie hole, hat das Feld gar kein Ende. Bei uns daheim wären das mindestens vier Farmen. Es ist November, und morgens unter der Decke hervorzukriechen, ist wie ins Wintermeer springen, die Arbeit ist dann aber so schweißtreibend, dass mittags keiner mehr ein Hemd am Leib hat. Das Feld ist nur Lehm. Ich habe Lehm an den Hosen, Lehm am Kartoffelsack, Lehm an den Armen. Ich kriege Lehm in die Stiefel. Wenn ich eine Kartoffel hochhalte, verstehe ich sie nicht. Ich versuche, mir ein Stück davon mit Butter und Salz am Ende einer Gabel vorzustellen. Es geht nicht.

Der Yorkshireman kommt abends gut abgefüllt zurück und pisst einem Schwein ins Maul. Ich höre ihn unten brüllen vor Lachen.

Ich liege auf meinem Strohsack. Ich kann mich kaum rühren, Arme und Rücken und Beine brennen noch von der Arbeit. P. J. sitzt auf der Schlafstelle neben meiner und liest ein Buch über Sternkunde. Mir stehen die hübschen Blumen auf unserem halben Morgen Kartoffelland

daheim vor Augen. Dann denke ich an das große Feld, das uns morgen bevorsteht. Wie viele Kartoffeln für ein Hemd, einen Ring, eine prächtige Golduhr für Ma? Wie viele, bevor ich Kate Creevy etwas zu sagen hätte, sollte ich das Glück haben, ihr auf dem Fahrweg zu begegnen? Wie viele musste Da für Joes Akkordeon ernten?

P. J. schlägt das Buch zu und legt es neben seinen Strohsack. »Mir unbegreiflich, weshalb Gott überhaupt noch einen Gedanken an uns verschwendet, bei dem, was im Universum alles so los ist«, meint er.

Er versucht, aus dem kleinen Fenster in den Nacht-
himmel zu sehen.

»Hat mein Vater eigentlich je auf dieser Farm gearbeitet, P. J.?«, frage ich ihn.

»Nein. Aber bei Appleforth, knapp zwei Meilen weiter westlich. Dort waren wir zusammen. Beim Heuma-
chen war er unschlagbar, wegen der Kraft in seinen
Armen. Wie geht es ihm?«

»Mit dem Bein muss Dermot die ganze Arbeit allein
machen. Das drückt Da. Aber meine Mutter meint, jetzt
bringt er so einem jungen Burschen, Wilson heißt er, Flöte bei, der fährt dafür extra elf Meilen mit dem Bus. Pas-
torensohn.«

»Ein Jammer mit dem Bein.«

»Wie war es damals mit ihm?«

»Besondere Freude hatte er sonntags an den Karten.
Konnte gar nicht genug kriegen. Manchmal, wenn ich
gesehen habe, wie er einen Haufen Geld einsetzt, habe
ich versucht, ihn zu bremsen. Er hat einen besonderen
Spruch dafür gehabt. Hat mich angesehen, gezwinkert
und gesagt: ›Vorm Akkumulieren kommt Spekulieren‹.«

Ich halte ganz still, denn nirgends tut es nicht weh.
Ich male mir aber aus, wie ich aussehen werde, wenn ich
erst mit meinem Geld daheim den Fahrweg hochkom-
me. Ich begucke mich von allen Seiten.

»Ich hätte zu gerne ein Fernrohr«, sagt P. J.

Er stützt sich auf den Ellbogen auf und sieht in den
Himmel. Ich habe ihn noch nie so, von der Seite, ohne
Blick auf seine Augen, gesehen. Er wirkt älter.

»Wie lange arbeitest du in diesem Land, P. J.?«, frage
ich ihn.

»Jetzt im Juni siebzehn Jahre.«

»Und wie ist das?«

Er sieht noch eine Zeit lang aus dem Fenster, dann wendet er sich um und löscht das Licht der Laterne. Ich weiß nicht, ob er mich gehört hat. Ich höre es rascheln, als er sich aufs Stroh bettet.

»Es ist, als würdest du aus einem tiefen schwarzen Loch heraus zu jemand sprechen wollen«, sagt er.

14

Im Süden steht Orion. Gegenüber kann ich den Großen Wagen finden, das Siebengestirn, den Bären. Es gibt die Venus mit einem sehr weißen Stern darüber, und Kassiopeia. Den breiten Streifen der Milchstraße wie ein zerbröckeltes Rückgrat. Die Leier, Pegasus. Ich sitze an die Wand vom Schweinestall gelehnt, rauche eine Woodbine und denke über die Arithmetik des Weltalls nach, wie sie mich P. J. gelehrt hat.

Dick Lally kommt so leise daher, dass ich ihn erst bemerke, als er direkt vor mir steht. Er spricht nicht viel, aber sein Mund steht fast immer offen. Seine Lippen sind feucht, und er hat Augen wie ein Kind – oder eine alte Frau, die nicht mehr richtig im Kopf ist. Die Arbeit ist hart für ihn, armer Kerl, und er hat einen schlimmen Rücken.

»Sieh nur, was mein Bruder mir heute gut Verpacktes geschickt hat.«

Er hält eine kleine Glasflasche mit Korken hoch, in der eine klare Flüssigkeit ist, die im Sternenlicht ein ganz klein wenig glitzert.

»Doch nicht etwa Lourdeswasser.«

Er schenkt zwei Gläser voll, und wir spüren dem Poitín nach, der uns heiß die Kehle hinabrinnt.

»John O'Hagen brennt immer noch, sagt Martin. Er hat die Blase gleich bei sich im Haus stehen. Als Junge war ich einmal dabei; die Männer standen herum und starrten, während der Poitín pitsch-pitsch in die Flasche tropfte. Als würden sie einer Kuh beim Kalben zusehen.«

Conor Dowd nennt Dick neuerdings »den mit der Jacke«, weil ihm nämlich der rechte Ärmel bis zur Achsel aufgeplatzt ist. An den Ellbogen ist die Jacke schwarz, und schwarz auch dort, wo die Rockschöße auf

die Hüften aufstoßen. Vorn hat sie noch einen Knopf, an den Ärmeln gar keine. Hinten ist ein Riss drin, und er hat den und den Ärmel mit Sicherheitsnadeln geflickt.

Er rutscht auf der staubigen Erde ein wenig hin und her, dann füllt er die Gläser noch einmal.

»Ob du mir vielleicht alsdann einen Gefallen tun könntest?«, meint er.

Er sieht mich mit diesen Augen an.

»Jederzeit«, sage ich ihm.

»Es ist dieser Brief, von Martin«, sagt er. »Er hat schlechte Nachrichten. Am besten liest du selbst. Es geht um Sheila. Du weißt ja, wie das ist mit mir und dem Schreiben. Du wirst schon die rechten Worte finden.«

Er erklärt mir, was zu sagen ist, und überlässt mir den

Brief von seinem Bruder. Dann kehrt er in den Stall zurück.

Liebe Sheila, schreibe ich. Ich lege eine Guinee von meinem Wochenlohn bei, und noch je zwei Bob für die Mädchen, sie sollen sich zu Hallowe'en eine Freude machen. Wie geht es den beiden und dir selbst? Ich habe lange nicht mehr von euch gehört. Ich bin bei guter Gesundheit, und auch mit dem Rücken geht es an, dem Herrgott sei Dank. Die anderen von daheim sind auch alle wohlauf. P. J. redet von einem großen Straßenbauprojekt in der Nähe von Birmingham, und ein paar Jungs denken daran weiterzuziehen, wenn wir hier mit den Kartoffeln durch sind, aber ich möchte Weihnachten wieder bei dir und den Mädchen sein. Sheila, ich hatte heute Nachrichten von Martin, die mich beunruhigen. Er sagt, dass Brendan Flannery seit Juni fast jeden Tag bei euch Besuch macht. Er sagt, ihr wandelt abends zwischen den Hecken. Er sagt, er glaubt, zwischen euch ist etwas Unrechtes. Ganz Oola spricht schon darüber, sagt er. Nie hätte ich gedacht, dass ausgerechnet uns so etwas passieren könnte, Sheila. Du bedeutest mir alles, du und die Mädchen. Hier auf der Farm denke ich immerzu nur an uns alle beisammen in Oola. Ich weiß, dass es schwer ist, Frau eines Taglöhners zu sein, aber ich bin doch euretwegen fortgegangen. Ich würde so gerne von dir hören, dass nichts dran ist. Ich würde so gerne hören, dass alles gelogen ist oder ein schlechter Traum, aber ich befürchte das Schlimmste. Sodass ich dich nun fragen muss, Sheila: Ist das Kind, das noch vor Weihnachten zur Welt kommen soll, von mir oder von Brendan Flannery? Ich liebe dich doch von ganzem Herzen. Dein dich liebender Mann, Dick.

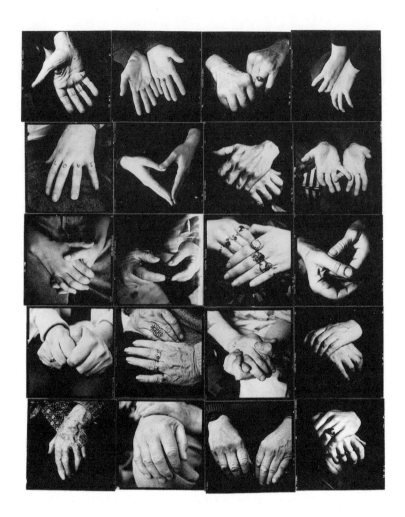

15

Als ich von Roscoes Tod höre, wasche ich gerade Socken und denke daran, wie Da »Anach Cuain« auf der Flöte spielte. Damit hat er immer alle still kriegen können, weil er die Flöte erst so mit Andacht hochnahm, an die Lippen hob, die Augen schloss und bestimmt fünf Takte wartete, ehe er den ersten Ton setzte. Am Anfang spielte er scheu, leicht und leise, kaum hörbar. Wie der feine Rauch, der vom Reisholz aufsteigt. Dann baute er auf. Am besten war es, wenn er für sich auf einem Stuhl an der gelben Wand saß, weil man gern nur ihn sehen wollte. Aber es verschwand sowieso alles, wenn er die Melodie erst mal hatte. Die ganze Welt konnte er mit seiner Musik vertreiben. Er baute die Melodie immer mehr aus, und du spürtest, wie sie in dich eindrang, sich hochrankte wie Efeu an einer Mauer. Seine Miene veränderte sich bei alledem kein bisschen. Die Augen niedergeschlagen. Höchstens, dass kurz ein Schatten über die Stirn flog. Ich kannte das Lied, bevor ich laufen konnte, und trotzdem wusste ich nie, wo der nächste Ton herkommt. Er kam immer überraschend. Aber pfeilgerade und sicher wie der Habicht im Fluge. Es gipfelte darin, dass du selbst weg warst. Du warst nur noch Musik. Und wenn er zum Ende kam, kehrte die Welt langsam zurück, aber anders. Das, was uns manchmal die Welt um uns herum vergessen lässt, war weg. Und alles brauste auf dich ein wie ein Sturm.

Conor Dowd kommt und sagt mir, er hätte gehört, Roscoe wäre in einem Kanalrohr an einer Straße nahe Brighton gestorben. Eine dieser großen Röhren, die unter der Erde verlegt werden sollten. Roscoe gehörte zur Arbeitskolonne, und scheints hatte er keine Bude. Er lebte in dem Rohr. Eines Morgens fanden sie ihn dort tot auf.

»Wir sind die Unsterblichen«, sagt P. J. Er trinkt ein paar Gläser auf Roscoe. »Wir haben einen Namen, und wir haben einen Körper. Wir sind immer in den besten Jahren, und wir sind immer arbeitsfähig. Wir graben die Tunnel, wir legen die Trassen, wir bauen Straßen und

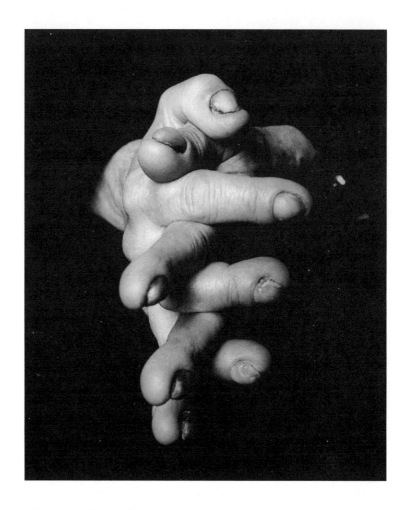

Häuser. Aber wir hinterlassen keine Spuren. Wir sind unbekannt und unbesungen. Wir haben viele Namen, aber uns gehören keine. Wenn dann die Glieder steif werden und die Schmerzen einsetzen und wir nicht mehr so können, wie jetzt Roscoe, dann verjüngen wir uns. Mit uns geht es immer weiter und weiter. Wir sind wie die Flasche, die nie leer wird. Wir sind unsterblich.« Er legt sich auf seinen Strohsack und seufzt tief.

»Es tut mir so Leid, wegen Roscoe«, sagt mir Conor.

»Er war ein rechter Spaßvogel. Und er konnte sich wie nichts einen Limerick ausdenken.«

Roscoe ging ohne Totenklage von uns. Ich stelle mir vor, wie Da an seinem Grab steht, seine Flöte hervorholt und dort vor dem Sarg »Anach Cuain« anstimmt. Er konnte das Herzweh Wunder wie schön. »Anach Cuain« höre ich manchmal, wenn ich mich schlafen lege. Und wenn ich dann mitten in der Nacht aufwache, höre ich es noch.

16

Was ich nicht konnte.

Eine Mahlzeit essen, zu der keine Kartoffeln gehören. Der Bank trauen. Eine Uhr tragen. Eine Frau fragen, ob wir ein paar Schritte gehen wollen. Mit Abflüssen klarkommen oder Dingen, die kleiner sind als ein Nagel. Ein Automobil steuern. Tomaten essen. Mir Busrouten merken. Ohne Qualen einen Hemdkragen erdulden. Beim Kartenspiel gewinnen. Die Queen anerkennen. Laute Stimmen ertragen. Manierlich grüßen und mich verabschieden. Geld sparen. Freude an der Arbeit in einer Fabrik haben. Kaffee trinken. Den Anblick von Wunden ertragen. Einem Cricketspiel folgen. Die Aussprache eines Mannes aus West Kerry verstehen. Schuhe oder Stiefel aus Gummi tragen. Im Streit mit P. J. das letzte Wort haben. Normal mit Männern reden, die Hemdkragen anhaben. Mich über Wasser halten. Ihre Witze verstehen. Mich zum Zahnarzt hintrauen. Einen Sonntag totschlagen. Nicht zurückdenken.

17

Ich drehe mich ganz um und betrachte die Männer. Sie knien, die Köpfe über die Schiebermützen und Rosenkränze gebeugt. Gesichter sehe ich keine, aber Matt ist da, seine Form würde ich überall erkennen. Die Köpfe bewegen sich nicht. Die Köpfe sind wie Eier, die ein Riesenvogel sacht in einer Reihe auf der hinteren Bank abgelegt hat. Die Haut auf ihren Köpfen ist trocken wie Papier und weiß, hier und da vielleicht spärlich mit den braunen Flecken des Alters gesprenkelt. Diese Haut sieht man überhaupt nur, wenn die Männer in die Kirche oder ins Bett gehen, sonst sind sie nie ohne Mütze.

Zwischen den Männern und mir sitzen die Menschen unserer Pfarrei. Sie rutschen nicht unruhig auf den Knien hin und her oder husten wie in einer normalen Messe. Sie heften den Blick auf den Priester. Wenn jemand bemerkt, dass ich schaue, senkt er kurz den Kopf und blickt dann wieder zum Altar hoch. Die Gesichter der jungen Burschen und Mädchen, die noch Kinder waren, als ich fortging, haben nun Gestalt und Kanten. In ihrem Blick liegt nicht mehr Einfalt, sondern Überzeugung oder Zweifel oder Nachdenklichkeit. Im Blick von Sarah McCabe schimmert Erwachen. In denen von Aunt Rosemary Tränen.

Das sind die Menschen, die Da vom Tag seiner Geburt an gesehen haben. Sie haben ihn am Fluss gesehen. Sie haben ihn Flöte spielen sehen. Sie haben ihn auf Brautschau gesehen. Sie sahen seine Kraft zu- und abnehmen. Manche waren mit ihm auf den englischen Feldern. Ihnen allen sehe ich das Gewicht der Arbeit an und

das Gewicht derer, die um sie herum geboren werden
und sterben. Wenn ich in ihre Köpfe schauen könnte,
würde ich alles herausholen, was sie von Da je gesehen
haben, und daraus einen langen Film machen, den ich
mir anschauen könnte. Ich würde ihm beim Tanzen
zusehen. Ich würde ihm an Deck eines Bootes zusehen.
Ich würde zusehen, wie er mit Ma zwischen den Hecken
ein paar Schritte macht, als sie noch jung waren.

Zwischen den Menschen in den Bänken und den
Männern, die hinten knien, ist der protestantische Junge, dem Da Flöte beigebracht hat. Er trägt einen schwarzen Anzug ohne eine einzige Falte und eine schwarze
Krawatte mit goldenen Streifen. Sein helles Haar ist sehr

ordentlich quer über den Kopf gekämmt. Er sieht aus, als würde er mit offenen Augen schlafen. Er hält die Arme gerade vor sich und hat die Flöte von Da. Bevor der Priester am Sarg das Gebet spricht, soll der Junge durch den Mittelgang nach vorne kommen und Da die Flöte auf den Sargdeckel legen.

Ich schaue auf diesen Sarg, Da ist darin. Ich sehe die Nägel blinken, die ihn verschließen. Mir fällt etwas ein, was ich fragen wollte, und ich drehe mich nach ihm um. Mir fällt ein, was ich von England gesehen habe, und ich überlege, wie ich es ihm beschreiben würde. Mir fällt eine Melodie ein, die ich ihm vorspielen will. Wie der Wind um die Mauern fährt und die Blätter über die Steine weht, wie der Priester das Gebet spricht, wie Dermots Schultern bis fast auf den Boden hängen, das alles ist deshalb so, weil er fort ist. Ma lässt den Priester nicht aus den Augen: als könnte sie auf seinem Gesicht die Zukunft lesen. Ihre Lippen sind schmal, fast weiß, die Haut um die Augen gespannt. Sie könnte aus Eis gehauen sein. Er ist nicht mehr von dieser Welt, denken wir. Und mir fällt dort an seinem Sarg außerdem ein, dass ich nie wieder einen lebenden Menschen so achten werde wie ihn, und jetzt, wo er fort ist, werde ich nicht mehr verhindern können, dass die Dinge aus ihrem gewohnten Platz fallen. Traurigkeit greift mir wie eine Klaue in Knochen und Eingeweide. Sie füllt die Zwischenräume. Sie ist schwer und mächtig. Ich glaube, diese Traurigkeit wird mir jetzt immer bleiben.

Der Priester steigt die Altarstufen hinab und gibt mit einem Nicken nach hinten das Zeichen. Ich drehe mich wieder nach dem Jungen um. Langsam macht er sich auf den Weg nach vorne. Wie er die Füße voreinander setzt,

das ist, als würde er auf wackligen Steinen einen Bach
überqueren. Einmal die Woche ist er vom Pfarrhaus seines Vaters aufgebrochen, ist mit dem Bus elf Meilen
gefahren, um bei Da Flöte spielen zu lernen, und am
Abend wieder elf Meilen zurück. Da hat gestaunt über
ihn, sagt Ma, über seine Ernsthaftigkeit, die Art, wie er
nach der Musik gefragt hat, wie er die Flöte gehalten hat,
wenn er spielen sollte. Als wäre es ein heiliges Relikt,
sagt Ma. Die ganze Woche sprach Da von dem Jungen
und wartete auf die nächste Stunde. Ich achte auf seine
Augen. Sie scheinen immer noch von diesem Schlaf
befallen. Die ganze Kirche schaut auf ihn. Dann wandert
sein Blick zu dem Sarg, und seine Augen werden groß.

Er holt Luft, als bekäme er keine. Sein rechtes Bein verweigert den Dienst, er tut den Mund auf und sagt »ich«. Er hat eine helle klare Stimme. Es klingt wie der Anfang von einem Lied. Es spricht seine Liebe zu Da. Und dann beginnt er zu fallen. Hände greifen nach ihm, und er sucht Halt am Gestühl. Aber es gibt keinen. Als er fällt, sehe ich in seinem Gesicht Leere und Schmerz. Ein dünner Faden Blut läuft von seiner Oberlippe, wie er dort auf dem Bretterboden der Kirche liegt. Die Flöte rollt ihm aus der Hand und durch den Mittelgang auf den Sarg zu.

18

Als er mir öffnet, nagt der Schneider an einer rohen Kartoffel. Seine Unterwäsche ist aus einem Stück, sie reicht von den Handgelenken bis zu den Fußknöcheln. Die Knöpfe stehen offen. Unter der Haut erkennt man alle Knochen seiner Brust. Das Haar wächst ihm in die Augen, aus der Nase, ins Gesicht, wie Binsengras, das aufgelassenes Weideland überwuchert. Er blinzelt im Hellen. In seinen Augen liegt eine Art Schrecken.

»Bist du's?«, fragt er mich.

»Ich bin es.«

»Was fehlt dir?« Seine Stimme ist dünn und hoch, als müsste er gleich weinen oder als hätte er Angst, dass die Antwort ihm schaden könnte.

»Ich hätte gern einen Anzug.«

»Einen Anzug.«

»Einen Anzug für sonntags, für Reisen und zum Tanzen.«

Er sieht mir ins Gesicht, als hätte ich ihm ein Rätsel
aufgegeben. Dann spricht er schließlich.

»Also gut«, sagt er.

Bei ihm im Haus riecht es nach umgestürzten Bäumen, die im Wasser gelegen haben. Dunkel ist es, es
brennt nur eine kleine Öllampe. Die Fenster sind mit
Zeitungspapier verhängt. Über dem Papstbild im Gold-
rahmen hat er mit Klebstreifen ein Taschentuch befes-
tigt, aber die Fingerringe und dicken Adern auf den
Rücken der gefalteten Hände sieht man trotzdem. Die
Kommode, einen Tisch und Stühle hat er in eine Ecke
geschoben und ein Laken darüber geworfen. Es gibt ein
Perdegeschirr und einen kleinen Pflug. Am Feuer steht

sein Stuhl mit den Zeitungen als Decke. Und mitten im Zimmer steht ganz für sich der Webstuhl, es ist nicht ein Staubkorn darauf zu sehen, und das feine Holz schimmert matt im Schein der Lampe.

Der Schneider zieht sich Hose, Hemd und Jacke über. Er fährt sich mit dem Kamm durchs Haar. Am Tisch holt er unter dem Laken aus der Schublade ein Maßband hervor, kniet sich vor mich hin und entrollt das Band innen am Schenkel.

»Sechs Jahre ist's her, seit ich einen Anzug gemacht habe«, sagt er.

Wie ein Nebelschwaden wandert er hinter meinen Rücken, dann kritzelt er die Maße an die Wand.

»Heute ist ihnen nur noch Ladenware gut genug«, sagt er.

Ich sehe seine braunen Finger die Ziffern runden, die Strähnen auf seinem Schädel, die nackten Knöchel in den Schuhen. Schuhen ohne Schnürsenkel. Ich sehe auf dem Fensterbrett aufgereihte Dosen, die vor Feuchtigkeit grünen Wände, die Zeitungen, mit denen er sich nachts zudeckt. Jetzt dreht er sich um, er schnauft schwer wie ein schlafender Hund, begegnet meinem Blick mit wässrigen Augen, öffnet und schließt den Mund, sucht nach Worten.

19

Seit der Beerdigung kann Ma ihre Hände nicht mehr still halten. Sie streicht Falten aus, zupft an Fäden, ordnet Haare, faltet Zeitungen, putzt die Augengläser, schürt das Feuer, bindet sich die Schnürsenkel, rückt

Bilder gerade, füttert den Hund, scheucht Hühner, zieht Schubladen auf, Strümpfe hoch, klopft im Takt zu unbestimmten Melodien. Es ist, als hätte sie innen ein Uhrwerk, das sie nicht ruhen lässt.

»Ob Dermot in der Stadt wohl auch zurechtkommt?«, fragt sie.

Sie sitzt am Feuer auf der Stuhlkante. Alle stieren zur Tür hinaus und sehen nichts. Niemand sagt etwas.

»Er holt das neue Gatter für die Weide mit den zwei Kühen. Hoffentlich denkt er an den weißen Zwirn, den er mir mitbringen soll.« Es ist, als wäre ihr Kopf eine Kreuzung, auf der viel los ist. »Und ich habe ihm gesagt, er soll nicht auf ein Bier bleiben.«

Jetzt wendet sie sich mir zu.

»Erzähl mir noch mal von Joe.«

Und ich muss ihr erzählen, wie er gewohnt hat, als ich ihn das eine Mal in Ipswich besucht habe, ob er mager war, ob seine Haut schlecht aussah, wie viel er trank.

»Hast du es bei der Polizei versucht?«

»Die würden mir nicht weiterhelfen können.«

»Das Register für die, die wählen?«

»Er wählt nicht.«

»Die Krankenhäuser?«

Ich antworte nicht. Sie trommelt mit den Fingern an die Wand.

»Mit meinem Uncle John war es das Gleiche. Am

Tag, als die Farm an meinen Vater ging, hat er ein paar Kleider in einen Sack geworfen und ist zur Tür hinaus. Wie hätten die anderen denn wissen sollen, dass sie ihn nie wieder sehen? Ein prächtiger Kerl. Stark wie ein Ackergaul, hieß es. Jeder, der aus England zurückkam, wurde gelöchert. Jeder, der rüberging, wollte Ausschau halten. Gebetet haben sie für ihn. Und du weißt ja, was passiert ist. Drei Monate hat er tot in einem Zimmer in Northampton gelegen, ehe man ihn fand. Masken mussten sie anlegen, um da überhaupt hinein zu können. An der Wand hing eine Fotografie von der Heimatinsel meiner Großmutter. Es war nicht einmal genug Geld da für die Überführung, damit er in der Heimat beerdigt werden könnte. Zweiundvierzig Jahre in England ohne eine Zeile nach Hause. Als hätte ihn eine Nebelbank verschluckt.« Sie steht auf, streckt die Hand nach dem Teekessel aus und setzt sich dann wieder. »Uncle John. Ja, den hätte ich gerne kennen gelernt.«

Dermots Frau erträgt es nicht mehr, sie geht in ihr Zimmer und zieht die Tür zu.

»Kannst du nicht eine Anzeige in der Zeitung aufgeben?«, fragt sie mich.

Sie murmelt etwas, es klingt wie Beten.

Am nächsten Tag bleibt sie lange im Bett, sie steht überhaupt nur auf, um mich zur Tür zu bringen. Die Schultern machen ihr neuerdings zu schaffen, sagt sie. Dann tritt sie einen Schritt zurück, um mich in meinem neuen Anzug zu bewundern. »Sehr ordentliche Arbeit«, sagt sie. »Ich hätte es ihm nicht mehr zugetraut.« Draußen ist der Himmel tief und sehr dunkel, und der Wind drückt das Gras und den Rauch aus den Schornsteinen runter. Wer überhaupt unterwegs ist, hält sich für sich.

Im ganzen Weiler bleiben die Türen verschlossen.
»Schlimmer Tag«, sagt Dermot auf dem Weg zum Bahnhof mehr als einmal. Ich ziehe ein Foto von Da aus der Tasche, das mir Matt geschenkt hat, an dem Tag aufgenommen, als Da in Dublin den Preis gewann. Er hält die Flöte ausgestreckt vor sich hin. Als könnte überhaupt nichts jemals schwer in seiner Hand wiegen. Matts Augen ruhen auf ihm, und auch die von der Frau in dem Umhang mit den Ringen. Ihre Hand ist erhoben, als wollte sie ihn etwas fragen, und sie lächelt auf eine Art, die ihm gefallen haben muss. Ihre Augen leuchten und sehen nur ihn. Ich würde gern wissen, was sie über ihn denkt, aber nicht, was sie fragen will, denn dieses Foto ist ohne Vergangenheit und Zukunft. Da höre ich plötzlich ein Heulen wie von einem Hund, der in einer Grube festsitzt. Es riecht verbrannt. Wir biegen mit dem Karren um die Ecke und sind jetzt auf der Höhe vom Schneider. Im Haus sehe ich ihn in seiner weißen Unterwäsche auf etwas zustürzen. Er hält eine Axt, und hinter ihm sehe ich Feuer. Er hebt die Axt, und als wir fast schon vorbei sind, sehe ich, was er tut. Er haut seinen Webstuhl in kleine Stücke, und er wirft die Stücke ins Feuer.

20

In der Rübenfabrik in Ipswich habe ich den Namen J. Brady angenommen, nach dem Namen in der Jacke, die mir Ma am Markttag gekauft hat. Als der Zahlmeister wissen wollte, wofür das J steht, habe ich fast gesagt: Jupiter, weil ich an P. J. dachte und seinen Wunsch nach einem Fernrohr. Aber ich brachte noch gerade

rechtzeitig »Joe« raus. Jeden Sonntag bin ich nach der Messe in ein anderes Pub gegangen, aber von Joe hatte niemand gehört. »Was hatte er denn sonst noch für Namen?«, fragte mich ein Mann aus Tipperary.

In der Rübenfabrik zu arbeiten war, als säße man an

einem heißen Sommertag in einer feuchten Heumiete. Ganz oben unterm Dach gab es klitzekleine Fenster, hinter denen man blauen Himmel sah, und die Pressen sorgten für mächtig viel Hitze und Dampf. Im Schweiße verrichtete man hier seine Arbeit und atmete praktisch nur Dampfwolken. Ich mochte es nie, wenn es im Salat rote Rüben gab, weder den Geschmack noch wie sie den Teller verfärbten. Es gab Maschinen zum Herankarren der Rüben, Maschinen für die Zuckergewinnung und Maschinen, die das übrig Gebliebene zu Nassschnitzeln zerstampften. Ich musste gebückt dastehen, einen Jutesack aufhalten und warten, dass die Schnitzel von der Rutsche geschossen kamen. Ich machte immer einen Zentner voll, nähte den Sack zu und stellte ihn beiseite, damit er abgeholt und ans Vieh verfüttert werden konnte. Lieber hätte ich gefüttert als gefüllt. Die Rübensaison war kurz, aber nähen habe ich gelernt, immerhin.

Wenn ich an Derbyshire denke, dann denke ich an den nebligen blauen Dunst morgens und die Bergleute darin. Warum sie so verloren aussehen, weiß ich nicht, eigentlich haben sie viel gelacht. Sie haben Hügel auf so ähnliche Art geköpft, wie man Frühstückseier aufschlägt. Wir mussten die Siebe für die Erzwäschereien aufstellen. Schwarz-Glücks-Johnny gehörte zu unserer Kolonne. Dann ein langes trauriges Laster aus der Gegend, das sie Niesel nannten. Außerdem Ackergaul McGurk, der Banjo spielte. Und Francie Meehan. Er nannte sich Gallagher, nach einem Hurler aus Donegal, und ich mich Rose nach einem von denen, die die Flöte gebaut hatten, die mit Da ins Grab ging. In der Unterkunft mussten wir beide, Francie und ich, uns ein Bett teilen. Er war wirklich elend lang, und er schlief auf dem Rücken, und wenn ich morgens aufwachte, sah ich als Erstes seine weißen Füße zur Decke zeigen. Manchmal zuckten sie, als wäre gerade eine Fliege darauf gelandet. »O weh, diese Füße«, sagte ich einmal zu ihm. Er sah mich an, als würden wir beide allein im Regen an einem Berghang stehen. »Ich weiß«, sagte er. »Es gibt kaum einen schlimmeren Anblick als ein anderes Mannsstück.«

Beim Goose Fair in Nottingham habe ich mit Francie und seinem Vetter Martin aus Glenties im Zelt auf einer langen Bank gesessen und zugesehen, wie ein Boxer, den sie den Tornado nannten, die Herausforderung eines schwarzen Mannes annahm, der in Hosen und Unterhemd gegen ihn antrat. Es war Sommer, und die Frauen draußen alle in ihren dünnen Kleidern unterwegs. Trotzdem war es ein Mordsspaß dort im Zelt. Für zwei Pfund gabs drei Runden im Ring gegen den Tornado, und wer ihn schlug, kriegte zehn. Einen Farmknecht und einen Turmarbeiter hatte er schon flachgelegt, aber dieser schwarze Mann, der trieb ihn Wunder wie in die Enge. Der ließ Schlag auf Schlag folgen, bis der Tornado die Hände sinken ließ. Dann setzte er nach. Die Kombinationen prasselten auf ihn ein wie eine Hand voll Steine, die man gegen die Wand schleudert. Er schlug eine lange Rechte an die Schläfe, und da ging der Tornado zu Boden, und das Blut schoss ihm in einem Schwall aus dem Mund.

»Jetzt«, sagte Francie, und drehte sich zu mir um. »Jetzt kannst du zeigen, was in dir steckt. Du bist der rechte Mann dazu. Er ist jetzt angeschlagen.«

Wir hatten draußen jeder zwei Pints und zwei Whiskey gehabt, und nachher sollten es noch ein paar mehr werden. Da war so eine Hitze im Zelt, dass ich mich gelockert und stark fühlte. Die Adern an meinen Armen standen vor, das Blut kreiste darin. Mir war, als könnte ich den ganzen Ring wegheben, notfalls. Francie und Martin gaben mir jeder ein Pfund. Ich musste an damals denken, als Da einen Sack mit Sand gefüllt und mir und Joe gezeigt hat, wie wir die Kraft für die Schläge aus den Beinen nehmen müssen. Ich schwenkte also in der Rechten die Scheine und stieg in den Ring. Ich dachte, ich könnte es wie John Joe damals im Zug machen und dem Tornado mit dem Umfang meiner Arme Respekt einflößen, aber als ich das Geld überreicht hatte und ihm vorgestellt wurde, maß er mich mit einem Blick und zwinkerte mir zu. Wir standen uns gegenüber. Ich schlug eine Linke und wollte mit einer Rechten in die Magengrube nachsetzen. Sechsmal holte ich aus, und alle Schläge schob er weg. Wie einer, der an einem Sommertag müde Bienen verscheucht, weil sie ihm lästig werden. Er tippte mir zweimal an die Stirn und landete eine rechte Gerade unter meinem Auge. Das war, als würden aus dem Himmel Baumstämme auf dich herunterpoltern. Dann schob er mich an den Achseln in die Seile.

»Wo kommst du her, Kleiner?«, fragte er. Ich sagte es ihm. »Wusst ich's doch. Ich bin von zwei Pfarren weiter. Leg dich brav hin, wenn ich jetzt zuschlage, dann können wir zusammen einen trinken gehen.«

»Der vor mir hat dich geschlagen, und das werde ich auch«, sagte ich. Ich dachte an die zehn Pfund und wie Francie und Martin mich ansehen würden. Ich stieß ihn zurück.

»Ist dir denn nicht klar, dass der und ich Partner sind?«, meinte er.

»Feiner Partner, dass er dir die Visage zerschlägt«, sagte ich.

»Beim Kampf haben wir beide einen kleinen Ballon mit Wasserfarbe im Mund«, sagte der Tornado. Es klang flehentlich. Ich holte mit der Rechten zu einem Haken aus, der eine halbe Armlänge an seinem Kopf vorbeiflog.

»Hast du Frau und Kinder?«, fragte er.

»Nein.«

»Ist es nicht schrecklich, was ich tun muss?«

Ich schlug nach seiner Oberlippe, er ging leicht in die Hocke, als wollte er die Rechte von ganz unten auf dem

Boden hochbringen, dann schlug er aber eine linke Gerade, die ich nicht einmal kommen sah, einen Volltreffer aufs Kinn. Ich ging wie eine abgeschossene Krähe zu Boden. Komisch, dass es gar nicht weh tut, wenn es sauber gemacht ist.

Welchen Namen ich in Nottingham benutzte, weiß ich nicht mehr. Wir verbrachten am Abend des Goose Fair noch schöne Stunden im Pub; der Schwarze erzählte uns, er wäre in Amerika Sparringspartner von Sugar Ray Robinson gewesen. Damals bauten wir gerade eine Straße, ich machte auf der einen Seite vom Stampfer den Beton glatt, Francie auf der anderen. Uns blieb selbst nach dem, was nach Hause ging, noch reichlich Geld über, und wir haben alles vertrunken. Cleary nannte ich mich, glaube ich, nach einem Priester.

In Kent haben wir Luftschutzbunker abgebrochen. Die waren die Hölle, manche jedenfalls, weil in die Mauern und Decken Stahltrossen gezogen waren. Francie wurde von einem Betonbrocken getroffen, der vom Meißel des Presslufthammers sprang. Das Blut lief ihm ins Auge, und er sah mich an, als müsste die Welt sich darauf gefasst machen, seinen Tod zu beklagen, aber ich sagte zu ihm, das sei nicht halb so wild wie der Treffer, den ich beim Goose Fair vom Tornado hätte einstecken müssen, als er mich in den Ring geschickt hätte, und da war er still. Schön waren die Obstgärten am Sonntag, der Duft der Äpfel. Es gab dort ein Mädchen. Margaret Bracewell. Sie verkaufte in einem Laden Zeitungen und Süßigkeiten. Ich schaute abends bei ihr rein und blieb manchmal eine geschlagene Stunde. Sie hatte wegen der Bomben im Krieg bei Nonnen in Dorset gewohnt, und die seien sehr gut zu ihr gewesen, sagte sie. Sie hatten ihr beige-

bracht, Spitze zu häkeln, und in der Zeit, die sie dort
verbrachte, hatte sie ein Altartuch gefertigt. Sie hatte
wunderschöne kleine Hände. Eines Sonntags sind wir
ein paar Schritte gegangen, über Hügel und an den Obstgärten und dem Apfelduft vorbei, und haben die ganze
Zeit ununterbrochen geredet, aber als wir am Gartentor
angelangt waren, wo sie wohnte, gingen mir mehr Dinge
durch den Kopf, als im Mund Platz hatten, und ich
stand auf der Straße und konnte nichts sagen. Ich weiß
noch, wie sie seufzte. Ich weiß noch, wie sie die Achseln
hob und durch die Gartenpforte zur Tür ging. Sie hatte
Backen wie die Äpfel. In Kent legte ich mir den Namen

Patterson zu, nach einem Ort in Amerika, wo Verwandte von Ma wohnten.

In Bedford habe ich Platten gelegt. In Coventry waren es Abflussrohre. Dann gab es die Baustelle in Barnet, vier Morgen waren das bestimmt, da habe ich hauptsächlich Fensterläden angebracht. In Blackheath habe ich eine Woche die Tragmulde geschleppt, aber es haperte bei mir mit dem Gleichgewicht. McNamara habe ich mich zeitweilig genannt, nach dem Lied, das die Amerikaner singen. O'Neill nach dem großen König aus dem Norden. Loss nach dem Kapellmeister. Damals konntest du sonstwo auf einer Baustelle sein, und die Hälfte der Männer nannte sich Michael Collins, aus Jux. In Chelsea habe ich mit Francie untermauert. Damals lag er singend auf den Knien im Dreck.

Voll Motten in der Liffey Street musst Möbel ich verkaufen,
und für die Bank mit einem Schild den lieben Tag lang laufen.
Heu schlug ich in der New Street los, in Spitalfields war's Speck.
Und Körb' ich flocht nach alter Art an der Fishamble Street am Eck.

Um den englischen Zahlmeister zu ärgern, nannte er sich Nasser, und ich benutzte den Namen Wilson, nach dem Jungen, der bei Da Flöte lernte. Wilson fühlte sich komisch an, aber ich dachte, ich versuche es. Francie und ich waren vor zwei anderen Männern auf der Kilburn High Road unterwegs. »Die sind aus Clare«, zischelte Francie mir zu. »Das erkennt man an der Art, wie sie pfeifen.« Sie waren vielleicht zehn Jahre älter als wir. »Die Heimat werdet ihr nicht wieder sehen, Jungs!«, rief der eine mit dem weit zurückgeschobenen schwarzen

Strohhut uns zu, und da lachten die beiden. Wir hatten
eine Bude in der Cavendish Road bei einer Wirtin
namens Chandler. Ich will mich jetzt nicht mit ihr aufhalten. Sie hatte uns an diesem Sonntagmorgen Eier und
Speck vorgesetzt, mit Blutwurst, und wir gingen in der
hellen Sonne ohne die Messe ganz bis nach Cricklewood
und dort gleich Schlag zwölf in den Crown. Es war der
Tag vom Endspiel im All-Ireland, und es wurden Wetten
notiert und die Pints jagten sich nur so. Mein Akkordeon
war auf der Bude, aber ein Kerryman ließ mir das seine,
und ich spielte für alle »The Golden Castle«. Wir kauften
uns Stout in Flaschen zum Mitnehmen und zogen mit
unseren Transistorradios zum Alexandra Palace, Francie,

Martin, ich und noch ein Vetter von den beiden, ein weißgesichtiger Hänfling namens Ivan, der über die heimatliche Pfarrei nie hinausgekommen war. Sein Lebtag hatte er in den Bergen mit dem Vater Schafe gehütet. An der Kreuzung Archway mussten wir den Verkehr abwarten, und er war am Schlottern. »So schnell, diese Wagen!« Er hängte sich an Martins Arm wie ein Ertrinkender. Ein Bus hielt, und als er wieder losfuhr, standen wir in grauem Rauch. »O je, Martin!«, hörte ich Ivan rufen. »Der Bus!« Ich konnte ihn vor Rauch kaum erkennen. Dann beugte er sich vornüber und gab sein ganzes Frühstück von sich, direkt vor uns auf die Straße. Ich sah, wie sich der gelbe Glibber vom Ei, das er gegessen hatte, durch das andere zog. »Der Bus«, wiederholte er. »Ich würde ja nichts weiter sagen«, meinte Francie, »aber er hat im Crown doch nur Sprudel getrunken.« Als wir am

Alexandra Palace ankamen, war der Hügelrücken schwarz vor Iren, die an ihren Radios drehten und den Sender von daheim suchten. Wir tranken unser Stout und lauschten dem Aufschrei am Hügel, wenn Punkte gemacht wurden, und später – die Sonne schien immer noch nieder – spielten wir eine Runde Twenty-fives. Das war der Tag vom Endspiel im All-Ireland, und ich gewann beim Kartenspiel vier Pfund. »Habt ihr gewusst, dass sie hier ein Standbild von Oliver Cromwell haben?«, fragte Francie. »Ich habe es mit eigenen Augen gesehen.« Wir waren im Oberdeck vom Bus auf dem Weg nach Kilburn. Ivan hielt ein Taschentuch, das mit einem roten Zwirn zu einem Beutel gebunden war. Er löste den Zwirn und hielt mir mit einem breiten Grinsen sein Tuch hin. »Heimaterde aus Donegal«, sagte er. »Er hat eigentlich Priester werden wollen«, sagte Martin. Zur Erklärung. »Aber er trinkt einfach nicht genug!«, bemerkte Francie, und wir mussten alle lachen, auch Ivan. Wir aßen alle eine Portion Bauchspeck und machten uns dann auf den Weg in den Old Bell. Ein kleiner runder Mann mit einem zornigen Gesicht unter der Hutkrempe schob uns eine Kinderkarre entgegen. Auf dem Sitz hatte er einen Karton, und er bahnte sich mit schrillen Misstönen auf seiner Mundharmonika den Weg frei. Wer nicht schnell genug beiseite ging, den verfluchte er. Ich musste an Baby denken und wie Da sie immer gegrüßt hat, und da holte mich alles wieder ein. Wir hatten im Old Bell ein paar Pints und im Volunteer ein paar Pints und im Black Lion. Das war der Tag vom Endspiel im All-Ireland und ein Tag, an dem mich das Glück nicht im Stich ließ, denn an dem Tag sah ich erstmals Maggie Doyle. Sie trug ein sandfarbenes Kleid und rote Schuhe, und sie ging durch den Raum wie auf einer Wolke, nur ganz wenig vorgebeugt, das rote Haar wie ein Vorhang vor dem linken Auge, ihre Miene verschlossen, der Mund leicht geöffnet, aber dann ging ein Lächeln über ihr Gesicht, breitete sich von den Mundwinkeln in die Augen aus, bis sie Wunder wie strahlte, als sie sich schließlich neben einer Frau mit einem breitkrempigen Strohhut niederließ. Ich erinnere mich nicht nur, wie sie aussah, als sie in den Pub hineinkam, sondern genauso an das Gefühl im Pub unmittelbar vorher, den Rauch, der von den Zigaretten aufstieg, den Jungen, der Zeitungen verkaufte, den Sligoman im grauen Anzug mit dem Geigenkasten auf den Knien, der sich mit dem Finger leise an die Augenbraue tippte. Francie, der Ivan beschwor, einen Whiskey zu trinken. Dann kam Maggie, und in meiner Erinnerung verschwimmt alles andere. Ich glaube, einmal schaut sie von ihrem Platz kurz zu mir herüber, aber vielleicht auch nicht. Ich habe mein Akkordeon mit, und als ich »Come West Along the Road« spiele, steht Ackergaul McGurk auf, zieht Hemd und Unterhemd aus und tanzt mit einem Stuhl zwischen den Zähnen um die Tische. Ich denke an die Fältchen um ihren Mund, wenn sie lacht, den wachen Geist, der sich darin zeigt. »Prächtig gespielt«, sagt sie zu mir auf dem Weg hinaus. Sie sieht dabei über die Schulter zurück. Der Tag vom Endspiel im All-Ireland. Vielleicht will sie es schon sagen, seit sie die Melodie erkannt hat.

21

Wenn unsere Wirtin die Tür auflässt, ist das für Francie das Zeichen, dass ihr Mann zum Busdepot aufgebrochen ist und er hochkommen soll. Das ging schon in der zweiten Woche mit ihm los, und danach ist er, sobald die Tür nur angelehnt war, zur Stiege gehetzt wie ein Windhund. Ich habe nie etwas zu sehen bekommen. »Wie sieht es da drinnen aus?«, habe ich ihn gefragt. »Alles rosa«, hat er in einem Ton gesagt, als wäre es ein großes Wunder.

Einmal hat sie ihn zwei Wochen ausgesperrt, weil sie ihm nämlich wegen der Sache mit dem Rauch grollte. Ich komme aus dem Bad ins Zimmer zurück, das Haar nass zurückgekämmt, den Anzug vom Schneider an, denn es ist Mittwoch und ich will zum Bamba-Tanz. Francie sitzt auf einem Stuhl, hat die Füße aufs Bett hochgelegt und den *Donegal Democrat* auf dem Schoß liegen. Auf dem Gaskocher dampft im Topf ein Schweinskopf vor sich hin. Francie trägt noch Arbeitskluft, und seine Lider flattern. »Schlaf bloß nicht ein«, sage ich zu ihm, ehe ich gehe. Maggie ist nicht zum Tanz erschienen, das weiß ich noch. Ich habe die Tür im Auge behalten. Als ich in die Cavendish Road auf unsere Bude zurückkomme, liegt Francie dick und fett auf dem Bett und schnarcht, Zeitung auf dem Gesicht und das Zimmer von Rauch eingenebelt wie frühmorgens in den Bergen, Topf mitsamt Schweinskopf schwarz wie ein Stiefel. Am nächsten Morgen hat uns Mrs. Chandler beim Frühstück beäugt, als müsste sie über das Strafmaß erst noch nachdenken, Verbannung vielleicht, statt dessen hat sie ihn dann ausgesperrt.

Eines Morgens bin ich ihm auf der Stiege begegnet, er trug die Schuhe in der Hand. Er sah aus wie ein zerknittertes Laken. »Eine Stunde Schlaf hat sie mir nur gelassen«, sagte er. »Immer, wenn ich gerade einnicken wollte, fing sie wieder an. Schlimmer als im Regen einen Graben ausheben.« Wir legten zu der Zeit Bahntrassen, und das war eine rechte Knochenschinderei. Als dann irgendwann die Katze mit den grünen Augen ins Zimmer geschlichen kam und Francie ansprang, hat er sie gleich mit einem Fußtritt durchs offene Fenster befördert. Wenn Francie seinen Schlaf nicht kriegte, konnte er ungemütlich werden. Wo immer die Katze gelandet ist, sie muss wohl am Küchenfenster vorbeigefallen sein, denn gleich darauf stand Mrs. Chandler in der Schürze im Zimmer und pfefferte unsere Sachen die Stiege hinunter. Wir stapften die Kilburn High Road entlang. »Der Wirtin darfst du's besorgen«, meinte Francie, »aber vergreif dich nicht an der Katze.«

22

Als Francie nach Portsmouth geht, Gasleitungen legen, bin ich auf der Bude sehr einsam. Diesmal sind wir in einem Untergeschoss in der Quex Road. In diesem Zimmer hängt nur ein Bild von einem blonden Jungen beim Kühemelken in einem blauen Holzrahmen, und das macht alles bloß schlimmer. Das Zimmer kriegt so gut wie kein Licht. Unter der Woche genehmige ich mir im Old Bell ein paar Pints und esse auf dem Rückweg in die Quex Road was in Zeitung Eingewickeltes zum Mitnehmen. Eines Abends sehe ich nach der Polizeistunde vor mir auf der Straße einen Kerl mit rotem Haar, verdreckten Stiefeln, Hängearschhose und einer aufgerollten Zeitung in der Jackentasche hergehen, wegen der Biere braucht er die volle Breite vom Gehweg, und ich weiß, das bin ich. Das sind wir alle. Sonntags erst in die Messe und dann in den Crown, und ab zwei ist es die Hölle. Ich hänge über dem Geländer und rauche Zigaretten, die nicht schmecken. Ich lese die Zeitung und schaffe keine Geschichte ganz. Ich drehe das Radio auf, aber die Wörter gehen an mir vorbei. Wir haben eine Uhr, da hefte ich den Blick drauf. Die Minuten vergehen wie Wasser, das aus dem Hahn tropft. Irgendwann so gegen sechs rücken die Wände immer näher.

Ich weiß, es wird etwas Schlimmes passieren.

Im obersten Stock lebt ein Mann aus Belfast, der trägt immer Anzug und Krawatte. Bei dem ist es unter den Augen ganz dunkel, und in den Augen auch, du findest ihn nicht, wie in einem Keller, wo nur ein winziges, schmutziges Fenster Licht hereinlässt. Er hat Manieren wie ein Mesner. Er lupft den Hut ganz vom Kopf, wenn er dich grüßt. Schauspieler ist er: Albert Maskey aus der Ormeau Road in Belfast. Man wundert sich, wie er das macht, denn kaum will er etwas Schwieriges erklären, kommt er ins Stottern. Im Staub und grauen Licht vom

Stiegenhaus sehe ich ihn ein Schälchen Milch für die Katze rausstellen. Wenn er nicht anderweitig beschäftigt ist, säubert und feilt er sich die Fingernägel. »Ein Schauspieler muss allzeit gepflegt sein«, sagt er. Wenn er etwas in der Art gesagt hat, schiebt sich seine rechte Augenbraue Richtung Stirn hoch, als würden ihn seine Worte selbst überraschen.

Abends Punkt sechs genehmigt er sich gern ein Glas Scotch, und irgendwie hat es sich so ergeben, dass ich donnerstags zu ihm raufgehe. Nie habe ich bei ihm das Bett ungemacht gesehen oder in der Tagesdecke auch nur eine Delle. Socken und Pullover zusammengefaltet auf einem Bord. Für die Flaschen eine Glasvitrine. Auf dem Tisch schon fürs Frühstück Tasse und Untertasse und Teekanne. In der Ecke steht eine kleine Flasche mit abgeschraubtem Deckel und einer grünen Flüssigkeit, die Wunder wie frisch nach Bäumen riechen soll. Es könnte das Zimmer von einem sein, der einen Bischof oder so jemand im Wagen herumfährt, wären da nicht die gerahmten Bilder von Frauen auf dem Bord über dem Bett. Daneben liegt eine Krone aus Gips, mit Goldfarbe bemalt. Hat er sie auf der Bühne getragen? »Noch nicht«, sagt er mir, die Augen dunkle Schatten.

Ich frage ihn nach den Frauen.

»Ich habe sie alle gekannt, weißt du«, sagt er. Er lacht, aber das Lachen stirbt schnell wie das Bellen eines müden Hundes. Er steht von seinem Stuhl auf und setzt sich die Brille auf die Nase. Er nennt jede beim Namen. Rita, Eustace, Marie-Thérèse, Lucy. Hat er die aus dem Hausbuch der Heiligen? Es gibt eine, die er die Prinzessin nennt, mit schwarzem Haar, sie wirkt überrascht, aber das gefällt ihr. Alle haben sie Zähne von diesem leuchtenden Weiß, wie man es von den Stars kennt. Einige tragen Reifen im Haar, und man sieht ihre Figuren genau, weil ihre Kleider so eng sind. Eine trägt ein langes Gewand, gold und weiß, bis zum Boden, ihr blondes Haar ist hochgesteckt und ringelt sich im Nacken, an den Ohren hat sie Diamanten. Zu jedem Namen erzählt er mir die Romanze. Mit der einen hat er auf dem Kreuzschiff gearbeitet, das in Barcelona ablegte. Das Mädchen aus Dublin wollte Nonne werden. Die in Derby, die die Kleopatra gespielt hat, hat er einem anderen Schauspieler ausgespannt. Die Grönländerin hat er im Museum kennen gelernt, wo er Grabkunst bewunderte. Irgendwie spielen Orte wie Lissabon, Istanbul und Tanger eine Rolle. »Ich war viel beschäftigt, ich bin viel herumgekommen«, sagt er. »Ich habe viele geliebt.« Und wieder das ersterbende Lachen, dem du nicht so recht glaubst.

Francie kehrt von der Arbeit in Portsmouth zurück, und ich lebe wieder etwas solider. Wir essen jeden Abend im Café. Wir wechseln die Schuhe, ehe wir in den Pub gehen. Wir bringen die Sonntage mit Karten rum oder langen Spaziergängen.

Manchmal kündigen sich Dinge, die passieren, vorher an. Wie damals im Pub, als sich rings um mich alles weiterdrehte, ich aber ganz still wurde, und dann Maggie erschien. An diesem Abend sitze ich plötzlich senkrecht im Bett, als hätte mir jemand mit der Trillerpfeife ins Ohr geblasen. Ich lasse mich ins Kissen zurücksinken, aber an Schlaf ist nicht zu denken. Die Uhr zeigt zehn nach zwei. Draußen geht ein leiser Wind, und die Schatten der Bäume im Garten tanzen über das Bild von dem Melkjungen und der Kuh. Ich liege im Bett am Fenster,

Francie drüben an der Wand. Ich sehe, wie sich sein Rücken im Schlaf hebt und senkt. Was soll ich machen, während ich warte? Ich versuche, mich durch sämtliche Noten von »The Green-Crowned Lass« zu denken. Dann höre ich einen Krach, irgendetwas stürzt durch die Äste, Holz splittert, dann rumst es, als würde eine Ladung Holz heruntergedonnert kommen, weil ein Zugseil reißt. Ich höre ein schwaches Stöhnen, dann Stille, stiller noch als zuvor. Den Wind höre ich nicht mehr. Ich ziehe die Gardine auf. Von der Erde starren mich die weiten dunklen Augen von Albert Maskey an. Oben ist sein Kopf etwas eingedrückt auf der Seite, wo er aufgeschlagen ist, und ein gebrochener Arm liegt quer über Brust und Schulter, Handteller nach oben und offen, als würde er um etwas bitten. Er hat Dreck im Mund. Er trägt Anzug und Krawatte, alles tipptopp, und die goldene Krone vom Bord über seinem Bett.

Ich bin nie dahinter gekommen.

An dem Abend, als er mir von den Mädchen erzählte, habe ich mir die Fotos genauer angesehen, ehe ich ging. Wie sie sich aufgebaut hatten, Hand in der Hüfte, Blick über die Schulter. Das Papier war ganz dünn, und bei manchen waren die Ränder ungleich. Er hatte sie aus Zeitschriften ausgeschnitten und gerahmt.

Das war schlimm, was Albert Maskey passiert ist, aber es war nicht das, was mich bedrängte, als die Wände immer näher rückten.

23

Um zum Friedhof zu gelangen, muss man über Sand
gehen. Der Friedhof ist ein von Seewinden blank
geblasenes Rund aus Erde und Gras und Stein im Wasser und nur durch die schmale Sandbank vor Babys Haus
mit dem Festland verbunden. Als Da hier die Stute
begrub, hat es nachmittags geregnet, aber jetzt ist es klar.
Im Abendlicht wird das Grün vom Gras noch grüner, die
Steine sind mit Silberstichen gesäumt, Gold dümpelt
glitzernd auf dem Wasser, steigt und sinkt, und die
Schatten der Grabsteine sind lang. Alles wie eh und je

auf den Gräbern. Kinderschuhe, halb fertige Pullover, Blumen, Münzen, Fotografien, eine Mundharmonika, eine Kappe. Im Hals einer Stout-Flasche steckt eine Nachricht auf einem zusammengerollten Zettel. Der Totengräber mit dem blonden Haar und den unteren Zähnen, die über die Oberlippe hochstehen, fegt mit seinem Besen, wo es eben geht. »Das Unglück von den Gräbern fernhalten«, sagt er wieder und wieder.

Auf dem Grab der Stute liegt nichts weiter, nur die Matschklumpen nach dem Regen vom Nachmittag. Als er sie erschossen hat, um ihrem Klagen ein Ende zu machen, meint Da, er will dem Fohlen ein Stück vom Schweif schneiden und ihr aufs Grab legen. Ich sitze auf der Mauer und sehe zu, wie die Sonne hinter dem Friedhof versinkt. Matt ist dagewesen und hat seiner Frau einen Teller Brombeeren aufs Grab gestellt, aber er und der Totengräber sind jetzt beide fort. Die Schatten zerrinnen zu nichts, als die Sonne versinkt. Für ein Pferd muss das Grab zweimal so lang und so breit sein wie beim Menschen. Ich höre ein Jammern, einen halb erstickten, kläglichen Laut. Ich kann ihn nicht orten, aber ich weiß, dass er aus der Erde kommt. Er wird schwächer, dann schwillt er an zur wilden Klage. Ich kenne ihn. Es ist das Wehklagen der todkranken Stute. Dann sehe ich, wie sich der Dreck auf ihrem Grab bewegt, mahlt, wie die Klumpen, von unten heftig umgewühlt, aufbrechen, zerbröckeln und rollen. Ich spüre die enorme Kraftanstrengung dahinter, während sich meine Finger um die Mauersteine krallen, eine Kraft, die stärker ist als die lastende Erde von oben. Ein Huf bricht hervor, scharrt in der Luft, eine Liebkosung. Dann beide lehmverschmierte Vorderläufe. Sie strampeln und treten, die Hufe sinken

tief in den Dreck, dann geht ein Ruck verhaltener Kraft durch die Erde, noch mal, und nun hievt sich die Stute mit einer gewaltigen Anstrengung hoch, klitschnass, verdreckt, dass die Lehmbrocken fliegen, und aus der Wunde am Kopf, wo Da die Flinte aufgesetzt hat, läuft immer noch Blut. Sie schüttelt das Grab ab und wirft den Kopf. Dann richtet sich ihr Auge auf mich.

Gott im Himmel. Vier Uhr früh. Mir ist, als wäre ich im Dunkeln von einem Baugerüst ins Nichts getreten. Mein Herz rast. Ich höre auf der Stiege den Tritt des Mädchens, das unter mir wohnt. Sie hat Mühe, das Schlüsselloch zu finden. Das eine oder andere Glas zuviel, vermutlich, und warum auch nicht. Draußen fährt

der Nachtbus vorbei. Einsame Geräusche. Das ist das
Bett, in dem Maggie sich an Träume erinnerte. Sie konnte einem Träume bis ins Kleinste erzählen. Ich will keine Träume mehr. Es gibt keinen, der mir nicht irgendwie
zu schaffen machen würde. Wo habe ich bloß so ein
Pferd her?

Der Friedhof. Mrs. Carney sagt mir, dass ihr Mann
krank ist und dass ich für das Grab wohl selbst sorgen
muss. Sie verschwindet in einem Schuppen, kommt mit
einem Spaten zurück und drückt ihn mir in die Hand.
Dermot trinkt seit Mas Todesstunde Whiskey, also ist es
an mir. »Wo soll ich denn graben?«, frage ich sie. »Du
wirst den Sarg deines Vaters hochholen müssen und

das Grab groß genug machen für alle beide.« Sie geht wieder hinein und zieht die Tür zu. Da stehe ich vor dieser Tür, der roten, blätternden Farbe, dem Türklopfer aus Messing mit Namen, den ihnen wahrscheinlich die eine Tochter in Schottland geschickt hat. Warum können sie sie nicht einmal ordentlich streichen? Warum kann er nicht graben? Am liebsten würde ich das Spatenblatt durch die Tür treiben.

Meine Mutter verstirbt im Monat November. Dunkle Wolken wälzen sich an den Hang, als ich mit Carneys Spaten über die Sandbank zum Friedhof marschiere. »Sie haben sie aufgemacht, und es war alles voll Krebs«, hat Dermots Frau gesagt. »Regelrecht schwarz. Besser, dass sie nicht lang hat leiden müssen.« Ich finde Da und fange an zu graben. In der Erde sind Holzsplitter, ein Knopf von einem Frauenkleid, Nägel, Muscheln, die die Möwen fallen gelassen haben, eine Scherbe von gutem Sonntagsgeschirr, eine Kaffeedose aus Amerika. Sie haben sie aufgemacht, und innen war alles schwarz. Wie viel halte ich aus? Ich grabe. Alles bebt. Ich grabe, bis ich Da habe. Mir ist, als könnte schon die Luft mir die Knochen brechen. Ich schaufele den Sarg frei und hieve ihn hoch. Nicht herausfallen, flehe ich ihn an. Es beginnt zu regnen. Ich steige wieder ins Grab, um weiterzugraben. Ich sinke auf die Knie. Ich bitte um Hilfe, egal von wo. Als das Grab tief genug ist, will ich herausklettern, aber ich gleite im Lehm immer wieder ab. Ich greife nach Grasbüscheln, nach den Seiten der Grabsteine, ich ziehe mich hoch, dann schiebe ich den Sarg näher an die Grube heran. Ich liege bäuchlings im Dreck und lasse ihn sachte hinunter. Bitte, lieber Gott, lass das Holz ganz bleiben. Ich höre ihn drinnen herumrollen. Dann habe

ich den Sarg schließlich unten im Grab, ich bringe ihn in
die Waagerechte und bette Gras darüber. Was ist mir? Ich
weiß noch, wie sich der Zorn angefühlt hat, als der Zahl-
meiser in Blackheath mich um den vollen Lohn prellen
wollte. Ich weiß noch, wie es sich angefühlt hat, als Kate
Creevy in den Zug stieg. Ich weiß noch, wie sich die Ein-
samkeit angefühlt hat, und die Mauern der Quex Road.
Ich weiß, wie sich schiere Trauer anfühlt. Das hier ist
nichts von alledem, oder vielleicht von allem ein bisschen und noch mehr. Nur, was ist dieses Mehr? Ich sehe
mich über den Friedhof hetzen, über die Mauer und ins

Meer. Denn es wird weder im Schlaf noch im Trunk Trost geben. Es ist, als legte sich etwas auf mich, das mir die Luft nimmt. Es ist, als würde sich etwas bewegen, was in mir was zerbricht.

Als ich in London ankomme, habe ich keine Ahnung von Ziegeln mehr. Der Zug fährt durch Tunnel und Schächte und an Gebäuden vorbei, die alle aus Ziegelsteinen von der Farbe getrockneten Bluts gemacht sind. Aus Ziegeln werden Mauern, aus hartem pockennarbigen Lehm werden Ziegel. Ich stelle mir die vielen, vielen Ziegel und die vielen, vielen kleinen Löcher vor, manche kaum größer als Nadelstiche. Wie kann es nur so viele Ziegelsteine geben? Wie kann es nur die Zeit geben, sie alle Schicht für Schicht aufeinander zu mauern? Wenn ich in der Quex Road im Bett liege, stelle ich mir ein Gebäude vor und wie viele Ziegel für die ganze Vorderseite nötig sind. Dann gehe ich über die Gesamtlänge nach oben und zähle die Reihen. Ich stelle mir die fehlenden Steine vor, wo Türen und Fenster sind und wo das Gebäude aufhört, denn es kann ja nicht bis in den Himmel hochwachsen, und ich versuche, die Zahl der Ziegelsteine in der Wand auszurechnen, auf die ich blicke. Ein Gebäude hat Vorder- und Rückseite, und vielleicht noch zwei seitliche Wände, oder sogar mehr, dann gibt es außerdem noch die Ziegel der Innenwände und Ziegel unter der Erde, Ziegel für die Straßen, Ziegel für die Kanalisation. Die Ziegel der Gebäude, wenn ich vor die Tür gehe, Ziegel die Kilburn High Road rauf und runter, und Ziegel in alle Ewigkeit in die weite Welt hinein.

In den Mauern gibt es Ziegelsteine jeden Alters. Im Vorbeigehen versuche ich, mir die Männer vorzustellen, die sie gelegt haben. Wer hat ihnen denn gesagt, wo die

Ziegel hinmüssen? Wie haben sie sich rasiert? Was haben sie am liebsten getrunken? Ich reihe mich unter sie und die Zeitalter der Stadt.

Ackergaul McGurk bedient den Kran. Er schwenkt die Paletten mit Ziegeln, als wäre er Hammerwerfer. Wir bauen Wohnungen in Spitalfields. Er setzt die Paletten mit Ziegelsteinen in regelmäßigen Abständen an der Mauer ab. Der Einweiser hat es mit den Zeichen längst aufgegeben, weil er weiß, dass der Gaul sowieso nicht drauf achtet. Er ist jetzt fast da, wo die Mauer einer Kurve folgt, und er muss die Palette mit der schlingernden Ladung unter dem Gerüst durchbringen, ehe sie runterkracht. Ich stelle mir vor, wie es wäre, auf der Palette gegen die Mauer zu fliegen. Der Einweiser raucht eine Zigarette. Das Gewicht der vielen Steine hängt an dem einen Stahlkabel. Verfehlt der Gaul jetzt die Lücke, trifft er Mauer oder Gerüst. Er holt mit dem Kranarm ein paar Mal aus, um den richtigen Rhythmus zu kriegen. Ich stelle mir vor, wie die Steine zu Ziegelstaub zermalmt werden. Er nimmt Anlauf und bricht ab, weil er sieht, dass der Versuch danebengehen würde. Und wieder beginnt die Ladung zu schwingen. Ich suche Finsternis. Die Palette holt ein letztes Mal aus, und ich springe auf. Als die Ladung vorsaust, zieht in mir alles nach unten. Ich fühle die gewaltige Wucht das Aufpralls schon vorher. Ich sehe, dass wir auf die Seitenmauer zurasen, und ich versuche, mit dem eigenen Gewicht nachzuhelfen. Staub von Ziegeln, Blut, Knochen und Finsternis. Die Mauer fliegt auf mich zu. Ich sehe die Löcher in den Steinen. Ich warte.

Der Gaul hat eine ruhige Hand. Er setzt mich sanft auf die Erde ab.

24

Die Tür ist nicht grün. Drinnen sind weder Priester noch Porter noch Lieder. Die Tür ist aus Eisen und steht offen. Drinnen ist Feuer.

Was ich damals konnte. Ich konnte meinen Namen vergessen. Ich konnte eine Woche im Bett liegen. Ich konnte die Finsternis suchen. Ich konnte die Schultern hochziehen, wie ein Idiot grinsen und fragen: Haben Sie nicht vielleicht Arbeit für mich? Ich konnte an die falsche Tür geraten. Ich konnte Francie Angst machen. Ich konnte mir die Musik entgleiten lassen. Ich konnte durch die Stadt ziehen wie ein Gespenst, sie war selbst gespenstisch. Ich konnte gehen, ohne es zu merken.

Ich sehe noch den Jungen auf dem Rücken seines Bruders, der die Tür mit den Händen anmalt. Wenn ich ihm aber über die Kartoffelfelder, durch die Orte und die Räume dahin zu folgen versuche, wo alles brannte, kenne ich mich nicht mehr aus. Ich erinnere mich an das Gift und die Schande und die Hitze. Ich erinnere mich, auf den Frieden gewartet zu haben, der nicht kam.

Der Pub ist voll Rauch, und die hohen Fenster lassen das Abendlicht herein. Es muss Sommer sein, dem Licht nach zu urteilen, der Art, wie die Leute in Hemdsärmeln vor ihrem Bier sitzen. Ich trinke Gin, weil ich den noch nicht kenne. Ich kenne weder den Pub noch weiß ich, wie ich hier gelandet bin. Ein Radio läuft. Man hört eine Ukulele, und eine Frau singt vom Strand. Ich stelle sie mir dick und blond vor, das Haar an den Spitzen steif hochgebogen wie Draht. Ich stelle mir den roten Lippenstift vor. Sie klingt fröhlich und gemein, und ich möchte, dass alles weggeht. Männer studieren Rennseiten, Männer stieren durch den Rauch ins Licht der Fenster. Am Tresen sitzt ein Mann mit beinahe mahagonifarbner Haut für sich auf einem Hocker, Kopf in den Händen. Ich leere mein Glas Gin und hole mir ein zweites. Während ich warte, betrachte ich den Mann, die Falten in der Haut in seinem Nacken. Vielleicht ist er aus Pakistan oder Bangladesch. Er starrt in sein Bier, und seine Lippen bewegen sich, er redet. Er wiegt sich im Takt von dem, was er sagt. Ich verstehe kein Wort. Ich frage mich, ob er wohl betet. Ich frage mich, ob wir gleich sind. Ich beuge mich tiefer, um zu hören, was er sagt, und er spürt, dass wer da ist. Er blickt hoch. Seine Augen sind gelb und braun und rot. »Ich wünschte, Gott würde die Welt zerstören«, sagt er.

25

Ich habe den Tee ausgetrunken und die Tabletten geschluckt, die mir die Schwester in einem kleinen Papierbecher gebracht hat. Sie reckt sich in ihrer weißen Uniform, um den Vorhang zuzuziehen, und sagt uns, dass wir jetzt schlafen sollen. Der Neue neben mir tut, was man ihm befiehlt, und der alte Knabe gegenüber schläft sowieso schon. Es ist halb drei Uhr am Montagnachmittag. Ich habe einen sauberen Schlafanzug, saubere Laken, ein sauberes Gesicht. Ich sitze aufrecht im Bett, die Hände im Schoß und starre mit weit aufgerissenen Augen gegenüber auf einen Fleck an der Wand. Ich bin so wach, als hätte mich jemand mit einem Eimer Meerwasser übergossen.

Jetzt kommt, mit einer Schachtel Pralinen, der Onkel meiner Mutter ins Zimmer, Uncle John. Er kommt geradewegs zu mir und setzt sich ans Fußende vom Bett. Ich weiß nicht, wie ich ihn so hingekriegt habe, aber er ist ein rechter Prachtkerl: schmales Inselgesicht, blaue Augen voll Meer und Himmel, und die Falten um Augen und Mund wirken mit am Lachen. Wie er wohl aussah, als die Männer mit den Masken ihn aus seiner Bude in Northampton holten? Er trägt eine Jacke, die Roscoe gefallen hätte, und einen goldenen Ring. Die Mütze ist neu, er legt sie sich aufs Knie. In der Kilburn High Road gibt es Männer, bei denen sieht man in den Augen nur

Baustellen. In seinem Gesicht sieht man nichts von der
Stadt. Dort sieht man das Meer. Man sieht ihn mit der
Hand am Ruder des Boots die Wellen teilen. Er sieht
goldrichtig aus, so wie das Haus, wenn ich es mir im grünen Hang von Labasheeda vorstelle. Aber während die
Falten lachen, kann sein Mund es nicht, denn vom linken Nasenflügel verläuft wie ein Tausendfüßler, der sich
windet, eine Narbe über die Lippe bis in den Mund.
Dieser Teil an ihm ist unbeweglich.

»Als ich aus der Heimat fort bin, habe ich zunächst in
New York gelebt«, sagt er. »Zwischen Gebäuden und
Beton habe ich einen Flecken Gras gefunden, und da bin

ich sonntags hin und habe drauf gesessen. Es war genau
wie das Gras auf dem Rücken des Tullaherin.« Er lacht
und kneift durchs Laken mein Bein, als würde ich die
Galle in seinem Scherz schon verstehen.

Er beginnt mit den beiden Häusern auf dem Tullaherin und geht im weiten Bogen den ganzen Weiler durch.
Er nennt mir die Farben der Türen an dem Tag, als er
auszog. Er nennt mir die Weiden, auf denen die besten
Tiere standen. Er nennt mir den, der schwere Steine am
weitesten warf, das beste Stroh zum Dachdecken machte, im Stehen ein Pferd reiten konnte, ganz allein ein *curragh* heben und ins Meer tragen konnte, am lautesten

rufen, am schönsten singen, am meisten trinken, Frauen am besten umgarnen. Von diesen nannte er mir die, welche Kinder großzog, die schnell wie der Wind liefen, jene, die das schönste Haar hatte, am leichtfüßigsten war, französische Wörter kannte, dem Priester Widerworte gab, die Alten ehrte, die beste Butter machte.

»Ich habe einmal ein Buch gelesen«, sagt er. »Ich habe einst viele gelesen. Bei einem Buch ist es ja so, dass der, der es schreibt, die Leben von beliebig vielen Orten nimmt und sie alle in einen Strom fließen lässt. Und während sie auf das Ende zufließen, gibt es Schlingen und Schlupflöcher und Formen, die alle Wunder wie gut zusammenpassen und ein einziges großes Ganzes ergeben. Dann blickst du zurück und siehst ganz genau, wie alle dahin gelangt sind, wo sie sind. An dem Punkt aber bringt nun der, der es schreibt, sein Buch zu Ende, und was danach kommt, erfährst du nicht. Ich würde gerne einen treffen, der so ein Buch geschrieben hat, und ihn fragen, wo er die Leben hernimmt. Mir ist so etwas mein Lebtag nicht begegnet. Ich blicke zurück, und ich sehe ein großes lehmiges Feld, da schlittern die Menschen und Tiere herum, und ich mit ihnen. Es gibt kein Ende. Es gibt bloß Zeiten, wo die einen stehen und die anderen fallen.«

Dann sagt er mir, dass er von der Musik gehört hat, die ich dem Akkordeon entlocke, und ich möchte so gern für ihn spielen, damit er bleibt. Er wird immer wieder schwächer, wie ein Radio bei schlechtem Empfang.

Er lässt mir die Pralinen am Bett, dann steht er auf. Er legt mir eine große warme Hand auf die Stirn und macht das Kreuzzeichen wie der Priester an Aschermittwoch. »Du kannst denen daheim, denen, die sich an mich erin-

nern, sagen, ich hätte mich nach ihnen erkundigt. Wir gleichen uns, du und ich. Sag ihnen, dass wir ihnen vergeben und sie uns vergeben mögen.«

Dann geht er, das gallige Lachen, das mir gilt, reißt auf und schließt sich hinter ihm wie ein Rauchkringel.

26

Der Spaten liegt schwer in meiner Hand. Auf dem Gerüst habe ich Angst zu stürzen. Wenn es lustig wird, wende ich mich beschämt ab, weil mir die Worte zu langsam kommen und zerbrechen. Am schlimmsten ist es mit dem Akkordeon. Es hat so viele Knöpfe, und ich kann sie nicht mehr alle finden oder mich erinnern.

Sie lassen mich fegen. Ich fege den Staub und die Hölzspäne und die Essensreste auf. Wenn ich diese Arbeit verrichte, habe ich nur mich mit dem Besen in der Hand vor Augen. Ich konnte mal Sättel aufpolstern. Daran kommt keiner vorbei.

Mit den anderen warte ich morgens in Camden Town im Dunkeln am Zaun. Alle sind im Mantel, stützen sich auf, rauchen Zigaretten. Männer, die einem im Pub die Ohren abkauen, jetzt schweigen sie, blicken ernst drein. Sie blicken drein, als würden sie auf einen Fluss hinabsehen, in dem welche um die Wette schwimmen. Wir warten, dass das Tier kommt und seine Kolonne zusammenstellt. Wenn er aus dem Transporter steigt, zieht er den Mantel aus, selbst im Winter, weil er nicht will, dass jemandem seine Arme entgehen. Von hinten sieht er aus wie eine Torfmiete und von vorne zum Davonlaufen. Vom Auge abwärts zerteilt eine Narbe das Gesicht wie ein Graben, seine Augen sind Halfpennies. In der Mitte sitzt eine Nase. Sie gleicht einer dicken Kartoffel, die durch die Krume bricht. Von der Nasenwurzel bis zur Spitze wächst sie mal hierhin, mal dahin und wieder zurück. Nicht wenige von denen, die am Zaun warten, wären Wunder wie gern derjenige, der sie ihm gebrochen hat. Sein Mund läuft ums ganze Gesicht herum wie bei einem Hund. Ihm ist nicht zu trauen. Du konntest dich im Pub mit ihm ganz friedlich über Greyhounds oder den Bierpreis unterhalten, und plötzlich geht er auf dich los. Zerschlägt das Pintglas an der Tischkante und hält dir die Zacken direkt unters Auge. Wenn er geht, zeigen seine Hände nach hinten. Seine Rechte baumelt wie ein

Gewicht am Ende einer Kette. Die haben ihm ein paar Jungs aus Connemara übers Knie gebrochen, als sie ihn mal in ihrem Hass in Willesden im Spotted Dog auf die Toilette geschleift haben.

Ich warte dort morgens mit Francie und Martin und den anderen auf Arbeit. Fast immer kriege ich eine, und sei es Fegen. Ivan ist das erste Mal auch mitgekommen, Schal und Wollmütze auf, und in seiner schweren Tuchjacke mit dem Lederbesatz auf den Schultern sah er aus wie eine Wäscheklammer mit Zelt dran. Kaum war das Tier aus dem Transporter gestiegen und hatte ihn erblickt, war er ein gefundenes Fressen. »Und was kannst du, Hampelmann?«, fragte er. Schon die Stimme machte einen nieder. »Ich kann graben«, sagte Ivan. »Du? Du gräbst doch nicht mal die Scheiße aus deinem eigenen Arsch«, meint das Tier. Er krümmt sich, klatscht die Hände auf die Knie und brüllt vor Lachen. Wer nicht mitlacht und erwischt wird, kriegt keine Arbeit. »Da arbeite ich lieber auf den Bussen«, sagt Ivan zu uns.

Ich sitze allein auf dem Zimmer mit dem Akkordeon und taste mich langsam heran. Lupfe es immer wieder ein bisschen hoch, wie ein Schoßkind, damit ich das Gewicht kennen lerne. Ich lasse die Finger über die Knöpfe gleiten. Ich spiele Lieder, die Da Joe beizubringen versucht hat, als der klein war. Am Samstagnachmittag sitze ich mit Francie beim Buchmacher auf der Bettkante und versuche es mit »She Moves Through the Fair«. Ich rutsche von einem Knopf ab und kriege einen gequetschten Ton wie den Schrei einer Gans. Ich fange von vorn an. Ich kann die schwermütigen Töne genau lang genug halten, bevor sie sich verschieben und mit den nächsten verschmelzen. Und da begreife ich, dass

man nicht wegen dem spielt, was man anderen gibt oder
was sie von einem halten, sondern um des Liedes selbst
willen. Das hält und hält, bis es fast aussieht, als würde
mir die Melodie entwischen, um ein Haar, aber ich kann
sie halten. Ich kann sie halten wie im Tanz. Das sind
Momente, da kann dir nichts und niemand etwas anhaben. Gerade so einen habe ich, als ich Francie bemerke.
»Herrgott, kannst du es nicht mal gut sein lassen?«, sagt
er. Er steht mitten im Zimmer und macht ein Gesicht
wie jemand, der aus Durst auf den Straßen um Münzen
bettelt. »Es ist nicht zum Aushalten so traurig«, sagt er
und geht hinaus.

27

Im Fenster erscheint übergroß das Gesicht des Königs. Die Hütte liegt in Kennington an der Straße, und die Scheibe ist vom Regen und Kohlestaub und den Abgasen der Busse verschmiert, aber ich sehe das lange, kräftige Kinn ganz deutlich und die kleinen runden Ohren, die seitlich vom Kopf abstehen wie Kronkorken. Ich trinke Tee. Der König klopft leise ans Fenster. Schon die Hand ist groß wie ein eiserner Torfstecher. »Hier trinkt keiner Tee ohne königliche Genehmigung«, sagt er. In Coventry hatte ich vom König gehört, in Luton wurde von ihm geredet und in London, wo immer ich auch hinkam. Jetzt steht er vor mir.

Ich trete hinaus, um ihn zu begrüßen. Er streckt mir die Hand hin, ich schlage ein. Er schiebt sein Gesicht dicht vor meins, und ich sehe die tiefen Furchen und die Narbe an seinem Hals von dem einen Mal, als beim Tunnelieren ein Stützpfeiler wegbrach und er begraben wurde. »Ich bin in sämtlichen Pubs von Camden und Kilburn und Cricklewood gewesen und habe keinen finden können, der ›The Mason's Apron‹ für mich spielt. Bis nach Glasgow bin ich rauf, aber auch dort konnte es niemand. Ob du wohl der Mann bist, den ich suche?«

Ich sage ja, das Lied kann ich, und er dreht für sich und für mich eine Zigarette, und wir lehnen uns an die Hüttenwand zurück und rauchen. Der grüne Transporter fährt vor, und das Tier steigt ein, der Wagen geht in die Knie bei dem Gewicht. »Erst seit ich diese Missgeburt kenne, sind mir meine Landsleute aus Louth verleidet«, sagt der König.

Zwei Burschen im Unterhemd, die das Maurerhandwerk lernen, wuchten einen Sack Zement von der Ladefläche eines Lasters und schleifen ihn hinter sich her. Wenn er auf eine Scherbe kommt oder einen spitzen Stock, platzt alles auf die Straße. Sie gelangen an eine niedrige Mauer und versuchen, den Sack auf die andere Seite zu heben. Aber sie kriegen ihn nicht zu fassen. Er rutscht ihnen immer wieder weg. Beide greifen sie zur gleichen Zeit unten um den Sack, und da stoßen sie dumpf mit den Köpfen zusammen. »Hat man so was schon gesehen?«, meint der König. Er legt seine Zigarette auf einem Fensterbrett ab und geht rüber. Sie sollen mal einen Schritt beiseite treten, sagt er ihnen. Er beugt sich aus der Taille vor, packt den Sack mit den Zähnen und hebt ihn über die Mauer. Dann kehrt er zu mir zurück und nimmt seine Zigarette wieder hoch. »Die Sache mit der Missgeburt, mit dem Tier, ist nämlich die«, sagt der König, »im Grunde ist er ein Feigling.« Alle, wie sie da sind, ob sie Zement mischen, Steine und Rohre schleppen oder nur vorbeigehen, alle schauen ihn an. Von Francie kenne ich die Geschichte, er hat mit eigenen Augen gesehen, wie der König einmal mit dem Presslufthammer dastand, als eine Frau daherkam und nach dem Weg zur Post fragte. »Dort bitte, Gnädigste«, hat er gesagt, den Hammer mit links angehoben und ihr den Weg damit gewiesen.

Keiner auf der ganzen Welt konnte graben wie der König, das sagten alle. Er grub Wasserleitungen aus Holz aus, verborgene Tunnel, alte Gemäuer und Knochen. Er sah Stützen wegbrechen und einen Tunnel zum Grab werden. Man konnte ihn allein unter eine Straßendecke schicken, mit nur einer Kerze, und dann trug er den

Dreck selbst im Zinkeimer raus. Als ich ihn kennen lernte, hatte er seine besten Jahre hinter sich, und doch habe ich ihn an jenem Tag in Kennington einen Sack Zement mit den Zähnen heben sehen. Später dann musste ich mit ansehen, wie er saftlos wurde und seine Knie schwach, hörte das Rasseln in seinen Lungen von den vielen Tagen unter der Erde im nassen Lehm. Und es kam die Zeit, da einem keiner sagen konnte, wo er steckte. Egal, wen man fragte, jeder wusste eine wundersame Geschichte über seine Bärenkräfte zu erzählen, aber gesehen hatte ihn keiner, oder irgendetwas gehört. Er ging in die Vergangenheit ein.

Eines Tages musste ich an ihn denken, als der Zug aus Leyton auf den Gleisen oberhalb vom Friedhof stehen blieb. Es war Winter, schwarze Wolken rollten heran wie Brecher bei schwerer See, der Wind zauste das lange Gras. Auf dem Friedhof war weit und breit niemand, bis auf eine Beerdigung direkt unter mir. Im Wind hielt der Bestatter seinen hohen Hut fest, die gemieteten Sargträger schulterten den Sarg, der Geistliche las aus der Heiligen Schrift, die Worte verwehten. Keine Frau, keine Kinder, keine Nachbarn, nur ein Mann im Trenchcoat mit weißem Haar, das ihm der Wind um den Kopf drehte. Es war die Ecke vom Friedhof ohne Steine und Blumen, wo alle die hinkommen, die bettelarm sind, die Namenlosen, die keine Spur hinterlassen. Der Sarg ist aus Fichtenbrettern. Die Beleuchtung im Zug scheint auf die Gesichter der Reisenden. Sie lesen oder sehen stur geradeaus oder in die Ferne. Es gibt niemanden, der von der Beerdigung Notiz nimmt. Es gibt niemanden, der die letzte Ehre des weißhaarigen Mannes im Trenchcoat bemerkt. Ich kann mir nicht vorstellen, wen er betrauert. Ich denke stattdessen an den König. Niemand machte seine Bekanntschaft, ohne die Macht des Königs zu spüren. Aber er nahm sie leicht, sodass man sich in seinem Beisein gestärkt fühlte. Wäre das seine Beerdigung, ich wüsste nicht mal, unter welchem Namen.

28

Francie steht am Mikrophon, in der einen Hand sein Glas, die andere ausgestreckt, und singt »I'll Take You Home Again, Kathleen« im Stil von John McCormack. Alle im Mother Redcap haben einen Heidenspaß daran, nur der Amerikaner beugt sich über sein Aufnahmegerät und dreht an den Knöpfen. Als mit der Maschine alles soweit stimmt, bittet er Francie, Platz zu nehmen und den Clareman mit seiner Geige nach vorn. Es ist Sonntagnachmittag, nach der Sperrstunde, aber es wird weiter ausgeschenkt, weil der Amerikaner bezahlt. Wir sind gekommen, um den Clareman zu hören, und weil es an einem Sonntagnachmittag sonst nichts zu tun gibt.

Der Clareman spielt Wunder wie gut, finde ich, er hat einen ganz zarten Strich. Er führt den Bogen so leicht, dass er der Melodie zwar vielleicht etwas Schwung nimmt, aber dafür kriegt sie einen rechten Glanz. Und schmeichelt sich ein. Bei »The Star Above the Garter« komme ich mit dazu, und wir klingen Wunder wie zusammen. Der Amerikaner gibt mir fünf Pfund und lässt mir noch ein Pint bringen. Zwischen den einzelnen Liedern fuchtelt er mit den Armen wie ein Verkehrspolizist. Und er ist so laut, wie er groß ist. Als er sich wieder seinem Gerät zuwendet und der Clareman zu spielen be-

ginnt, kommt Maggie herüber und setzt sich an meine Seite. Was hatten wir zu der Zeit miteinander? Wir hatten dreimal im Pride of Erin getanzt und waren einmal am Sonntag am Kanal ein paar Schritte gegangen, da war ich ihr zufällig begegnet. Der Clareman spielt »Spailpín a Rún«, und so schön habe ich es noch nie gehört. Schon wie er die Melodie erhascht, macht mir Lust zu spielen. Maggie beugt sich zu mir herüber, Hand auf meinem Knie. Darin ist sie so unbekümmert wie ein Mädchen vom Lande. »Es heißt, du musstest mit Verbrennungen ins Krankenhaus«, sagt sie. Sie schiebt ihr rotes Haar mit beiden Händen hoch und lässt es dann über das linke Auge zurückfallen. Das andere blickt mich an, braun und warm und klar. In so ein Auge kannst du nicht sehen und dann lügen. »Verbrennungen, weil ich im Archway Tavern hinten in den Fernseher kriechen wollte«, gestehe ich. Da greift ihre rechte Hand hoch, und ich denke, jetzt berührt sie mein Gesicht, aber sie überlegt es sich offenbar anders und lässt die Hand auf meine Schulter sinken und an meinem Arm herabgleiten. »Ich weiß doch«, sagt sie. »Aber jetzt ist ja alles wieder in Ordnung.« Ihre Berührung ist leicht wie ein Lufthauch, nie werde ich vergessen, was sie wog und wie lang sie anhielt und dass es mir wie unter Strom den Rücken hinauffrieselte bis in den Kopf. Ich kann das alles auch jetzt in der Erinnerung noch wachrufen, so leicht und warm und dabei so mächtig, dass es mich vom Boden hebt.

29

Als der Priester die letzten Nummern ausruft und Con Hogan aus Belmullet nichts gewonnen hat, zerreißt er seine ganzen Tombolalose in kleine Fetzen und wirft sie hoch in die Luft. Sie schneien ihm aufs Haar und auf die Schultern und Oberschenkel. Die Woodbine versengt ihm gleich die Finger, der Rauch kringelt sich durch seine Locken und um die Fitzel der Lose. »Damals waren noch alle zusammen. Auf ihren Fahrrädern«, sagt er. Er redet von etwas, was zuvor schon in seinem Kopf begonnen wurde. »Man sah gleich, wer da

kam. Jetzt sitzen alle in Automobilen. Wie soll man im Automobil sehen, wer da kommt?« Er zieht an seiner Woodbine und merkt nicht, dass er sich die Finger verbrennt. Er hat die Beine übereinander geschlagen und sitzt ganz schief, und ich frage mich, ob er wohl gleich vom Stuhl fällt.

»Siehst du den Mann dort?«, fragt der König. Er hat eine Flasche John Powers dabei, und die stellt er uns auf den Tisch, ehe er Platz nimmt. Wir, das sind er selbst, ich, Francie, Martin, Maggie und ihre Kusine Helen Maguire, die gerade erst aus Tyrone angekommen ist. Dass er sich zu uns setzt, gibt mir dasselbe Gefühl wie damals, als ich am Markttag mit Joe Brennan durch den Ort ging und als mich Casey dann nahm. »Der war frisch aus Belmullet eingetroffen, da bin ich mit ihm ins Kino. ›Moment‹, sagt er unterwegs, und tritt in einen Laden, ich hinterdrein. ›Ich hätte gern vierundzwanzig Mars‹, sagt er zum Mädchen hinter der Ladentheke. Sie sieht mich an. ›Stimmt mit dem irgendwas nicht?‹, fragt sie mich. ›Wieso?‹, frage ich. ›Er hat eben vierundzwanzig Schokoladenriegel verlangt.‹ ›Dann verkaufen Sie ihm die‹, sage ich bloß. Als wir wieder auf der Straße stehen, mustere ich ihn scharf und sage: ›Du machst mich zum Gespött.‹ Ich habe zwei gegessen und er zweiundzwanzig. Con Hogan aus Belmullet.«

Das Tier kommt in den Gemeindesaal marschiert, links und rechts zwei Kumpel, falls jemand auf ihn losgeht. Der eine war aus Newcastle, das weiß ich noch, und der andere aus Louth. Sie setzen sich unter eine Fotografie von einer afrikanischen Missionsstation. Hinterm Tresen öffnet eine Nonne Flaschen, eine andere reicht Teller mit Broten herum. Als sie vorbeikommt, bedienen wir uns alle, und als nur noch eins auf dem Teller liegt, beugt sich der König zu mir rüber und sagt: »Heb mir das auf, ich komme gleich wieder.« Er verschwindet zur Tür hinaus, und als er wiederkommt, ruft er dem Tier zu: »Schau her, John. Du sollst nicht leer ausgehen«, und das Tier nimmt das letzte Brot. »Jetzt kannst du was erleben«, sagt der König zu mir. Das Tier beißt einen faustgroßen Brocken aus dem doppelt geklappten Brot, unter der roten Nase mahlt der Unterkiefer. Dann stutzt er, das Brot fällt ihm aus dem offenen Mund, er reißt die kleinen schwarzen Augen auf, so weit es geht. »Allmächtiger«, sagt er zu dem Mann aus Louth, »ich dachte, Hochwürden kauft sein Fleisch bei Corrigan«, und dann spuckt er, was er noch im Mund hat, auf den Boden.

»Was hast du ihm bloß gegeben?«, frage ich den König.

»Etwas, was in so einem Gemeindesaal wirklich Seltenheitswert hat«, sagt er.

»Und das wäre?«

Er beugt sich ganz nah zu mir her, damit ihn die Frauen nicht hören. »Scheißwurst im Kondomdarm.«

»Jesus, Maria und Joseph«, meint Francie. »Er hat Leuten schon aus geringerem Anlass die Knochen gebrochen.«

»Wisst ihr, was fast so schlimm ist wie ein Landsmann aus Louth?«, fragt der König. »Ein Mann, der in der Fabrik arbeiten geht oder auf Zügen.«

Das Tier kommt an unseren Tisch, um den Geschmack der Scheißwurst mit einem Schluck königlichen Whiskey hinunterzuspülen. »Abend, allerseits«, sagt er und grient verächtlich. »Stellt euch vor, weshalb dieses Armloch von Bauinspektor vom Gemeinderat mich am Sonntagabend rausklingelt«, meint er. Er stürzt den Whiskey hinunter. »Wegen einem verfluchten Zoll. ›Der Graben da‹, sagt er zu mir, ›der verläuft einen Zoll weiter zur Straßenmitte hin als auf den Plänen. Den müssen Sie wegmachen und neu ziehen.‹ Ist es zu fassen? Wegen dem einen verfluchten Zoll. Da mach ich doch eher ihn weg als das Loch.«

Wie spukhässlich das Tier ist, sieht man ganz richtig erst aus der Nähe: wie der Kopf von den Schultern weg immer spitzer wird. Die Lippen sehen aus wie mit Wasser gefüllt, die gewaltige Nase wie etwas, was ein Hund angenagt hat. Geredet hätte der auch in der Gegenwart

seiner Großmutter so. »Was zählt schon so ein furzelender Zoll?«, brummt er in die Runde.

Mit ganz ernstem Gesicht, so als ginge es um eine schwierige Rechenaufgabe, hebt Maggie den Finger und sagt: »An einer Nase kann das eine Menge ausmachen.«

Das Tier sackt plötzlich still und dumpf in sich zusammen wie ein gebolzter Ochse im Schlachthof. Dem König beben die Schultern, als er sich Whiskey nachschenkt. Martin sieht aus, als würde er gleich platzen, Francie, als hätte er eine Fünf-Pfund-Note auf der Straße gefunden.

Bei Maggie im Gesicht regt sich kein Muskel, aber ich glaube, in ihrem Innern steigt ein Lachen auf. Sie hat ihre Chance gesehen und seine Deckung durchschlagen, Geist scharf wie eine Klinge. Von dem Tag an konnte ich nicht mehr von ihr lassen.

30

Zum Bild gehört auch ein junges Mädchen im rotweißen Kleid, das Blumen in den Kasten vor ihrem Zimmer pflanzt. Jeden Tag, eine ganze heiße Sommerwoche lang, während wir unter ihrem Fenster in der Ladbroke Grove den Gehweg aufreißen, können wir hochschauen und sie sehen. Freitag kennt sie uns alle längst mit Namen. Myles Walsh ist dabei, Pat Kennedy und der Irokese aus Glasgow. John Conneely aus Connemara sitzt an der Mauer auf der Erde und isst einen Apfel, da kommt das Mädchen vom Fenster herunter und bringt ihm einen Holzstuhl. John war zu der Zeit dreiundsechzig, und man sah ihm seine steifen Knie an. Francie hat einen Fuß auf ein Mäuerchen gesetzt und trinkt Milch aus einer Pintflasche. Eine Biene brummt herum und stört ihn dabei, und als er die Flasche wieder an den Mund setzt, geht ein schwarzer Mann mit Strohhut und blauweiß gestreiftem Anzug vorüber, blitzende Goldringe an den Fingern und zwischen den Zähnen eine Zigarette mit Spitze. Er trägt das feinste weiße Hemd, das ich mein Lebtag gesehen habe.

Wir reden vom Tier.

»Er ist kein Gentleman«, sagt John. »Er hat einer Katze eine brennende Zigarette in den Arsch gesteckt. So etwas tut ein Gentleman nicht.«

»Das möchte ich meinen«, sagt Myles.

Francie stellt die Milchflasche weg und nimmt den Presslufthammer hoch.

»Neulich Montag gräbt Martin unter der Marylebone Road, als er mit dem Spaten gegen etwas Hartes kommt. ›Was haben wir denn da?‹, denkt er sich und scharrt den Dreck weg. So ein großes dunkles Ding und beschriftet. Aus Blei war's. ›Was sagst du dazu?‹, fragt er Jack O'Rourke, der im Gang neben ihm schuftet. Jack setzt seine Brille auf und besieht sich das Ding genauer. Nun ist ja Jack ein großer Bücherfreund, wie ihr wisst. Er besieht sich das Ding von allen Seiten, als würde er es eventuell kaufen wollen. Schließlich gibt er sein Urteil ab. ›Ein römischer Sarg‹, sagt er und steckt die Brille wieder weg. Martin kriecht aus dem Gang und ruft Muldoon drüben auf dem Platz an. Aber er kriegt nur die Krähe an den Apparat. ›Das Tier isst in der Princess Louise gerade zu Mittag‹, sagt die Krähe. Also ruft Martin im Pub an, lässt sich das Tier geben und erklärt das mit dem römischen Sarg. Pause, während das Tier überlegt. Dann sagt er: ›Zerkloppt das Scheißding und vergrabt es‹. Er wollte nicht, dass einer vom Museum die Arbeit aufhält. So ist das Tier, Freund der Künste und Wissenschaften.«

Francie setzt den Meißel vom Preßlufthammer auf den Gehweg und legt los. Ich sehe ein kleines Mädchen in einem Fenster sitzen und ein Buch lesen, die Sonne scheint ihm aufs Gesicht. Ich sehe, wie sich der Schwarze mit den Goldringen eine Rose ins Knopfloch steckt. Ich sehe Francie grinsen. Dann faucht und zischt es lichterloh, und die Luft um Francie flimmert heiß auf. Flammen schlagen aus seinen Stiefeln, seinen Hosen, seinem Hemd. Auch sein Haar steht in Flammen. In seinem Mund brennt Feuer. Auf seinen Händen brennt Feuer. Seine Haut lodert auf und wird schwarz. Der Presslufthammer fällt hin und Francie auch. Myles und John und Pat und der Irokese und ich und das Mädchen und der Schwarze sehen auf den toten Francie auf dem Gehweg neben dem Schacht herunter und auf das dicke Kabel, das er mit dem Hammer aufgebohrt hat, an dem die Isolierung kocht und qualmt und aus dem bunte Drähte vorstehen wie die Stängel frisch geschnittener Blumen.

31

Ich sehe, wie über mir auf dem Kopfteil des Betts die Asche am Ende der Zigarette immer länger wird. Ich sehe die Asche reißen, abknicken und neben mir aufs Kissen fallen. Dann sehe ich zu, wie sich die Glut der Zigarettenkippe ins Holz brennt. Von links nach rechts ziehen sich längliche Brandflecken über das Kopfteil wie die schwarzen Tasten am Klavier.

In Maggies Zimmer ganz oben im Haus an der Elgin Avenue waren ins Kopfteil ihres schmalen Bettes Ranken und Blumen und Perlen geschnitzt. Es war dunkelbraun, von genau derselben Farbe wie Stout. Neben dem Bett gab es einen kleinen Tisch mit einer Spitzendecke, und manchmal, wenn wir uns zueinander in das Bett legten, nahm sie die Kerze vor dem Herz-Jesu-Bild weg und stellte sie auf das Tischchen, damit wir sehen konnten. An ihrem Anblick war in diesem Licht etwas, das für mich ungemein friedvoll war. Wenn sie schlief, konnte ich mir vom Bett aus in Ruhe ansehen, wie sie sich mit allem eingerichtet hatte. Sie hatte ein Bord für Bücher und ein Bord für Schallplatten und dazwischen eine Landkarte von Irland. Die Karte zeigte nicht nur Städte und Dörfer und Flüsse, sondern es gab außerdem kleine Bildchen, die zeigten, was sich zugetragen hatte. Es gab ein Bildchen für Angriffe, ein Bildchen für Schlachten, ein Bildchen für Blutbäder und eines für niedergebrannte Städte. Die Wände waren weiß, und der Teppich hatte die Farbe von Gras, wenn es auf Sand wächst. Es gab ein Bild von ihrem Vetter Eddie Furlong, dem besten Geiger aus Monaghan Stadt. Es gab ein Foto von ihrem Vater, der auf einem Knie Blumen für ein Kind pflückt. Es gab ein Foto von mir auf der Brighton Pier in dem Anzug vom Schneider, der so ordentlich gearbeitet war, Hände in den Hosentaschen und mehr Haaren als heute. Auf dem Foto trage ich Maggies Sonnenbrille. Ich hatte so gern, wie sie im Schlaf sanft an meinen Hals hinatmete. Wenn sie aufwachte, richtete sie sich das Haar nicht so, dass es über das linke Auge fiel. Ich konnte den

Tisch mit dem Spiegel sehen, wo sie ihre Flaschen und
Scheren und Kämme aufbewahrte, und jedes Mal, wenn
ich kam, lagen sie anders da. Ich konnte den Schrank
sehen, und wenn er manchmal offen stand, dann konnte
ich das Kleid sehen, das die Farbe von Sand hatte, und
auch die anderen Kleider und ihre Hüte und Blusen und
Mäntel. Mir gefiel es, wenn irgendetwas nicht aufge-
räumt war, wenn zum Beispiel einer ihrer roten Leder-
schuhe mit den hohen Absätzen umgekippt war. Da
konnte ich mir besser vorstellen, dass sie Dinge tat. Das
Zimmer lag ganz oben unterm Dach, und die Decke fiel
zu beiden Seiten vom Bett ab, und du fühltest dich
geschützt und ungestört wie in einem Zelt.

Es gab ein Fenster, das seitlich in der Dachschräge saß, und ich sehe dort noch wie heute ein hohes Glas mit Schwertlilien stehen. Sie waren im ersten Licht des Sonntagmorgens, nach durchspielter Nacht bei der Geburtstagsfeier der Frau des Vermieters im Weaver's Arms, sehr still und blau. Es war im Monat Mai und das Morgenlicht ein sehr blasses Blau. Was hatten wir einen Hunger nacheinander, den ganzen Weg heim durch die Straßen und die vielen Stufen hinauf bis in ihr Bett, wo ich endlich die ganze Hitze und den Sog und die Macht ihres Körpers kennen lernte. Wir tranken dort im Bett Brandy, die Laken und Decken geriffelt wie Sand unter Wasser, und das blasse blaue Licht stahl sich an den Schwertlilien vorbei ins Zimmer. Die ganze Luft schien voll von ihr, wenn ich einatmete, und als sie mir die Lippen ans Ohr legte und mich bat, für sie zu spielen, wusste ich, dass ich noch nie so vom Wunder eines anderen Menschen ergriffen worden war. Ich sehe mich noch wie heute nur im Unterhemd aufrecht im Bett sitzen, die nackten weißen Beine gekreuzt, das Haar auf meinem Kopf auch fast ganz weg, sehe, wie ich mich mit meinem Akkordeon ein klein wenig hin und her wiege, und Maggie neben mir mit der Hand auf meinem Knie, das rote Haar auf ihren weißen Schultern, während ich ihr zuliebe ganz langsam und gefühlvoll »My Lagan Love« spiele.

32

Weißt du noch, wie lang ich damals das Haar trug? Dass ich es wegheben musste vorm Hinsetzen. Und Da hat mich angefleht, es nicht abzuschneiden?«

Sechzehn Leute sind an diesem Tag, an dem ich Maggie heirate, im oberen Wirtszimmer vom Eagle's Nest versammelt, und nie hätte ich geglaubt, unter ihnen Eileen zu sehen. Mary war zu der Zeit in einem Kloster in Wales. Bernadette bei ihrem Mann in dessen Pub in Belfast. Sie haben ein Telegramm geschickt. Vincent arbeitete, dem letzten Stand nach, in Australien mit Rennpferden. Joe habe ich nie gefunden, obwohl ich immer noch suche. Eileen war mir auch lange verloren gegangen, aber nicht Brid, obwohl die selbst mit sechs Kindern und einem Mann, der mit Häuserbauen Millionen verdient hat, in Philadelphia saß. Aber Brid gab Eileen wegen der Hochzeit Bescheid. Brid würde ich

gerne wieder sehen. Ich weiß noch, wie eines Tages ein Mann aus Galway daherkam, den Da von Musikwettbewerben kannte, und der ließ eine Tinwhistle auf dem Stuhl liegen, und Brid nahm sie hoch und konnte gleich spielen, obwohl sie damals erst acht war und noch nie gespielt hatte. Sie spielte »The Soldier's Song«.

Eileen lacht. Wenn sie lacht, klingt es, als würde ihr jemand die Kehle zudrücken. Der Weg, den sie aus Labasheeda bis zum Tag meiner Hochzeit im Wirtszimmer in Cricklewood zurückgelegt hat, liegt für mich im Dunkeln. In ihr Gesicht sind viele Falten gestrichelt, ähnlich wie die Verästelungen auf Landkarten, die anzeigen, wo Flüsse sich auffächern, ehe sie ins Meer fließen. Ihr Haar ist grau mit einem leuchtenden Orange darin, mit dem man gut Eiscreme einfärben könnte. Sie ist dünn, und wenn du sie ansiehst, denkst du sofort an Knochen, deren Härte. Ihr Kleid hat zwar auch weiße Stellen, aber hauptsächlich ist es orange wie ihr Haar. Ihre Stimme ist rau geworden, und es liegt darin wie fernes Laubfeuer in der Luft ein Hauch Yorkshire, wo sie nun lebt. Sie raucht eine nach der anderen.

Sie spricht von ihrem Mann.

»Ich bin ihm eines Tages im Nebel begegnet, als ich auf der Holloway Road um die Ecke bog. Nebel so dick, du hättest ihn löffeln können. Es war das erste Mal, dass ich Leute mit Laternen herumgehen sah. Wie diese Frostnebel, die es in Russland geben soll, wo du durchgehen kannst und dein Körper einen Abdruck hinterlässt. Ich begegne ihm also in diesem dicken Nebel, und aus dem habe ich bis zum Tage seines Todes nicht mehr herausgefunden. Er war zu nichts nutze. Zu nichts. Weißt du, dass ich ein Sofa beziehen kann? Ich kann den

Wert alter Uhren schätzen. Ich kenne mich mit Hüten und Putz für feine Damen aus und dem Kaufen und Verkaufen von Automobilen. Ich habe ein Hotel geführt. Das alles habe ich gelernt, weil er sein ganzes Leben keinen Finger gerührt hat, und was ich an Geld nach Hause brachte, hat er versoffen. Was musste ich auch in den Nebel hinausgehen.«

Dann dieses Lachen, das klingt, als wäre unten in ihren Lungen schweres Wasser. Wenn ich sie mir ansehe, denke ich, es ist vielleicht weniger bitter als zäh. Es werden Sets getanzt. Eileen sieht zur Tanzfläche, und wo ihr das Wirbeln der Paare übers Gesicht und Haar streicht, erkenne ich von der Seite in Stirn, Nase und Augen etwas von dem wieder, was sie früher als junges Ding gewesen war, als sie noch keine Enttäuschung gekannt hatte. Je länger sie beim Tanzen zusieht, je mehr verliert sich das, was die Jahre in ihre Augen gelegt haben, und verfliegt.

»In der ersten Zeit hier war ich Hilfsschwester. Im Krankenhaus in Hackney. Einmal ist einer mit schrecklichen Verbrennungen gebracht worden, dem klebten die Kleider an der Haut, und ich sollte sie ihm abziehen, und da bin ich gleich auf der Stelle umgekippt, ohne ihn überhaupt angefasst zu haben. Da wusste ich, das ist nichts für mich, aber bevor ich kündigen konnte, kam noch St. Patrick's Day, und wir sind in einer ganzen Clique im Bus zum Tanz in die Seymour Hall gefahren. Damals sind wir auch oft zum Tanztee ins Astoria gegangen. Für Sixpence. Alle fein herausgeputzt.« Sie lässt die Tänzer nicht aus den Augen.

»In der Seymour Hall bin ich bei der Damenwahl raus auf die Tanzfläche. Wir gehen also im Kreis herum, und

163

als wir stehen bleiben, habe ich einen Mann gegenüber, also haben wir getanzt. Er in der Tanzjacke. Wie aus dem Ei gepellt. Nach dem Tanzen haben wir uns einen Moment hingesetzt. Er sagte, er sei Teepflanzer und gerade aus Assam zu Besuch in der Heimat. Ich sehe ihn vor mir wie heut. Er war groß, dunkelhaarig, und er trug eine Hornbrille. Sah sehr gut aus. Ich würde ihn heute noch auf der Straße erkennen. Wir haben noch zwei-, dreimal miteinander getanzt, dann hat er gefragt, ob er mich heimbringen darf. Als ich das den anderen erzählte, haben sie gemeint, das wäre zu gefährlich und ich soll doch lieber mit ihnen im Bus zurückfahren. Aber ich bin trotzdem mit ihm mitgegangen. Er hatte einen wunderschönen Wagen, und da saß ich vorn neben ihm und stellte mir vor, wie wohl ein Leben auf einer Tee-plantage in Assam wäre. Er brachte mich bis direkt vor die Tore zum Krankenhaus, dann reichte er mir die Hand und sagte: ›Ich danke Ihnen für den wunder-schönen Abend.‹ Ich habe es nie vergessen. Ein wahrer Gentleman. Und so ein schöner schwarzer Mantel mit Pelzkragen.«

Dann steht sie auf und hält mir die Hand hin. Ich nehme sie, und wir gehen hinaus auf die Tanzfläche. Martin ist da, er strahlt über beide Backen, und von sei-ner Stirn rinnt der Schweiß. John Conneely steht da mit seiner Frau und wartet, er klopft den Takt mit dem Fuß. Maggie bindet ihrer Nichte die Haarschleife, dann dreht sie sich zu mir um. Ihr Gesicht ist hell wie ein Tal, aus dem sich der Dunst hebt. Alle haben noch vom letzten Tanz rote Gesichter, glühende Haut, Brustkörbe heben und senken sich, während alle Welt nur darauf wartet, dass die Musik wieder einsetzt. Auf dem Sprung wie

Langstreckenläufer vor Beginn des Rennens. Die Bedeutung von Dingen, die Freude machen, dämmert einem meist erst allmählich, aber wie reich das Bild vor meinen Augen ist, begreife ich schon im Sehen. Jack Dwyer setzt den Bogen auf die Saiten. Artie Sweeneys Schultern sausen hoch, als er sein Akkordeon zusammenschiebt. Der Mann am Klavier stürzt sich in die Tasten und trifft den Ton wie ein Schwimmer, der vom Fels hinabtaucht. Das Lied klingt auf. Eileen ist so leicht. Ihre Knochen könnten aus einem ganz leichten Holz sein. Die Musik ist wie ein elektrischer Strom, der uns speist und über die Tanzfläche schickt. Eileen kennt die Schritte, ohne überlegen oder hinsehen zu müssen. Die Schritte sind in ihr zu Hause. Sie wirft den Kopf in den Nacken und lacht lauthals, und es ist, als würde in ihrem Gesicht etwas aufbrechen und wegfallen, eine Maske aus verkrustetem Lehm. Wie sie mich daheim am Stations-Day herumgewirbelt hat. Jetzt sind ihre Füße wie Möwen, sie wiegen sich auf Luft. Wir fliegen an den Tänzern vorbei, weiß und rot blitzen die Kleider, es kommt Wind auf. John Conneely galoppiert auf steifen Knien mit seiner Frau durch eine Lücke. Der Herzschlag der Musik und der Herzschlag der Tänzer. Wir sind alle ein Tanz. Der Klang, den ich daheim aus der Küche gehört habe, als ich an der Tür wartete, die ich grün angemalt hatte. Da, der mit leuchtenden Augen das Akkordeon aus dem Kasten hebt und Joe hinhält. Wie er Flöte spielen und dir die Noten von »Anach Cuain« ins Herz setzen konnte wie Stiche in einen Stoff. Joe Connor, der uns nach dem Schweineschlachten das steinige weiße Donegal herbeisingt. Matt, der Lieder braucht wie an einem heißen Tag einen Schluck Quellwasser.

Das Akkordeon, das mir in den Händen erblüht. Die Lieder, die auf der Überfahrt nach Liverpool im eisernen Schiffsbauch verklingen. Wie ich auf der Bude, die ich mir in Kilburn mit Francie teile, »She Moves Through the Fair« finde. »My Lagan Love« für Maggie, als sie darum bittet. Musik passiert innen. Sie bewegt das, was da ist, von einem Ort zum anderen. Sie verleiht Flügel. Sie bringt dir die Vergangenheit. Sie bringt dir Dinge, von denen du gar nicht wusstest. Sie bringt dich zu dem, was gerade ist. Sie bringt dir Heilung.

33

Wie Maggie war. Sie konnte einen Hut goldrichtig aufsetzen. Sie kannte die Namen der Bäume. Sie konnte einer Melodie oder Vorstellung oder Geschichte folgen und da noch Sinn finden, wo andere keinen sahen. Sie konnte weben. Sie konnte trinken, und nichts war zu merken. Sie konnte Wunden heilen. Sie konnte so sprechen, dass es klang, als wäre ihre Stimme in dir selbst drin. Sie konnte Kleider nähen. Sie wusste etwas über spanische Städte. Sie war bei allen Kartenspielen unschlagbar, für die man ein gutes Gedächtnis braucht. Sie konnte eine Leere füllen, auch ohne etwas zu sagen. Sie konnte weit schwimmen.

Ich erinnere mich, wie sie das Taschentuch an die Lippen führte. Ich erinnere mich, wie sie Gemüse hielt, wenn sie es klein schnitt, wie sich ihre Hände bewegten, die zarten Knochen und langen Finger, alles so leicht und sicher und unhastig. Sie hatte eine Art, die Lippen so und das Auge so zu bewegen, wenn sie etwas belustigte. Sie konnte gut addieren. Sie hat mich ins Museum geführt, um mir die bunten Südseevögel zu zeigen. Sonne vertrug sie schlecht, vor allem im Gesicht. Dann sah sie bedrängt und verlegen aus. Sie konnte die Füße nicht still halten, wenn sie Musik hörte. Sie klagte nie, wenn sie krank war. Als ich sie fragte, weshalb sie ihr langes rotes Haar auf beiden Seiten hochbauschte und es so fallen ließ, dass es das linke Auge bedeckte, nahm sie ganz sacht meine Hand und sagte mir, dass das verdeckte Auge aus Glas ist.

Wie sie war? Sie war nicht wie ein Tier oder eine Farbe. Sie war nicht wie der Himmel oder das Wetter oder irgendeine Speise oder irgendein Stein. Sie war wie ein Wald. Darin lebten und verwandelten sich ihr unbekannte Dinge. Dort war das Licht immer in Bewegung. Uralter Wald und ganz junger Wald. Sie konnte einen umschließen. Ihre Stille. Vorm Wind schützen.

Sie war eine Frau. Es gab an ihr nichts, was weniger war, ihr Schritt, wenn sie um die Ecke bog, ihre Stimme aus der Nähe, ihre Ringe, ihre Berührung, ihr Anblick beim Aufwachen. Ich gebe mir Mühe, sie hierher zurückzubringen. Ihr Rosenkranz ist hier, das Kleid mit den Glockenblumen, die Fotografien. Ihr Bein wird in einem langen Schwung vom Knie abwärts schmaler. Ihre Haut ist warm wie Brot frisch aus dem Ofen. Um die Schultern schimmert sie matt wie poliertes Holz, nach einer Zeit an der Sonne. Wenn sie die Schultern hebt, weil sie etwas erklärt, gibt es über den Schlüsselbeinen Mulden. Die Haut riecht nach Sonne, nach Bettwärme, Lavendel. Bei ihr kommt das Lachen nicht aus dem Hals, sondern tief unten aus dem Körper. Ich sehe ihre anmutigen Linien, Muster in der Haut, ihre Bewegun-

gen. Ich folge ihnen. Ich bin Teil von alledem. Und dann kann ich nicht anders. Ich sehe die sonnige Straße und die hohen Platanen, deren Rinde die Farbe von Asche haben, den Motorradfahrer, der vorbeibraust, den Hund, der vorauseilt. Maggie kommt mir im Gedränge entgegen. Das sehe ich wieder und wieder und wieder. Sie legt eine Hand oben auf den Hut, mit der anderen winkt sie. Die Hand erstarrt, dann sinkt sie herab.

34

Als Dermot die Wiese aussucht, die wir von ihm bekommen sollen, beginnen wir über einen Wohnwagen nachzudenken. Wir stellen uns vor, wie er aussehen wird und wo er stehen soll. Am Ende der Weide ist eine weiße Felswand mit grauen Adern. Dort wollen wir den Wohnwagen aufstellen, im Windschutz. Das Stück Land fällt zum Fluss hin ab, und der Fluss stürzt von dort als Wasserfall herab. Die Sonne wird hinter der Felswand aufgehen und überm Fluss unter. Maggie spricht vom goldenen Licht auf dem Wasser am Abend. An der Steinmauer, die den Weg zwischen den Hecken begrenzt, wachsen Brombeeren, und zwischen den Wiesen Weißdorn, Eschen, wilde Kirschen und Schlehen. Am anderen Flussufer stehen in Lord Masboroughs aufgelassenem Obstgarten Apfel- und Birnbäume. Dort wachsen wilde Orchideen, und man findet Fischgräten und die blauen Schalen der Krebse, die die Otter verspeist haben. Ich soll Kartoffeln und Mohrrüben und Kohl pflanzen, Maggie kümmert sich um die Blumen und Minze.

Wenn man dem Weg am Wohnwagen vorbei über die Hügelkuppe folgt, kommt man an eine Weggabelung. Rechts geht es zum Meer hinunter, wo Matts Neffe Hugh den ganzen Tag mit seinen Hummerkörben und den Strandschnecken und Rotalgen herumschafft. Links kommt man nach nur einer Meile zu Honor Caseys Pub und dem Laden mit den Speckseiten, den Gummistiefeln und den Pints. Dort können wir an jedem beliebigen Abend hingehen, denn die Arbeit ist bis dahin vollbracht. Im Wohnwagen sollen zwei Räume sein. Wir werden den ganzen Sommer frische Blumen haben und Gardinen aus Belfast. Wir werden das Eichenbett aus Monaghan herbeischaffen, in dem Maggies Mutter zeitlebens geschlafen hat. Wir wissen, von welchen Tellern wir essen werden, aus welchen Gläsern wir trinken werden und welche Bilder wir an der Wand sehen werden. Wir werden wissen, wie es an einem klaren Morgen durchs Schlafzimmerfenster aussieht. Wir werden wissen, wie im Mai der Weißdorn aussieht und die Vogelbeeren im September. Wir wissen, wie es riecht, wie das Licht ist, die Luft. Als ich jung war, hatte ich weder Vergangenheit noch Zukunft. Dann gab es die Arbeit. Ich habe Straßen gepflastert, Beton aufgebrochen, ich habe unter Häusern gegraben und Dreck weggeschafft. Ich habe Schaufeln gezählt, Kartoffeln und Ziegel. Das war die Zeit, als ich eine Vergangenheit kriegte. Die Vergangenheit war schwer, wie die Steine im Kiel, mit denen man Boote austrimmt. Ohne Vergangenheit wäre ich gekentert. Ich dachte, ich hätte auch eine Zukunft, aber ich konnte sie nicht sehen. Sie war das, was ich hob und schleppte und was ich dafür bekam. Es war eine Zukunft, die schnell flackerte und erlosch, wenn ich genauer hinsah. Dann gab es ohne Vorwarnung Maggie, und plötzlich war Licht und ein Weg voraus, der nur wartete.

35

An dem Sonntagabend, als ich Maggie mit dem Hund entgegen gehe, schlüpft die Sonne unter den Wolken durch und bringt die Straße zum Leuchten. Die Zeitung lag noch auf dem Tisch und daneben stand die Teetasse noch da, wo sie sie stehen gelassen hatte, um zur Messe zu gehen. Als ich die Straße erreiche, an der die hohen Platanen in dem Jahr dicht im Laub stehen, sehe ich an denen, die mir entgegenkommen, dass die Messe vorbei ist. Nach der Messe gehen die Menschen immer langsam. Im Park höre ich jemand einen Tennisball schlagen. Es ist ein herrlicher Abend Anfang August, und das letzte Licht ergießt sich in einem satten goldenen Glanz über weiße Hemden und die Kleider, und zwischen den anderen sehe ich Maggie mit ihrem Hut auf mich und den Hund zukommen. So lange ich sie auch kannte, ich habe mich nie an ihren Anblick gewöhnt. Immer war da irgendetwas: wie sie den Kopf hielt oder die Hand hob, um das Haar vor ihrem Gesicht zu richten, die Knochen ihrer Hände, der Laut, den sie machte, ehe sie losplatzte, die Lachfalten plötzlich um ihren Mund, wie ihr Fuß leise den Takt zu einer Melodie schlug, die sie sich ausdachte, wie anmutig sie sich beugen oder drehen konnte, die Art, wie sie zuhörte, als wären Worte oder Musik Wasser, das sich über sie ergoss, die Art, wie sie bis ins Herz der Dinge hineinsehen konnte, die andere taten, wie sie staunen konnte. Manchmal kam sie mir vor wie ein Forscher, wie sie mitbekam, wie Menschen waren, ihre Winkelzüge. Diese Dinge waren immer wieder neu und immer sie. Nichts, was sie tat, erinnerte mich an irgendetwas, was ich schon gesehen hatte. Wie um alles in der Welt habe ich sie bloß gefunden? Sie legt die Hand oben auf den Hut, um ihn im Wind festzuhalten, und winkt. Sie machte größere Schritte, wird schneller. Dann erstarrt ihre Hand in der Luft, sinkt herab. Es sieht aus, als hätte sie etwas vergessen. Sie wankt nach rechts, als würde sie fallen, fängt sich aber wieder. Sie stützt sich mit den Fingerkuppen auf einem Mäuerchen auf. Dann dreht sie sich in einer langsamen Bewegung, in der der ganze Tag Platz hätte, fast ganz um die eigene Achse, Arme hochgeworfen, Kopf vornüber gesackt, und dann stürzt sie zu Boden. Ich sehe ihren Kopf einmal auf den Steinplatten hüpfen. Ich sehe ihren Hut im Wind flattern und die Straße zurück auf die Kirche zurollen, als ich zu ihr hinlaufe.

Nun werde ich Kentish Town nur noch in einer braunen Kiste verlassen, um dann in Labasheeda bei Maggie zu liegen. Ich habe alles genau hinterlegt. Die Kleine, die in der Wohnung unter mir wohnt, weiß, was zu tun ist. Auch der Chef im Gloucester Arms. Und die Frau, deren Hund ich unter der Woche nachmittags ausführe. Und ich habe es trotzdem alles noch mal auf das Blatt Papier niedergeschrieben, das neben dem Bett auf dem Tisch liegt. Da liegt auch der Schlüssel zu der Schatulle mit dem Geld. Wie viele Fuß Tunnel graben für einen Sarg? Wie viele, um mich nach Labasheeda zu überführen? Diese Hände. Zerschunden und vernarbt wie alle unsere Hände. Was muss durch die Tunnel? Wer fährt auf den Straßen? Was geschieht hinter den Mauern und Wänden aus Ziegeln? Denken die Menschen dort je an die Männer, die sie erbaut haben?

Nach der Trauerfeier in Monaghan miete ich ein

Taxi, das uns nach Labasheeda bringt. Ich glaube, im Norden ist die Erde nur ein Zoll tief, darunter ist alles Lehm. Hügel über Hügel gibt es und rauschendes Wasser, wie überall in Irland. Ich blicke auf einen Hügel und sehe Maggie als Mädchen auf einem Pferd den Hang hinabpreschen, und mir ist, als hätte ich an eine offene Leitung gefasst. Woran soll ich aber sonst denken als an sie? Über allem liegt die Farbe ihres Todes.

Als wir an der Grenze entlangfahren, sehe ich auf der anderen Seite zwischen den Hügeln, die nicht anders sind als die Hügel um Monaghan, die hohen Türme der Engländer mit ihren Gewehren und Hubschraubern und der ganzen technischen Ausrüstung. Es brennen auch Feuer in den Hügeln, Laubfeuer. Ich muss an die Feuer denken, die wir zu Hallowe'en entfacht haben, um die Geister der Toten zu vertreiben. Die Straßen, die hier über die Grenze führen, enden in Schutthaufen, weil die Posten in den Türmen sie gesprengt haben.

Was heißt es, jemanden zu vermissen? Es ist nicht wie das heiße Pochen einer Wunde. Es ist nicht der Schmerz, der vom Rennen unter den Rippen sitzt. Es ist kein besudeltes Gefühl, nicht wie im Schlamm stecken. Es ist, als wärst du an einem fremden Ort und würdest dich nicht mehr zurechtfinden. Es ist ein Gefühl wie schauen, ohne zu sehen, essen, ohne zu schmecken. Es ist Vergesslichkeit, die Unfähigkeit, dich zu rühren, die Unfähigkeit, Verbindung aufzunehmen. Es ist eine Strafe, die du absitzen musst, und wenn der Mensch, der dir fehlt, tot ist, dann sitzt du lange.

Ich stehe, als ich Maggie auf dem Friedhof beerdigt habe, da, wo die Straße oberhalb von Labasheeda ansteigt. Und wieder höre ich die schwarze Erde auf

ihren Sarg fallen. Dann die Stille. Es gibt keinen Trost
und nichts ist zu Ende, nur weil sich die Erde über ihrem
letzten Ruheplatz schließt, aber es gibt Mitgefühl und es
gibt Frieden, oder wenigstens eine Vorstellung von dem
Frieden, der eines Tages sein wird. Der Himmel ist
schwarz und tiefblau und sehr still. Ich sehe jedes Steinchen im Belag auf der Straße, den gelben Strich, wo früher nur Fahrwege aus Schotter und Dreck waren. Das
Gelb leuchtet. Am Straßenrand blühen blaue Disteln.
Ich gehe los. Die Schreie der Vögel hallen unter einem
tiefhängenden Himmel. Ich komme am Haus von Philly
Concannon vorbei, einer der besten beim Gaelic Foot-
ball, das grüne Eisentor ist verrostet und von Sonne und

Regen gebleicht, zwischen den Gitterstäben mit Winden gestopft, und vom Fußweg, den sie benutzt haben, ist nichts mehr zu sehen, alles ist von hohem Gras überwuchert. Ich gehe merkwürdig gequält die Straße entlang, stockend, als hätte ich Steine in den Schuhen. Ich höre den Fluss. Er klingt sanfter als früher, weil auch die Böschung, wie die Pfade, mit Gras bewachsen ist. Am Hang bei Knocksouna weiden Schafe, ein Mann zieht mit seinem Hund langsam zu ihnen hin. Es gibt Kühe. Drei sehe ich und höre auf einer tiefergelegenen Weide eine vierte. Aber es sind wenig Tiere. Die Weiden sind feucht und starren vor Binsen, die Steinmauern verfallen. Das ist die Tageszeit, zu der ich einmal wusste, wo alle sind. Ich komme an der Pumpe vorbei, die Betonplatte davor ist voller Rostflecken, der Schwengel baumelt lose wie ein gebrochener Arm. Ich gehe weiter auf die Kurve in der Straße zu. Die Stille ist lastend, wo nur Vögel im Flug schreien. Hinten auf dem Hügelrücken am Weg nach Killycolpy sehe ich drei Häuser. Es sind Hülsen, schwarze Hülsen jetzt gegen Abend im schwindenden Licht. Dort lebten einst viele Brennans und Murtaghs und Dolans. Alle fort. Ich lehne mich am Wegrand über eine Mauer und stecke mir eine Zigarette an. Hinter mir fährt ein Auto vorbei und geht langsam in die Kurve. Ich blicke ihm nach. Es fährt beim Schneider vorbei, auch dort fehlt das Dach, wächst das Gras aus dem Küchenboden um die Beine eines einsames Tisches. Es fährt bei Dermot vorbei, dem kleinen Haus auf der Weide, in dem Ma ihre Hühner gehalten und das er dann rosa getüncht hat. Sein Wagen steht in der Einfahrt. Daneben ist die große Blechschüssel für den Fernsehempfang. Das Auto, das hinter mir vorbeigefahren ist, schlängelt sich an den Häusern vorbei und hält auf der Straße vor den drei Häusern auf dem Kamm. Ich sehe einen Mann hinten aussteigen und dem Fahrer Geld geben. Er steigt den Pfad zu den Häusern hinauf. Da stoße ich mich von der Mauer ab und folge. Ich höre kleine Steinchen unter meinen Sohlen zerspringen. Ich höre meinen Atem. Im Vorbeigehen sehe ich zu Matts Fenster hinein: Sie haben die Küche mit Kartoffeln vollgekippt, da stehen Eierbecher voller Nägel, und auf der Fensterbank liegt immer noch Matts Pfeife. Ich bleibe auf der Straße stehen und drehe mich nach dem Haus um, in dem ich geboren bin. Die Tür ist jetzt blau, sie hängt nur noch an einer Angel. Könnte ich Musik aus der Luft ziehen, würde ich sie

hinter die Tür packen. Ich würde die Zimmer mit Leben
füllen. Ich würde allen in die Gesichter sehen und hören,
was sie reden. Aber ich finde sie nicht. Sie vergehen. Es
gibt nur den Fluss, der durchs Gras streicht, einen auf-
kommenden Wind. Es gibt den Geruch von nasser Asche
und nassem Holz. Auf dem Hügelrücken oben sehe ich
den Mann um die verlassenen Häuser gehen. Er trägt
einen braunen Anzug, der zu klein ist, und zieht das
rechte Bein nach. Wieder gehe ich los. Die Namen der
Orte um mich her werden schwächer und verblassen. Das
Autowrack, in dem Tom Connor sich einst Schweine
hielt, steht immer noch, ganz bis auf die Achsen her-
untergerostet, auf dem Hof. Am Weg, der zum langen

Feld führt, begegne ich Baby. Sie hat einen chromblitzenden neuen Kinderwagen mit hohen Rädern. »Du bist ja noch da, Baby«, sage ich. »Irgendjemand muss doch die Fußstapfen machen«, sagt sie. Wir gehen ein Stück Weges. Wir gehen ohne Grund in die Richtung, wo der Mann auf dem Hügel die Häuser umrundet. Der Wind weht jetzt stärker, und Baby meint, es gibt wohl noch Regen. »Der unerbittliche Nordwind«, sagt sie wissend. Als wir die Stelle erreicht haben, wo der Mann aus dem Taxi gestiegen ist, bleiben wir stehen. Wir sehen durch die Lücken in den Mauern zu, wie er durchs mittlere Haus wandert. »Weißt du, wer das ist?«, frage ich Baby. »Das weiß ich. Natürlich. Tommy Murtagh. Ist vor langer Zeit nach England gegangen und mäht das Gras in den Parks.« Der Mann taucht jetzt hinter dem Haus wieder auf und überquert langsam den Hof. Er rutscht auf den nassen Steinen mehrmals aus. An einem Baum bleibt er stehen. Der Baum ist geduckt, die Äste sind schwarz, sie sehen ganz zerquält aus von dem Wind, der sie so lange gepeitscht hat. Er kniet sich vor dem Baum ins lange Gras und faltet die Hände. »Kommt jedes Jahr einmal und sucht das Haus heim«, sagt Baby. »Sucht den Baum heim.« Sie riecht nach Leder und Seife. Noch niedrigere, noch schwärzere Wolken rollen von Norden herein, und mit ihnen kommt der Regen. Ich hebe die Jacke über den Kopf und sehe zu, wie der Mann im strömenden Regen auf die Wurzeln des Baums starrt. Vögel schreien am Himmel, und da blickt der Mann hoch. Es ist, als hätte er die Laute noch nie gehört, als wüsste er nicht, wo er ist. Ich rieche wieder Leder und Seife, und dann steht plötzlich Babys Gesicht dicht vor meinem. »Weißt du denn gar nicht, was unter dem Baum liegt?«,

fragt sie. Ihre Wangen sind um den zahnlosen Mund herum eingefallen. Sie macht ein Gesicht, als wäre etwas zum Lachen. »Weiß ich nicht«, sage ich. »Tommy Murtaghs Zwillingsbruder. Tot geboren und nie getauft. Also haben sie ihn unterm Baum begraben.« Sie nickt einmal zur Bekräftigung dieser wunderlichen Tatsache. Ich blicke an ihr vorbei auf den Mann. Er hat sich jetzt von den Knien erhoben und sieht sich um. Er schlägt den Kragen seiner Jacke hoch und tritt auf die Straße.

Im Regen scheint das Land alles loszulassen, was auf ihm lag. Wer wäre denn noch da, der wüsste, was der Fisch im Brunnen treibt, wo der Schlag Joe Roddy gefällt hat, oder wie viel Sand Matt auf dem Esel herbeigeschafft hat, um sein Stück Feld zu bauen? Wer wird noch die Geschichten derer kennen, die unter den Grabsteinen auf dem Friedhof liegen? Ich gehe jetzt ohne irgendwas, keine Geräusche, keine Bilder, nichts von dem, was in Freude oder Leid war. Ich gehe in Vergessenheit, und wo ich vorbeikomme, entschwindet alles.

36

Im Zimmer kommt jetzt eine Brise zum Fenster herein, und sie bringt den Geruch des Frühlings mit. Unten dreht die Kleine ihr Radio auf. Ich liege im Bett und lausche der Musik. Es kommt eine Zeit nach langer Arbeit, wo du Kraft suchst und nichts findest. Es kommt eine Zeit des Vergessens und dann eine Zeit, wo du wieder weißt, was du kannst. Und es kommt zuletzt eine Zeit, da ist die Arbeit vollbracht.

Im Morgenlicht lasse ich los.

Danksagung

Viele irische Emigranten haben uns reich mit ihrer Zeit und ihren Geschichten bedacht. Darunter Willie Barratt, Ann Connolly, James Dunleavy, Dermot Grogan, Mary Hall, Martin Hayes, Evelyn Haynes, Maureen Heston, Joseph Hynes, Gerry McLaughlin, Peggy Moore, J. M. O'Neill, Tim O'Sullivan, Jessie Stafford, Michael Sullivan, Peter Woods sowie Bewohner und Mitarbeiter des Arlington House. Peter Woods gestattete uns auch den Abdruck seines Gedichts. Andere waren, auf ganz unterschiedliche Weise, von unschätzbarer Hilfe, etwa John Adamson, Jackie und Campbell Bruce, Zelda Cheatle, die Familie Clifford, Willie Collins, Hannah Dawes und Gary McKeone vom Arts Council, Seamus Deane, Catherine Eccles, die Familie Faherty, Vince Goodsell, Chris Jones, Declan Kiberd, Phillip Kirwin, Dewi Lewis, Gordon MacDonald, Christy McNamara, Metro Imaging, Michael Mitchell, Chrissie Redmond, Mark Sealy, Sarah Westcott, Jonathan Worth und alle bei der Harvill Press. Dermot Healy war eine Quelle wertvoller Anregungen, John Berger gab ebenfalls und in ganz entscheidender Weise Anstöße einmal durch seine eigenen Gemeinschaftsprojekte mit Jean Mohr und durch seine Schilderungen des Lebens von Wanderarbeitern, dann auch als einer unserer ersten Leser und Ratgeber zu Fragen der Darstellung, und er hat darüber hinaus ein Vorwort verfasst. Nichola Bruce war eine große Hilfe bei der Zusammenstellung von Bild und Text.

Viele andere, nicht zuletzt die auf den Fotos Porträtierten, haben – auch wenn sie hier nicht namentlich genannt werden – wesentlich zum Gelingen beigetragen, und auch ihnen möchten die Autoren an dieser Stelle herzlich danken.

Bilder

END GAME

'Tipping Point for Planet Earth', by Cheng 'Lily' Li

ANTHONY D. BARNOSKY
AND ELIZABETH A. HADLY

END GAME

Tipping Point for Planet Earth?

WILLIAM
COLLINS

William Collins
An imprint of HarperCollins*Publishers*
1 London Bridge Street
London SE1 9GF
WilliamCollinsBooks.com

First published in Great Britain by William Collins in 2015

1

Copyright © Anthony D. Barnosky and Elizabeth A. Hadly 2015

The authors assert the moral right to be
identified as the authors of this work

A catalogue record for this book is
available from the British Library

HB ISBN 978-0-00-754815-6
TPB ISBN 978-0-00-757566-4

Printed and bound in Great Britain by
Clays Ltd, St Ives plc

All rights reserved. No part of this publication may be
reproduced, stored in a retrieval system, or transmitted,
in any form or by any means, electronic, mechanical,
photocopying, recording or otherwise, without the
prior permission of the publishers.

This book is sold subject to the condition that it shall not, by
way of trade or otherwise, be lent, re-sold, hired out or otherwise
circulated without the publisher's prior consent in any form of
binding or cover other than that in which it is published and
without a similar condition including this condition being
imposed on the subsequent purchaser.

MIX
Paper from
responsible sources
FSC C007454

FSC is a non-profit international organisation established to promote
the responsible management of the world's forests. Products carrying the
FSC label are independently certified to assure consumers that they come
from forests that are managed to meet the social, economic and
ecological needs of present and future generations,
and other controlled sources.

Find out more about HarperCollins and the environment at
www.harpercollins.co.uk/green

*To our parents, Emma & Michael Barnosky and
Jane Grassman Hadly & William McKell Hadly,
whose work to make a better world, each in
their own way, made us who we are.*

*And to our daughters, Emma and Clara,
who carry on with the future.*

CONTENTS

Introduction

THE JOURNEY

This is a story of a journey. Like most journeys, it started out as a personal quest, but for us it has also been a professional one. It began when we were young scientists, driven mostly by curiosity and looking for the next big adventure. We found adventures aplenty, because our jobs as palaeoecologists – people who study how our planet changes through time – took us to remote places all over the world. Along the way we fell in love and got married, and then the personal and professional adventures started inexorably to intertwine. We had one daughter, and a few months later got her a passport and hopped a plane to Australia. Then another daughter, same routine, but this time it was six weeks in Patagonia. By the time our kids were two-year-olds, they'd spent many nights in wilderness tents with us, buried their fingers in koala fur, been carried on our backs as we forded waist-deep rivers and stared down grizzly bears, and fallen sound asleep in their snugglies as we skied back-country trails. By the time they were fifteen, they had their own list of exploits: they'd hunkered down in their own tent as lions paced through camp, taught our graduate students the Latin names of various species, trapped rodents in Patagonia, faced off angry rattlers in the Oregon desert, and watched grapefruit-

1

sized chicken-eating spiders lead around their hundreds of young on a dark Amazonian night.

By now we've travelled to every continent in the world, save Antarctica; sometimes together, sometimes alone, sometimes with our daughters, sometimes not. All those trips were research expeditions as well as adventures, each of them undertaken to learn something about how nature worked in the places on which we hoped humans had not yet laid a heavy hand. And we did discover answers to some of the questions we were asking – like how animals respond to climate change that isn't caused by people, what causes mass extinctions, how ecosystems are assembled, and how evolution works at the genetic level to keep species alive.

But we also discovered that as the years went by and the personal and professional experiences added up, the questions we were asking ourselves began to change. From the personal perspective, the more different places we visited, the more they seemed the same in a very important respect: the values that people hold dear. Eventually we came to understand that the basic wants, needs and emotions that draw people together are much more deep-seated than those that separate cultures and countries. It didn't matter whether we were with the native Inupiat in an Arctic fishing village, with an indigenous tribe in the jungle of Peru, with scientific colleagues in India, or with executives imbibing at a fancy hotel in one of the great cities of the world. Everyone seemed united in wanting a healthy, comfortable life, putting family and friends first, and in the joy they took in basic pleasures like a good meal, a good laugh, or a pleasant stroll through a pretty place. And without exception, no matter the religion, the country, the political views or the economic class, everyone wanted the best for their children, and hoped that as their sons and daughters grew up, the world would just get better and better. As we watched our own daughters grow up, listening to their own dreams and hopes, we realised that we were no different from anyone else in those respects. Adventure and curiosity were no longer the be-all and end-all; giving our kids, and everyone else's, the future they deserve became much more important. And our lives in science began to change.

The more we saw, the more our professional perspective shifted. At some point the individual expeditions came to seem more and more like beads on a string, each bead distinct, but when all were taken together, forming a pattern that was hard to miss. And the pattern was that the world was changing before our eyes, much faster than any past changes we were familiar with from our studies of the deep-time history of the planet. Much of our earlier work had revolved around climate change before people got in on the act, so we knew what pace and magnitude of warming temperatures could be considered normal in the planet's history, and there was no doubt about it: what was happening today was way too much and way too fast. Likewise, we'd worked hard to figure out why species died out in the past, and what normal levels of bio-diversity should be, both in terms of numbers of species and their genetic diversity. Again, the losses we were seeing now – from giant otters in Amazon lakes, to wild dogs in Africa, to amphibians in the Rocky Mountains – were way too many.

We started to wonder, long and hard, about what exactly was driving the unusual and rapid changes that were happening all over the world. We knew, of course, the broad brush of the answer: people. The ecologists whose articles we had studied and who we now worked with on a daily basis were more senior than us, and had been publishing research about how people were changing the planet for decades. In some cases they had been reaching out and trying to spread that message to the world. But reading it in a scientific journal or book, or hearing about it in a professional presentation, didn't resonate at the gut level as much as it should have. Yes, we knew we'd been born into a world that held fewer than three billion people, and that as we progressed through our lives and careers, that number had more than doubled. But like most people, we'd also grown up in a world of limited horizons that made it pretty hard to observe first-hand the connection between more people and planet-sized changes – Tony was born into a poor working-class family in small-town Colorado and never saw much else until well into his twenties, and Liz grew up as a military brat, moving from one army base to another every couple of years, each one looking very much like the next, albeit in many different states and different countries. But eventually we began to connect the dots from all the places we'd travelled to in our careers, and we saw the links between the added billions of people in our lifetime, and hunger, poverty and unhappiness.

Through the years we also saw how it was getting harder and harder to find places that felt they hadn't been changed in a big way by people. The haze from faraway cities or power plants or wildfires would often obscure our view, even when we thought we were in the middle of nowhere. On our plane journeys from one part of the world to the next, the features we saw on the landscape below were usually farms and pastures, unless they were barren desert, open ocean or rough mountainous terrain. On night-time flights, the lights from cities and highways seemed to spread out below us everywhere. When we started compiling some numbers, we knew why: almost 50 per cent of Earth's land has been changed from forests and prairies to farms and pavement. That meant that each person on Earth requires about two acres of land, on average, to survive, given current diets, expectations and ways of doing business. We realised that the ratio of used land to people can't keep up for very much longer, given how fast we're adding human bodies to the world, and that we've already used up nearly all the good land.

As more years went by, we did more research, and we found that the number of humans and their domestic livestock on Earth now is about ten times higher than the planet could support before we – people – discovered how to increase its carrying capacity for big animals, including us, by mining fossil fuels from the ground. We watched HIV/AIDS take the world by storm, and realised that new diseases can, and do, crop up to kill us, and can change things as basic as people's sex lives. We went into the jungles of Costa Rica and found out that as far as disease goes, HIV/AIDS is not unusual in being transmitted from wild animals to humans, and that such transfer of disease happens more frequently as more people, looking for places to live and make a living, take over rapidly diminishing areas of wild lands.

All of these things made us wonder, just what was the future up against? It didn't help that in recent years we read seemingly ever more often about conflicts and genocides that were springing up around the world, many of them triggered by scarcities in such basics as food, water or oil. We knew about wars from our growing up – in elementary school, duck-and-cover drills, which amounted to hiding your head so you wouldn't see the nuclear bombs fall before they vaporised you, were an ingrained part of the routine. We dodged that bullet, but not the Vietnam War – Liz's dad did two tours of duty, and our generation lost friends there. Nobody wants that for their children. And then came the ever-present crises in Africa, the breakup of Yugoslavia and the USSR, 9/11, Iraq, Afghanistan, Ukraine, recurrent Israel–Palestine tensions, and now the rebel Islamic State. Was the world going into a downhill slide?

We grasped that, strange as it would have seemed to us when we started out as palaeoecologists, the kinds of data we had spent decades examining held the answer to that question. At that point our lives and careers, as lives and careers do, took an unlikely turn. About the time we were pondering the magnitude of current global changes and how they compared with those past, along came one of the most exciting and revolutionary realisations in ecology in

5

recent years: that what we like to think are gradual environmental changes in fact turn into sudden ones that we don't expect. In popular parlance, these are tipping points, and they happen because, in all walks of life, gradual change accumulates slowly until it hits a certain threshold, and then all hell breaks loose. We saw that in our own lives, when we fell in love – a gradually developing friendship, and then, boom, things suddenly changed forever, luckily in a good way. The sudden changes can just as easily be bad, though – like the death of a loved one, which also changes lives forever. On a larger scale, ecologists and theoreticians now know that sudden tipping points are not unusual in biological systems of all scales – think about a lake going overnight from clear, clean water to green algae scum, once the water reaches a certain temperature and nutrient load.

As we reflected on our palaeoecological research, we realised that we'd actually seen the entire Planet Earth hit tipping points before. Times like sixty-six million years ago, when an asteroid struck the planet and acted as the coup-de-grâce in killing three out of every four of the species known at the time. Or twelve thousand years ago, when the one–two punch of natural climate change and growing human populations wiped out half the big-bodied animals on Earth, at the same time that it went from a cold planet largely covered in ice to the warmer one we know today, which then fostered the growth of human civilisation.

Those past tipping points made us sit up and take notice. Since it has happened before, could Earth be headed for yet another planetary tipping point? And if so, just what does that mean for our children, and for theirs? Or, for that matter, given the lightning speed at which we have seen the world change, what does it mean for our own future?

We've now spent a few years, along with many other scientists, trying to answer those questions. And what we've discovered has surprised us: first dismaying us, and then giving us hope. The dismay is that if we keep on with the way we've been doing things, it is inevitable that the world will soon tip into a permanent state that is worse than what we are used to now. That end game will not be one we want for ourselves, and certainly not one we want for our children. The hope comes from learning that there are feasible ways to change the future, heading it towards an end game with the outcome of a better life, a better world – but only if we, as in all of us, act fast.

These things are what this book is about – our journey of discovery about ourselves, and about the planet we love. We hope that reading it will be a journey for you as well, one that ends in your own personal tipping point, where you comprehend that you really do have the power to change the world.

1

PAST OR FUTURE?

Liz, in the Himalayas of Nepal, April 2012

It all happened pretty fast. One minute, I was sitting outside sipping my tea. The next, I was hunkered down in a cold, smoky hut, patching up a Tamang woman's bloody scalp, which she was lucky to have at all, given the machetes that were swinging around. Like most activities around sundown in that part of the world, it was a race against time, because darkness was coming on fast, and candlelight just wasn't going to be up to the task.

When I had boarded the plane for Nepal a few days before, that kind of adventure was the last thing on my mind. I had set out with one of my Ph.D students, Katie Solari, to meet up with my Indian colleague, Uma, and her Nepali student, Nishma Dahal, in Kathmandu. Our four-woman crew was then going to head into the Himalayas to figure out which species of pika, a fluffy but short-eared cousin of rabbits, occupied which elevations in the world's highest mountain range. We wanted that information in order to learn how the pikas are responding to the rampant climatic warming that is now heating up that part of the world, as a kind of bellwether for predicting how global warming will change wildlife in

9

general. Pikas, it turns out, are the perfect natural experiment in that regard, because their physiology prevents them from tolerating warm temperatures. As warming climate causes mountain environments to heat up, the pikas move upslope, taking advantage of the fact that for every hundred metres of rise in elevation, temperature falls by a little less than 1°C. Our thought was that by tracking their upslope movement over a series of years, and performing genetic tests on them to see how the animals we trapped were related to each other, we could use the pikas as the proverbial canaries in the coalmine to help forecast Earth's ecological future.

Since we left Kathmandu, we'd been moving upslope at a much faster rate than the pikas, and we were glad of it. After hiking for two days we were above three thousand metres. The high mountain air felt fresh, if a little thin, after our time in the valley, where brick kilns and fires thickened and darkened the air with a blanket of dense smog. That was far behind and below us now, and we revelled in being in one of the world's treasured landscapes, ascending through hillsides covered with startlingly vivid arrays of red, pink, white and purple rhododendrons. I scanned the forests for signs of the red panda, since we were in one of the last strongholds of the species. What caught my eye instead, though, was that there was no real forest understorey, and although the trees were straight and tall, all but the highest branches were gone, leaving no cover for birds, much less for red pandas.

Just before reaching the ridgetop that day we met a striking Tamang girl who invited us to stay at her family's teahouse overlooking the slopes where the red panda was said to reside. Her smile was warm, the afternoon was cold, and we did not hesitate about taking her up on her offer. We didn't have any better options anyway. Despite the constant signs of humanity along the trail – trash everywhere, even the steepest slopes levelled into slivers of land to grow a few meagre crops – dwellings were few and far between. Our hosts' hut was one of only two built on the narrow ridgeline, both doing double duty as homes and as teahouses for people like us. Outside each, the family matriarch was sitting in her Tibetan garb, knitting the woollen hats that are so popular among the trekkers who pass through. I shared my binoculars and field guide with a young boy in my hut's family; he was tan from being outside, and ready with his smile. He pointed to the birds he knew in the guide, miming the places in the forest where they lived. I scrambled around the rocks near their small cabbage garden, looking for evidence of pikas, but didn't find any. Nishma translated that the boy had not seen any for a while, and that he thought the weasels had eaten them all in the last couple of years.

So I sipped my tea outside, reflecting on the day, waiting for the daily dinner of dal bhat (Nepali lentils and rice). That's when the shrieks jerked me out of my reverie.

All of a sudden mothers, fathers, kids, aunts, uncles and who knows who else – all the residents of the two houses – were pouring down the hill. The boy who had been so interested in my field guide had been caught stealing wood from a pile collected by the son of the other family, who had done all the hard work shimmying up the trees, cutting off branches as he climbed. The fight was on. Both boys swung their kukris (curved machetes) at each other. Their entire families – parents and children alike – joined in the fray, beating each other with sticks, pulling at braids, grabbing at clothes, scratching and screaming. All the while, the kukris kept swinging.

At the end, all were bruised, some were bleeding, clothes were ripped and shoes were lost. While another trekker patched up the gash on the head of the matriarch from the other teahouse, the matriarch from ours asked me for medical help. Fist-sized clumps of her hair had been torn out, her face was cut, and large bumps had appeared on her head and brow. As I patched her up, the two families continued to hurl curses at each other.

The violence in this spectacular, top-of-the-world setting was jarring – the wood they were fighting over was for our evening's cook fire. For me, the pieces fell into place. Every day, young Tamang boys travel from higher, barren elevations down to the upper treeline to collect wood. That's why we noticed as we climbed higher that all the low branches were gone. The trees were being stripped bare where they stood, leaving no cover for the red pandas, which ironically are a major lure for the trekkers, the profits from whom the Tamang rely on for the few things they have that they don't take from the land – like mobile phones, and the small solar panels to charge them.

The problem is, the land is starting to let them down. Or maybe it's vice versa. For the days we worked in the Himalayas, we, through our Tamang hosts' cooking, depended on the wood collected from those trees that were being stripped bare, the water that was syphoned from the melting glaciers above, the cabbage and potatoes grown in small family gardens, and the rice and lentils carried up the mountain on their backs. I had climbed above five thousand metres, and thought I had escaped the smog and chaos of the 'modern world'. But what became all too apparent was that there is now no place clear of humanity's impact. And that the farther you get from our creature comforts, the closer you live to the land, and the more apparent is our dependence on Earth's natural resources.

Even more of a wake-up call was seeing that where those human impacts get to be too much, you end up in the middle of a machete fight, the result of tensions that boil over as an inevitable byproduct of depleting what you need to stay alive. I was left with an uncomfortable question in my mind. Had I seen civilisation's past in those mountains of Nepal, or had I caught a glimpse of the future?

* * *

Judging by the trends of the last few decades, that machete fight, and what led to it, is all too plausibly the world of the future. What is now normal – not only in places we usually think of as economically underprivileged like Nepal, India and Africa, but in fact through most of the world – is a landscape and seascape that has been so changed by humanity that our life-support systems are teetering precariously on the brink of collapse. And in systems as complex as those that keep society ticking along in the way we're now used to, collapse has a habit of sneaking up so stealthily that you're blindsided. Suddenly you're in the middle of a new normal, and suffering devastating consequences that are happening too fast to do anything about.

In popular parlance, that's known as hitting a tipping point. Things may seem to be changing gradually, or at face value even not at all, until you reach some critical threshold, and everything becomes different. Think, for example, of water heating up on the stove. The reason it seems a watched pot never boils is because you don't observe any major changes until the water reaches a critical temperature, which (depending on the heat of the flame) can take a long time to happen. When the temperature does hit the boiling point (about 100°C, or 212°F, at sea level), however, instantly everything changes. Bubbles roil, and the water changes its state, turning into steam. Boiling water exemplifies what scientists mean when they talk about tipping points: a rapid change from an 'old' state of being to a new, very different state, caused by pushing the system past some important threshold value. The actual change from the old state to the new one is called a 'critical transition'.

Tipping points (or, if you want to sound like a scientist, critical transitions) are not confined to boiling water. At just about any scale and in any system you care to name, you can think of one. The egg gradually rolls towards the edge of the counter, until it drops over it and reaches its new state of being broken on the floor. A butterfly metamorphoses from a caterpillar, or a frog from a tadpole. The canoe rocks, then all of a sudden tips over and is upside down. Your car runs perfectly well, then one day it won't start. Property values build up over decades, then crash in a year.

For people too, tipping points are the rule rather than the exception. In fact, if you think about what happens to you and your loved ones, tipping points are the defining moments. A woman is pregnant for nine months, then in the space of minutes a baby is nursing at her breast. Tipping point. The baby grows, gradually learns to talk, walk, play, reason, and then all of a sudden hits puberty. Big tipping point. More gradual change through the teen years, young adulthood, and then that special someone comes along and two previously separate lives join together in marriage – once again, a tipping point. Gradually the two grow old together, accumulating their respective aches and pains as middle age gives way to the retirement years, then a fall breaks a hip. Another tipping point. And finally, of course, the biggest state-change of all, from life to death.

The ubiquity of tipping points has prompted a great deal of research among theoreticians of late, which has made it very clear why living things tend to experience major changes in such fits and starts. Basically, it has to do with how many parts something is built of, and how those parts are connected to one another. The more parts there are, and the more intricate their connections, the greater the likelihood that the resulting system will remain stable for long periods of time. But by the same token in such systems, the greater the likelihood that when change does come, either by tweaking lots of parts simultaneously, or by damaging just one super-critical part, it will come fast, and it will hit hard, flipping the system from its 'old normal' to a 'new normal'. These sorts of systems – with many intricately connected parts that influence each other – are called, not surprisingly, 'complex systems' in the jargon of science.

Past or Future?

Living things are extremely complex systems, composed as they are of millions of mutually interacting parts that are connected to each other in spaghetti-tangle ways. The scale of the complexity begins to boggle your mind when you realise that anything alive is actually built of many smaller-scale complex systems, separate entities in themselves, but connected together to form ever-larger and even more complex systems. Starting at the molecular level, for instance, DNA replication itself is a complex system that we are just barely beginning to get a working knowledge of. That, of course, is intimately dependent on the workings of, and at the same time influences, the slightly larger-scale complex systems that we call cells. And so it goes, with connections between cells, organs, individuals, groups of individuals, species, communities, and entire ecosystems. The human body has more cells of microbes than human cells; the complexity of our own body's ecosystem is not remotely well understood. The most complex system of all is the global ecosystem, which is composed of all life on Earth, and the myriad ways that life forms interact with each other and with the inanimate environment around them (like air, water, soil, and so on).

Which means that humans, being life forms ourselves, are not at all separate from the rest of the global ecosystem; on the contrary, we're intimately embedded in it, just like every other animal (and plant, and microbe – it's a long list). We count on it for such essentials as a place to live, air to breathe, food to eat, water to drink, and for comfort and solace. But there is no denying that, unlike other animals, our place in the global ecosystem has taken on an unusual role – because we now dominate it. So much so that, just like the flame heating that pot of water towards a boil, we have been inexorably pushing key pieces of our planetary life-support systems towards a tipping point. The tipping point we are pushing towards, however, differs from the boiling of water in an important respect. Once you cool steam, it returns to its previous state, liquid. By contrast, there is no going back once we cross the sort of threshold we're marching towards, which is more like the one an egg crosses when it tips off the edge of the counter.

People who study tipping points for a living have a name for crossing those thresholds of no return – the system is said to exhibit 'hysteresis'. The resulting irreversible kinds of state-changes become more and more likely as the complex system gets, well, more and more complex. Intuitively, that makes a certain amount of sense. The more parts to a system, and the more interdependencies between those parts, the harder it is to get all the pieces back in the same order if it happens to fall apart – say because a critical part wears out, or because you inadvertently broke it. Think of the watch you took apart as a kid, or the cars we drive today.

At the huge scale of the global ecosystem, the number of parts, their diversity of function, and the number of connections between them are so enormous that it is little wonder that hitting a tipping point means big, irreversible changes. That isn't just theory: the geological and palaeontological record is replete with evidence of past threshold crossings that changed the planet forever. One of the most famous is dinosaur extinction, which happened about sixty-six million years ago. In that case, the global ecosystem was almost literally pushed past a critical threshold by an asteroid slamming into it, with cascading impacts throughout the planet. For tens of millions of years prior to that, the Earth had maintained a super-sized version of the food chain, where *Tyrannosaurus rex* and its cousins hunted prey that in some cases stood as high as a two-storey house and weighed thirteen tons or so. In the course of what may have amounted to a bad weekend, all that was over, and the new state of the world was one where puny mammals, and eventually us, began to rule the Earth.

Not all planetary-scale tipping points are caused by something as dramatic as an asteroid strike, but even so, they still show up unmistakably in the geological record. The most recent global state-shift was when the last ice age gave way to the interglacial warm time in which we still live. The glacial state featured ice, miles thick, covering much of the northern hemisphere and mountain glaciers throughout the world, a condition that had prevailed for about a hundred thousand years. Then, over the course of a few millennia, beginning about fourteen thousand years ago, the climate gradually got warmer, without much overall effect, until suddenly, with a last flicker from cold to warm between eleven and thirteen thousand years ago, the new interglacial state arrived, and it was a whole new world, one without massive continental glaciers.

That was an important global tipping point for humanity, because it set the stage for our domination of the planet. The cause was a complex interplay between three features of the Earth's orbit around the sun that vary regularly, but at different paces: how elliptical the orbit is, how much the Earth's axis tilts, and how the Earth wobbles as it rotates. As those three orbital features came into alignment over thousands of years, not much happened to the glaciers, until finally the Earth was in just the right position to maximise the amount of sunlight striking at critical seasons. With that, a warming threshold was crossed for the planet, the glaciers disappeared rapidly, and new ecosystems assembled virtually everywhere, as plants and animals formerly separated by ice came together. At the same time, humans finally arrived on every continent (except Antarctica), and began to grow dramatically in number, while other large animals died out rapidly. Then, around eleven thousand years ago, the global ecosystem stabilised into its interglacial new normal, where it has been right up until the last couple of centuries. This new normal caused formerly continuous landmasses to become separated by high sea-level stands, and their plants and animals set off on new independent ecological and evolutionary journeys. Now, though, the world has once again begun to change in a way, and at a speed, that signals a new planetary tipping point is just ahead.

This time it's not something from outer space or Earth's orbit that's pushing the planet towards a point of no return. It's us, pushing relentlessly towards thresholds on several different interconnected fronts: population growth, overconsumption of natural resources, climate disruption, pollution, disease, and killing anything that gets in our way. Some scientists think that going too far in any one of those arenas could push Earth past a planetary boundary that would have devastating consequences. Think, then, what would happen if we exceeded critical thresholds in more than one of them at once. Again, both intuition and data predict some very bad effects. Intuitively, two bad things hitting at the same time is clearly going to have much more impact than only one. We can again turn to the past to see that this is indeed the case when it comes to global tipping points. The kind of climatic shift that eleven thousand years ago turned an ice-age Earth into the warmer planet we're used to had in fact happened many times over the past couple of million years. But evidence about the last ice-age-to-warm critical transition suggests that it was different from any of the others in a very important respect. That last big climate change was also accompanied by the extinction of half of the big-bodied species on Earth – instead of the full complement of about 350 such species, the last global tipping point left us with only about 180.

The reason? It wasn't just hitting a critical threshold in the climate system. It was hitting that climate threshold at the same time that *Homo sapiens* expanded their populations, colonised the world, and began to hunt and to compete with other large-bodied species. Where climate change hit in places where humans had not arrived there were sometimes a few extinctions, but nothing too major. Where humans arrived on a continent before climate change hit – for example in Australia fifty thousand years ago – they caused more extinctions than happened with climate change alone, but those extinctions were spread out over several thousand years. But where human arrival and climate change hit at the same time – as in the Americas – the number of extinctions was multiplied many times over what you'd expect by simply adding up the anticipated effects of a few extinctions by climate change, plus a few more by human impacts. It is this multiplying effect that may be the big issue if we exceed several thresholds simultaneously, or if exceeding a threshold in one part of the global ecosystem causes a domino effect of exceeding thresholds in other interacting parts of the system. Unfortunately, those simultaneous threshold crossings are all too plausible from a complex systems point of view, because the individual systems of our world – human population growth and consumption, climate change, environmental contamination, and so on – are so interconnected.

Just how close are we to hitting those thresholds on the various fronts? Very close indeed. It's already happening in certain regions of the world – that machete fight in Nepal, and the lack of basic natural resources that caused it, is just one tiny indication. Substitute guns for machetes, and all of a sudden you have a world that is not too different from that portrayed in 1981's *The Road Warrior*, the second of the *Mad Max* movies, in which a leather-clad Mel Gibson defends one of the last remaining supplies of oil in the outback of Australia with his mute sidekick, the perpetually dirt-smudged 'Feral Kid'. In March 2013 in Egypt, at least briefly, that became reality, as reported by David Kirkpatrick in the *New York Times*: 'Qalyubeya, Egypt – A fuel shortage has helped send food prices soaring. Electricity is blacking out even before the summer. And gas-line gunfights have killed at least five people and wounded dozens over the past two weeks' (30 March 2013). And in developed nations like the United States and the United Kingdom, there are people who are so worried about something similar happening that they have been laying in stockpiles of guns, ammunition, food, and whatever else they think it will take to ensure the survival of themselves and their families if the worst should come to pass. A perusing of survivalist (or 'prepper') websites shows just how seriously these people take the threat of disaster, spending millions of dollars on be-prepared merchandise, setting up specialist dating websites and developing products like filters that can make urine taste like bottled water and the $449 'Centurian children's tactical vest'.

What the preppers are worried about are the things we are all reading in the news, realities that are pointing in the direction of crossing dangerous environmental thresholds, which would lead to huge societal problems, if not outright collapse. Climate change has already begun to ramp up storms so much that in 2005 the sea swallowed New Orleans. Waterfalls poured into the tunnels of New York City's subway system in 2012. Massive droughts sparked crop losses and wildfires over huge areas of the United States and Australia in 2012 and 2013. Shortages of things we once took for granted are now becoming commonplace, to the extent that even big business is getting worried. Coca-Cola, for example, cited water availability as one of the key challenges to its continued success in its 2010 report to the Securities and Exchange Commission. Environmental contaminants are so rampant that fish are growing two heads in some places, and that's just from the obvious pollutants. Sneaking in under the radar are things like hormones (such as endocrine disruptors), which we have unwittingly been spreading everywhere, recently implicated in causing such things as children hitting puberty earlier, increased heart disease, obesity and type II diabetes. Even small-scale oil and chemical spills, such as those occurring regularly in the North Sea, can dramatically impact local marine diversity. And global mercury levels in the ocean surface have tripled since Industrial Revolution levels, trickling into our seafood, which when eaten can result in developmental disorders in children.

Just how close we may be to a global tipping point becomes apparent when you take a helicopter view and see what is happening at the scale of the entire planet. The statistics look pretty stark. The deforestation that caused that machete fight in Nepal is all too common worldwide – as has already been noted, more than 40 per cent of the world's forests have been cut down, and we're continuing to clear-cut an area about the size of Greece every year. Nearly 50 per cent of all of Earth's land has been paved, bulldozed, dammed or turned into agricultural fields and pasturelands. That means we humans have caused more sledgehammer, chainsaw-style change on Earth than took place at the last global tipping point, when only about 30 per cent of the planet's surface was totally transformed, back then by retreating glaciers. We've used almost all the arable land that exists for agriculture, and we've fished 90 per cent of the big fish out of the sea.

If those obvious transformations aren't enough, we also have to add tremendous amounts of energy into the global ecosystem to keep society operating at its present level, and the way we have traditionally done that, by burning fossil fuels (the stored remnants of previous life on the planet), is beginning to bite us from behind, by raising Earth's temperature abnormally. If we keep going at the rate we have been, it will become hotter in the next six decades than it has been for some fifteen million years. The increase in temperature will be so fast that many of Earth's species won't be able to keep up, and in some places where lots of people currently live it will be too hot for any mammal – including us – to survive outside. That, of course, presumes that we don't run out of the easily obtainable oil first, which would escalate what happened in Egypt in 2013 by increasing energy prices across the world. Of course there are alternative sources of energy, but the world hasn't been pursuing them too actively.

You get the message – there's lots of global change under way. The underlying driver of it all is that there are just so many people now, all needing their slice of the pie. And we keep on coming. As of 2014 we were adding eighty-two million people per year. That is three orders of magnitude higher than the average yearly growth from ten thousand years to four hundred years ago (which averaged sixty-seven thousand people per year). Most of the population growth has been in the last century, over which time the number of humans has nearly quadrupled. Just since 1950, we've increased our numbers almost threefold, and since 1969, we've doubled ourselves. The problem is that each of us requires our own portion of air to breathe, a place to live that is comfortable and dry, enough water to drink and food to eat, and myriad ways to amuse ourselves. And we produce a lot of waste – waste from our bodies, waste from our structures and vehicles, waste from our fun.

As a result, each of us ends up requiring a lot of 'stuff' – the average American, for example, uses up about ninety kilograms of things each *day*. Some people, particularly those in developed countries, use more stuff than others, to be sure, but nevertheless, every one of us has needs and wants that we attempt to meet by tapping into the global ecosystem, which means that each of us leaves a usage footprint – in truth, an environmental footprint – that is much bigger than the actual footprint we leave in the sand. The average size of each individual's environmental footprint is truly staggering. For instance, it takes (on average) about 1.7 acres of land per person per year to sustain us in the manner to which we've become accustomed. The 'average' person uses about 4.6 barrels of oil per year (although the figure varies enormously: if you live in Singapore, you use eighty-one barrels; in the US or the Netherlands, twenty-two barrels; in China, three barrels; in Nepal or Bangladesh, about a fifth of a barrel). The average American's water footprint is about 665,000 gallons per year – enough to fill an Olympic-size swimming pool.

Multiply such numbers by the over seven billion people now in the world, and you begin to see the magnitude of the problems.

Then take into account that the population is continuing to grow, albeit at slower rates than in the last fifty years. Even conservative demographic projections indicate that we'll add two to three billion people to the world in just the next thirty-five years, each one of whom will require their own quota of 'stuff'. The multiplying factor is that if economic conditions continue to improve in developing and populous areas like China, India and Africa, the average environmental footprint per person is likely to grow even larger. That will accelerate us even faster towards those dangerous thresholds of global-scale impacts like climate change, environmental contamination and ecological losses that eventually manifest as societal problems, even if we are able to stall population growth. Not to mention that in the demographic revolution under way, the population is ageing. All of us collectively are living longer, hanging around on Earth, consuming more food and energy and stuff as we age. The twenty-first century will belong to the old. Currently, less than 10 per cent of the world's population are under four years old, while about 13 per cent are over sixty. The over-sixty crowd is going to almost double by 2050. In developed countries like those in western Europe, the age imbalance is even worse: by 2050, more than 30 per cent of the population will be over sixty. Who is going to produce all the stuff those old people need, and how will they be taken care of? This is in contrast to the developing world, particularly Africa, where the majority of the population is under the age of fifteen, and only 3 per cent are over sixty-five. What jobs will those young people have, and how will they spend their time?

Given the upward population trends and the corresponding downward trends in the health of the global ecosystem, it is not hard to see that if we simply continue doing business as usual, some very serious problems we already have will only get worse. Even now, about 80 per cent of the world's population (5.6 billion people) live below poverty level. A third (2.6 billion people) of us lack basic sanitation services. Over a billion have inadequate access to water. One out of every eight (870 million people) lack enough food. A billion have no access to even basic health care, at the same time that increased global travel and commerce are fostering and spreading new diseases that affect us and the plants and animals on which we depend.

That's where we are today. What happens if population pressures finally hit a threshold that tumbles the dominoes of food, water, energy, climate, pollution and biodiversity, which in turn break up the intricate workings of the global society? That would be a global tipping point, which would change the world from what is now one of relative comfort, to one where those machete fights in the Himalayas, or the *Road Warrior*-style gun battles at Egyptian petrol queues, rapidly spread throughout the planet. Lack of access to resources creates instability.

Those scenarios aren't way off in the future. They're already here, in many communities, in both developed and developing nations. Conflicts over water, for example, are already brewing all over the world, both within and across national boundaries, including in the western United States; between the United States and Mexico; between Mali, Niger, Nigeria and Guinea; within China; between Syria and Israel; and between Iraq, Syria and Turkey. The terrorist group Islamic State has captured dams and other infrastructure in Iraq in order to control access to water and electricity and to use catastrophic dam failure by bombing as a weapon of coercion over those downriver. In modernised Bangalore – known as the Silicon Valley of India – people have to lock up their water-storage tanks to guard against theft, and water is delivered to the taps so infrequently and irregularly that entrepreneurs are developing mobile phone apps to alert people when it is on the way, so they can rush home in time to fill their containers. Power there fails frequently, especially when the reservoirs that generate electricity run dry. Pakistan has long walked a tightrope of delivering enough water to its farms and people while still holding enough in reservoirs to provide the hydroelectric power it largely relies on to generate electricity. The situation often comes down to choosing between a drink of water and turning on the lights. In 2012 the sweltering summer – unusually hot and dry even by Pakistan desert standards – brought the situation to a head. Water had to be diverted from power generation to keep people alive, leading to a shortfall of nearly 45 per cent of the national demand for electricity, and eighteen to twenty hours per day of power outages.

The results were massive violent demonstrations and riots, and as a US National Research Council report on the social stresses of climate change put it, 'burned trains, damaged banks and gas stations, looted shops, blocked roads, and, in some instances, targeted [attacks] on homes of members of the National Assembly and provincial assemblies' (John D. Steinbruner et al., *Climate and Social Stress: Implications for Security Analysis*, National Academies Press, Washington DC, 2012). The drought and hot weather had been going on since 2010, and caused international tensions as well as unrest within Pakistan's borders. The Pakistani Foreign Minister blamed India for illegally diverting water from the Indus River system before it could reach Pakistan, while the Pakistan Commissioner of the Indus River System Authority put the blame on climate change, primarily caused by the developed countries of the West.

The same US National Research Council report pointed out that Egypt could easily erupt into violence and social unrest within a decade, posing a huge security concern for the rest of the world, as increasing drought from climate change begins to dry up the Nile. Water from the Nile is now required to irrigate fields that provide half of the wheat that is essential to feeding eighty million Egyptians (the other half is imported). The problem is that the river flows through Sudan and Ethiopia before it gets to Egypt, accumulating nearly half of its volume upstream of Egypt's borders, and there are no international agreements about apportioning water between the three countries.

What happens if Egypt's wheat fields turn into parched ground? Millions of people, already living on the edge and ready to erupt into violence – as the Arab Spring and the 2013 petrol-station gunfights in Egypt showed – get hungry and mad. Food prices rise and the economy goes downhill as more Egyptian pounds are diverted towards importing food. Unemployed, hungry people take to the streets, and leaders become powerless in the face of angry mobs. Meanwhile, border tensions with Sudan escalate, and the terrorist groups that have long called Sudan home take advantage of the social unrest to expand their influence. Egypt, desperate for water to irrigate its fields, attacks Sudan. In response, terrorists get their hands on a nuclear device. Suddenly the Middle East is at war, and the flow of oil from Saudi Arabia – the biggest oil producer in the world – is disrupted. The United States, still reliant on the Middle East for about 13 per cent of its oil, jumps into the fray to protect its national interests. And so it escalates further. The world is plunged into a crisis so all-consuming that any efforts to mitigate the longer-term global pressures – climate change, pollution, environmental contamination – go out the window, and our global die is cast for the future. The world becomes no longer as good as it is now. Instead, it becomes a world where the survivalists would rightly say, 'I told you so.'

Similar scenarios could play out in many parts of the world. The specific triggers differ from place to place – in New York, for instance, the straw that breaks the camel's back could be another inch of sea-level rise due to melting glaciers combined with more frequent superstorm Sandy-type deluges, whereas in Paris or Rome it could be environmental refugees who further strain already over-stressed societal support systems. But the common thread every-where is basic human needs meeting diminishing resources. That's when a final push – which in times of plenty might have little impact – can cascade into crisis that sends the world over the edge, and that's where fear for the future can begin to look very genuine. How palpable that fear should really be is what the rest of this book is about. And since the chief driver is how many of us there are on the planet, let's start with that.

2

PEOPLE

Liz, Tony, Emma and Clara, on the road to Kurnool, India,
February 2007

It was late afternoon, the sun getting low in a hazy sky, and our car
was the only one on a narrow ribbon of asphalt stretching off into
the distance, dusty brown fields on either side. Our Indian driver's
response to seeing the line of bandits blocking the road – stringy-
muscled, sun-browned men in all manner of well-worn baggy
pants and ill-fitting, mismatched shirts, kids in raggedy shorts and
T-shirts, even a few women in their saris – was born more out of
the last couple of days' frustrations than out of any ill will. His eyes
darkened and narrowed a little, he muttered what may have been
the Telugu equivalent of 'Dammit, not again!' and then he jammed
the accelerator to the floor. Our Indian colleague Uma yelled, 'Lock
your doors!' Just as we braced for impact, imagining who knows
what carnage, the bandits dropped the rope they were stretching
across the road, dived every which way to avoid being run over, and
with a couple of big bounces we were over the line of rocks they'd
placed in our path. One second, we were worried about being
robbed; the next, we were feeling a little as if we were the bad guys,

with angry, scared faces flying past the car windows, baskets rolling towards the barrow pit, and us leaving it all behind as we sped down the road.

That was the third time we had had a run-in with bandits in two days, which is why our driver was getting fed up with it. The first time he was downright scared, like the rest of us. Travelling with two daughters you're supposed to be watching out for – Emma was fourteen at the time, and Clara was ten – adds to the anxiety in those kinds of situations, but as a two-career couple, both needing to do the fieldwork our jobs demanded, we had only two basic parental options. One of them, leaving the girls back in California while we were off gallivanting in India for a month, wasn't something we were prepared to do. So there they were, with us, our Indian host Uma (the same Uma who was trekking up the Himalayas with Liz in the previous chapter) and our driver, the girls watching the adults to figure out the protocol in this foreign land, as the car was brought to a stop by people banging on the windows and shouting something or other in threatening voices. The odds were decidedly unbalanced from our perspective: a bunch of stern-looking fellows demanding money versus our group of two men, two women and two girls; them on their home turf, us strangers in a strange land; and none of us but our driver able to speak the language (even Uma did not speak this region's language – there are over a hundred languages in India, after all). As this was the first attempt at highway robbery since we had set out from Bangalore, our driver took the negotiation tack, something along the lines of (as was later loosely translated for us) 'You really don't want to mess with these foreigners, the cops would be all over you.' Whatever he said, it seemed to work, a small donation ensued, the brigands backed off, and we continued down the road.

We hadn't travelled much further, maybe a couple of hours, when once again we saw congestion up ahead, this time caused by a throng of women moving from car to car. Dressed in spotlessly clean saris of dazzling colours – the pinks, yellows and blues a startling contrast to the stark countryside – they were laughing, singing and playing tambourines, the bangles on their arms sparkling in the sun and adding their own chime to the rhythm. As we got closer, though, we sensed that something was a little off. The tambourine players seemed to be intentionally creating a distraction; then a different group of saris would swoop around the car that had been brought to a halt. And all of the sari-wearers' shoulders seemed a little broader, and their hips a bit narrower, than they ought to be. When we got closer still, we saw that the elegantly made-up faces and sari-clad bodies were in fact those of men. One more thing to explain to our daughters: it was a gang of transgenders (known as 'hijras' in India) who were holding us up. Honestly, there's not much to do in that situation but laugh, part with some money, and go on your way. Even Uma was surprised.

We had landed in Bangalore a few days before, and were journeying from there to some caves we needed to explore in the off-the-beaten-path Kurnool district, about a hundred miles south of Hyderabad. As we set out, our heads were still reeling a little from jet lag and the culture shock that inevitably hits a Westerner on their first trip to India. In Bangalore the sensory chaos was awe-inspiring, at times overpowering: what seemed like infinite numbers of sputtering, belching and roaring motorcycles, yellow tricycle taxis, cars, buses, trucks, bikes and pedestrians, with a few cows thrown in for good measure, jockeying for a space on the road or on the vehicles, no apparent rules, apparently every man and woman for themselves. The tempting fragrances of baking naan and exotic spices somehow found their way through the wood-, coal- and petrol-fumed air. Women completely shrouded in black burqas clustered in front of a shop window displaying sexy red underwear on otherwise naked mannequins. Well-dressed businessmen and fashionable ladies in all sorts of colourful attire milled through elegant shops and high-end restaurants, while beggars conducted their forlorn business right outside. Feral dogs roamed the alleys even in the centre of town. And as we walked down the streets – a mishmash of pavement and dirt – there was ubiquitous chatter, none of it understandable to us, coming from faces that radiated every expression from bright smiles, to curiosity, to in a few cases a touch of hostility.

After that full-on immersion in the human condition, the road trip – highway robbers and all – felt downright relaxing, except for what seemed to us several near misses of head-on collisions, but which our driver assured us were all in a day's work for him. Even the best roads have few signs, and many are barely wide enough for one vehicle. Passing means finding any wiggle room you can, sometimes pulling in your wing mirrors. As we drove we were barraged by pedestrians, oxen carrying their loads, crammed buses with people hanging out of the windows, sitting on the roofs or holding on to the rear bumpers, and the extraordinary Indian trucks, which are lovingly and beautifully decorated, often with little blinking Christmas-tree lights, tasselled front-window curtains, or hand-painted slogans like 'India is Great' in bold blue letters on a bright orange and yellow background.

We finally navigated to the caves, after driving through a village street so narrow that we could touch the walls of the houses on either side if we stuck our hands out of the window – and where surprised faces looked up from washing, cooking, napping and all manner of everyday activities to see the rare sight of a nice car with a family of foreigners basically driving through their living quarters. We were in a little-populated area by Indian standards, but still, there wasn't a square inch of land that did not have a heavy human footprint. And we had long ago left power and running water behind.

People

The purpose of our journey was to find some rich fossil deposits in those caves that would tell us something about what India's wildlife and the rest of the ecosystem were like before the country's human population grew to its present density – among the highest in the world, with close to 1.3 billion people packed into an area about a third the size of the United States, where only 316 million people live. The part of India we were in was particularly interesting to us in that regard, because humans (or our closely related progenitors) had occupied that landscape for more than a hundred thousand years.

The fossils were there, as was an enormous python Emma revealed in the beam of her flashlight – it probably fed on some of the millions of bats whose eyes shone down from the roof of the cave. But truth be told, we were a lot more concerned with the tens of millions of people we had been seeing all around us. Because we knew that by the time Emma and Clara were our age, the average population density of the whole world's habitable land will be about equal to India's now. We wondered, what might we expect to see in a world like that?

Paul Ehrlich presented one vision in his classic book *The Population Bomb*, published in 1968. Perhaps more than any other single effort, that book brought human population growth into the public consciousness, in no small part because it painted a near-future world that looked like a slum in one of India's most densely populated cities:

> I have understood the population explosion intellectually for a long time. I came to understand it emotionally one stinking hot night in Delhi a few years ago. My wife and daughter and I were returning to our hotel in an ancient taxi. The seats were hopping with fleas. The only functional gear was third. As we crawled through the city, we entered a crowded slum area.

The temperature was well over 100, and the air was a haze of dust and smoke. The streets seemed alive with people. People eating, people washing, people sleeping. People visiting, arguing, and screaming. People thrusting their hands through the taxi window, begging. People defecating and urinating. People clinging to buses. People herding animals. People, people, people, people. As we moved slowly through the mob, hand horn squawking, the dust, noise, heat, and cooking fires gave the scene a hellish aspect.

Although Paul (and his wife Anne, a powerhouse of facts, figures and logic also known for her own work on population growth) fully recognised that there is much more to India than that first impression, his point was a simple one: that night in Delhi was what he thought the world could look like if its population continued to grow as it had been doing in the years leading up to 1968. In fact, he thought there was a very real possibility that population growth would drive the world into despair before the year 2000 – let's call that Ehrlich's Hell – in large part because of the difficulties in producing adequate food and other resources.

To everyone's great relief (Paul's and Anne's included), Ehrlich's Hell didn't happen, at least not globally, and at least not yet, for reasons we'll talk about towards the end of this chapter. It hasn't even happened in India – cities like Bangalore are vibrant, thriving places; crowded yes, but exciting and full of opportunity too. The basic point made in *The Population Bomb*, though, and which Paul and Anne continue to make, remains a fact. There are biological limits for the human species, just as there are for every other species, our incredible technological achievements notwithstanding. And the world is moving towards those limits all too fast.

Here are the sobering realities. After we had colonised all the continents except Antarctica, the prehistoric human population averaged somewhere around ten million. It took thousands of years, until the early twentieth century, to grow to two billion, which is the number of people the Earth is thought capable of supporting without further major technological interventions. With those interventions, our population has almost quadrupled just since our great-grandparents' time, to more than seven billion of us today. If we humans, averaged worldwide, continue to grow our population at the rate we've done over the last decade, our numbers will rise to over twenty-seven billion by the year 2100.

Few, if any, people who make their living studying biology think that can actually happen, as we'll elaborate upon in later chapters. For one thing, there is not enough land to grow food, or enough fish in the sea, to feed that many people. For another, wars, disease and other catastrophes would almost certainly knock the human population back to significantly smaller numbers long before we hit twenty-seven billion – that is, sometime in the next few decades – as past history is all too clear in showing us. The infamous Black Death of the fourteenth century killed an estimated 30 to 60 per cent of Europe's population; the one–two punch of the First World War and the 1918 flu pandemic may have wiped out as much as 9 per cent of all the people in the world; and the Second World War felled as much as 4 per cent. Basically, as we tried to keep growing to twenty-seven billion, we'd be packed so tight that we would be like too many rats in too small a cage, and nature's version of population control would kick in. Ehrlich's Hell would almost certainly spread far and wide.

What does look inevitable, though, based on just about any reasonable population-growth model out there, is that we're destined to see a world with somewhere between nine and ten billion people by the year 2050, as we'll explain in a little more detail below. That virtual certainty means the world you'll be living in by mid-century is going to be very different from the one you are used to now. The big picture is that we have to pack a couple of billion more people into the relatively small proportion of Earth's land that is available for occupation. That's actually only about 20 per cent of the planet's land surface, which is what's left over after you subtract the 40 per cent we need to grow food and the 40 per cent that is such inhospitable terrain – rugged mountains, barren deserts, glaciers – that it can't be heavily populated. The upshot is that if you like rural living, kiss it goodbye; those wide-open spaces peppered by just a few houses will be no more. City life will even more resemble living in a sardine can. As Paul Ehrlich put it: 'People, people, people, people'.

To set what is going to happen in perspective, just think about current population densities. In 2013 India packed in (on average) about four hundred people per square kilometre, compared to the United Kingdom's 260, and the United States's thirty-two. By 2050, on average we'll see India's population density everywhere we can easily live. Of course, most people are crammed into cities, where population densities are off the charts compared to averages for a whole country. Greater Los Angeles has 1,400 people per square kilometre, greater Beijing 3,200, greater London 5,600, the New York metropolitan area 10,600, and Delhi twelve thousand. All you have to do is walk down a main street in any one of those cities – or worse yet, try to drive down one of them – to get a sense of what such population densities really mean for a way of life. Yet children growing up now are likely to look back when they are adults, and remember the cities of today as being sparsely populated. The United Nations estimates that by the year 2050, 70 per cent of humans, up from today's 50 per cent, will be urban dwellers – that is, 6.4 billion city folk versus the present 3.3 billion. Almost double the number of shoulders to jostle you as you try to walk down the pavement.

If you're from a developed country, as most of you reading this book probably are, and especially if you already live in a city and are pretty happy there, most things you've heard about population growth may well make it sound like somebody else's problem. After all, in developed countries, we like to think we've got fertility rates pretty much under control (although that's actually not the case in the United States, as we'll see). You probably already know that it's in poor countries that the population is growing fastest, and sad as it is to hear about deteriorating conditions on the other side of the world, you may think that things aren't apt to change all that much where you live. But if you reflect a little more deeply on that assumption, you'll realise you are already experiencing the impacts of population growth.

Here is one example from our own lives. It is a first-world problem, for sure, but it is illustrative in showing how growing numbers of people influence nearly everything. Emma and Clara have grown up a lot since they travelled to India with us. They've both finished high school and have gone off to college, but the angst of their college application process is recent enough that it still lingers in our minds. We are not alone there: college application angst infects millions of American households each year. But the elevated stress of that whole process is a new thing, because competition for college slots is just so fierce these days. Back when we were of high-school age, you threw in one or two applications, maybe three if you were really motivated, and you didn't worry too much, because, assuming you had decent grades and hadn't done anything too egregious, your chances of getting into where you applied were pretty good, even in top-tier universities. We'll use Stanford University as an example, simply because we live next door to it and Liz works there. About 22 per cent of 9,800 applicants were admitted in 1970.

Back then, we (and certainly not our parents) never thought to track those percentages (or of applying to Stanford, for that matter). But today, things have changed. High-school students and their parents are well aware that in 2013, only 5.7 per cent of nearly thirty-nine thousand applicants were admitted to Stanford, and in 2014 it was even worse: 5.1 per cent of 42,167 applicants. That's not confined to top-tier universities; it's a global trend. In fact, what's going on with Stanford applications is mild compared to what's happening at top-level universities in highly populous places like India, which are routinely turning away 98 per cent of their applicants. The Indian Institute of Technology usually receives up to five hundred thousand applications, and accepts only 2 per cent of them; Shri Ram College of Commerce, part of the University of Delhi, has just four hundred slots for twenty-eight thousand applicants – only 1.4 per cent.

Those kinds of numbers are what cause stress levels in American households with high-school-age children to go through the roof each college-application season. Families (at least, the relatively few who can afford it) spend thousands of dollars to increase their children's SAT and ACT scores by a few points, and then hundreds more dollars for them to apply to a dozen or more colleges, all carefully vetted and sorted into the categories of 'reach', 'target' and 'safety' schools. The reality is that the chances of getting into your top choice are slim at best, and random chance often dictates acceptance even into the safety schools. The net effect is that among high-school students (and their parents not infrequently get in on the act as well), competition can be fierce for grades, recommendations, internships, sporting teams and those other coveted achievements that make a college application stand out.

All this stress goes right back to the fact that there are so many more people in the world nowadays. Despite universities increasing their class sizes to provide places for more students, there just isn't enough money, available classroom and lab space or land to make it possible for universities to accept much higher percentages of the applicant pool. More people apply each year in part because there are simply more students of college age each year. Over the same time that applications to places like Stanford quadrupled, global population doubled (3.7 billion in 1970, compared to 7.1 billion in 2013). On top of that, proportionately higher numbers of all those new families worldwide moved into socioeconomic categories where a shot at a university education seemed worth taking – that's a good thing, but it still brings the overall chances of acceptance down. And, in the face of higher odds, more American students apply to multiple colleges to hedge their bets, further increasing the applicant pool for many colleges simultaneously.

Our point: intense competition for limited resources is the ubiquitous effect of population growth. Of course, supply-and-demand problems are not confined to higher education – we used that example to illustrate that even in areas where you don't normally think about the problems of population growth, it looms large. There are plenty of other examples of how increasing demand for limited space or goods has begun to change things in your own lifetime, especially if you have lived for a few decades. The traffic is worse. Housing prices have gone up. It is harder to find a job. The list goes on and on.

All of these things you may view as pretty subtle impacts of population growth, but one impact that is not subtle at all is immigration. It's in the news all the time these days, in country after country. Worldwide, at least every thirty-two seconds a migrant crosses some border between nations, and that's only the ones we know about. Immigration is where population growth in those poor places that you may regard as someone else's problem really hits home. More migrant workers are coming in, taking jobs and requiring basic social services that somebody has to pay for. Throngs of people are bowing to Mecca each evening outside Catholic churches in Italy and France. Children are streaming across the Mexican–American border each night, despite expensive fences and patrols attempting to keep them out. Those things are happening because in poor parts of the world, where population is growing fastest, the growth outstrips local resources, and little vignettes of Ehrlich's Hell emerge. Poverty, disease and death become the definition of normal in those places, and not surprisingly, the people suffering living there want to escape to new territory that offers a better way of life. So they come to your town.

The population is growing so fast in poor countries for what is actually a positive reason – death rates have been coming down. Population growth is a function of both the number of births and the number of deaths. If the numbers balance, the population remains constant; if there are more births than deaths, the population grows; and with more deaths than births, it declines. From the purely biological perspective, in order to keep your species going, you need to have at least two children per family to replace the parents when they die; most species hedge their bets by having a few more than two offspring per set of parents, and humans up to now have been no different. In historically poor places like India, Nigeria and Pakistan, to name just a few, until very recently living conditions were so bad that the only way for a family to be sure to have at least a few children reach adulthood was to have a lot of them. The very good news for many of those places is that they are now gaining access to basic levels of health care and more reliable food supplies, with the wonderful result of reduced childhood mortality; more children have been growing up to have families of their own. For instance, in India, mortality of children under five years old has fallen from about 120 deaths per thousand births in 1990, to about seventy deaths per thousand births in 2010.

But old lessons die hard. Even though survival rates in such places are now higher than they used to be, the ingrained cultural tradition is still to have lots of kids, because people still expect to lose many. Since more children are surviving to have their own babies, population growth rates skyrocket. This lag-time effect means that half of all the population growth between now and 2100 is expected to take place in only eight countries, seven of which are regarded as poor by developed-nation standards: Nigeria, India, the United Republic of Tanzania, the Democratic Republic of the Congo, Niger, Uganda and Ethiopia (listed in order of their contribution to world population growth). In the number-eight spot for countries contributing most to population growth is one that is not poor by any stretch of the imagination: the United States.

These, and other countries like them, now have fertility rates that are too high, that is above two. The 'fertility rate' is basically the average number of children born per woman; two is the magic number if you want the population to level off rather than continue to grow indefinitely, because at that number each set of two parents on average replace themselves with two kids; hence a fertility rate of near two is called the 'replacement value'. To be precise, the actual replacement rate is a little higher than two, presently 2.1 in industrialised countries and 2.3 on a worldwide average, because not all children survive to reproduce, but we round it to two for ease of discussion.

Given current demographics, if all of the countries that now have fertility rates above replacement (like those eight listed above) see a decrease that quickly brings them down to replacement, by 2050 we'd end up with a global population that stabilised at a little over ten billion people, and then remained constant after that. Just half a child over replacement rate, and we're at more than sixteen billion by 2100. Half a child under replacement rate would allow us to stabilise at around our present seven billion by 2100 – but even in that optimistic scenario we still hit nearly ten billion around the year 2050, before population finally begins to fall. So any way you cut it, we're adding close to three billion people to the planet over the next three decades. If you are interested in what goes into these models, and country-by-country data, the information is readily available from the 2013 United Nations Department of Economic and Social Affairs Population Division publication *World Population Prospects: The 2012 Revision, Highlights and Advance Tables*, and *Volume II, Demographic Profiles*, which provide most of the population numbers we use in this book.

Obviously, the population-growth impacts in poor countries, where the numbers of people are increasing very, very fast, are going to be different from the first-world impacts we've been talking about for developed countries. Today poor places – like India, Pakistan and especially many African countries – already find it hard to provide adequate food, water and health care, and basic services like electricity, toilets and sewage-treatment plants, and these problems will only get worse.

Take the best-case scenario of one of these growing-population countries, India. India is on track to decrease its birth rate to the replacement level of around two children per couple by 2050. Even so, between now and then births will add four hundred million people to the country, increasing its native-born population from the present 1.2 billion to about 1.7 billion. This is roughly double the number of people India added from 2000 to 2010, which contributed to dramatic changes in the country. Those changes are hard to miss. In 2012, on a return trip to Bangalore, it was obvious that the city had extended its urban sprawl radically compared to how it was when we visited in 2007. Where there had been open ground, new neighbourhoods, businesses and highways had sprouted. So had the number of shanty towns. Vehicles of every kind filled the streets, and people were ubiquitous, day and night. Seemingly everywhere you looked there was scaffolding made from bamboo-like tree branches, with barefoot workers hoisting buckets by rope, building supersized components of new concrete structures that were transforming the skyline. This, remember, in what is already the most densely populated large country in the world.

That was the on-the-ground expression of some rather startling statistics – while overall India's population increased by about 17 per cent from 2001 to 2011, Bangalore's population grew by a whopping 47 per cent. Even its urban sprawl, which tripled the area covered by the city (from 226 square kilometres in 1991 to 716 square kilometres in 2010), has not been enough to prevent a huge increase in population density in the last decade (from 2,985 people per square kilometre to 4,378 in 2010).

This trend to urbanisation as population grows is because people born into poor rural areas tend to move to the city in search of a better life, a pattern that repeats over and over in history, and which, as we noted above, the United Nations predicts increasingly for the future. In India, Bangalore is a particularly good city to come to if you're looking for work: it is one of the country's intellectual, economic and entrepreneurial engines. But not all cities experience equal immigration and growth as population increases. Delhi's growth (21 per cent) was just a little over India's as a whole (17 per cent) for the period 2001–2011. At the same time the area around Mumbai saw its population increase by only 4 per cent; however, all of that increase was in its suburbs, which grew by 8 per cent, whereas the city centre actually lost about 5.8 per cent of its population. This illustrates another point: when cities get too crowded, the only way they can grow is out. Mumbai now packs in more than twenty thousand people per square kilometre over an area of about five thousand square kilometres – equivalent to a square of real estate that measures a little over seventy kilometres on each side. And of course, if they don't have adequate infrastructure, as is the case with Mumbai and many other cities, living conditions are not very pleasant.

The lesson here is that as population grows, people flock disproportionately to the most desirable places, which, in the absence of equally fast growth of infrastructure, causes some major problems. In Bangalore, for example, the influx of people has outpaced both the infrastructure and the availability of natural resources, making it routine for electricity and water to be available for only parts of the day in those areas of the city that even have access at all. Yet that lack of supply leads to higher prices, so even as the quality of life goes down, the cost of living goes up. In the state in which Bangalore is located, Karnataka, the cost of keeping the lights on, and supplying the population with fuel and food, has more than doubled since 2005. This reflects a general trend in the ten most populous states in India.

The flip side is that if cities do develop adequate infrastructure to handle high population densities, the cost of living goes sky high because of limited supply of homes and office space in the face of high demand, and the costs of maintaining all that infrastructure. Manhattan, for instance, has a population density of 18,500 people per square kilometre, not too far below that of Mumbai. A nice place to live, for sure, if you like city living, but at $3,973 per month, the average apartment there will cost you about $2,800 more per month than the nationwide average for the United States. New York City as a whole, with 10,600 people per square kilometre, is the fifteenth most expensive city in the world. Greater London is even more pricey: with 5,600 people per square kilometre, it was the most expensive city in the world in 2014. Such figures drive home the point that it costs a lot – and to many people, is prohibitively expensive – to live in a city that is both densely populated and has a well-functioning infrastructure, although of course the correlation between population density and cost of living is modified by a host of other factors, such as governmental system, proximity and access to natural resources, town planning, and so on.

The general lesson of rapid growth of a city's population outstripping its capabilities to provide adequate infrastructure applies world-wide. In China, Beijing provides another cogent example. In the decade 2000–2010, China's population grew about 6 per cent, reaching a little over 1.3 billion people. In the same decade, Beijing's population increased 30 per cent, from about fourteen million to twenty million. The difference in percentage-growth is because, just as happened in Bangalore, many, many people migrated from the countryside to the city. As a result, Beijing too is experiencing problems: a water supply that can only support 60 per cent of the city's residents, inadequate housing and public transportation, lack of access to medical care and education, and air pollution so bad that on many days the only way to see what the sunrise would look like is to look at a stock picture on a big video screen in Tiananmen Square.

As far as nations with growing populations go, India and China are probably the lucky ones, because the end of their population growth is in sight. Given the pace at which birth rates have been decreasing in those countries, both are on track to see growth of their populations stop by mid-century, and then at least remain stable and possibly even decline. And both are large nations that are rapidly advancing their economies, technology and social systems with at least some foresight of population-growth impacts, and with the full awareness of their governments that slowing population growth is a priority.

Not so with many countries that are in much worse shape economically, and with even less adequate natural resources. According to the most recent demographic projections, it seems a *fait accompli* that by 2050, 'Five least developed countries – Bangladesh, Ethiopia, the Democratic Republic of the Congo, the United Republic of Tanzania and Uganda – will be among the twenty most populous countries in the world.' By 2100, three more least developed countries will climb into the top twenty list for most populous – Niger, Sudan and Mozambique.

In fact, it seems to be a general rule that the poorer the people, the faster their population grows. This correlation holds both within countries, and from nation to nation. In India, for instance, birth rates among higher economic classes are pretty much at replacement value; the growth that is still occurring is in the poor rural population. And at the global scale, it is the poorest countries that are the population-growth hotspots. The UN Population Division projects that most of the forty-nine least developed countries are on track to see their populations triple or more between 2013 and 2100, and several are heading for a *fivefold* increase, including Burundi, Malawi, Mali, Niger, Nigeria, Somalia, Uganda, the United Republic of Tanzania and Zambia. You might have noticed that countries in Africa seem to be showing up with high frequency on these lists, and indeed Africa is the place that promises to launch a tidal wave of global change from its rapidly growing masses.

Which brings us back to the impacts on developed nations. Sudan and South Sudan are regions that provide a window into where the world would be headed if population growth in Africa plays out as predicted. The two countries' combined populations grew from 8.3 million in 1950 (Sudan 5.7 million; South Sudan 2.6 million), to 45.5 million in 2010 (Sudan 35.6 million; South Sudan 9.9 million), to 58.5 million in early 2014 (Sudan 47.5 million; South Sudan eleven million). That sevenfold increase of numbers of people in the region has been accompanied by a twenty-two-year-long civil war that in 2011 finally split what used to be one country into two; genocide in Darfur that has gone on since 2005 as Janjaweed (the 'devils on horseback') militia and Sudanese forces maraud through villages on ethnic-cleansing missions; and widespread hunger, disease and death. These are life-and-death problems for the countries' inhabitants – in South Sudan alone, in February 2014 a third of the population, nearly four million people, were desperately hungry, nearly a million people had been displaced from their homes, many thousands had been killed, and government forces and rebels were razing towns for what seemed no good reason.

That translates to some very noticeable global impacts. The cost of humanitarian aid to South Sudan quickly rose to over £800 million, and the conflict drew in neighbouring countries, in this case army and rebel fighters from Uganda. At an even larger scale, war-torn, unstable countries become breeding grounds and safe havens for international terrorist groups, which is exactly what happened as far back as the 1990s in the Sudan region, and which continues to be a problem there today.

The link between rapid growth, local wars and escalating global conflict is one of the most important population-growth impacts. We devote Chapter 9 to that topic, but a pertinent issue to mention at this point is that with rapid population growth usually come important changes in the so-called population pyramid. The 'population pyramid' refers to the number of people in infant, child-age, teenage, young adult, older adult and geriatric age groups. Rapid population growth bulges the teenage and young adult categories, which means there just get to be too many curious, energetic young people with no productive way to channel their energy. You can see that bulge in recent trouble spots such as Sudan, South Sudan, Egypt, Somalia, Pakistan and Afghanistan, where about 20 per cent of the population is fifteen to twenty-four years of age. In much of Africa, about half the population is aged fifteen or below, and just 3 per cent are sixty-five or older. Contrast that with more stable countries, like the United States, the United Kingdom, France, Germany, Norway or Japan, which have only about 17 per cent of their populations under the age of fifteen, and 16 per cent aged sixty-five or older.

The problem with swelling the ranks of young people relative to the rest of the population, especially in poor countries, is that unemployment increases disproportionately among young people as well. Indeed, unemployment among young people was one of the key drivers that led to the Arab Spring uprising that toppled rulers throughout the Middle East, including Hosni Mubarak's regime in Egypt in February 2011. The same problem was still causing huge protests that threatened Mubarak's successor Mohamed Morsi in early 2014, when eight out of every ten jobless Egyptians were under the age of thirty. The projections of the population pyramids for these and other poor countries, even assuming they drop their current higher-than-replacement birth rates to replacement values, suggest that the fifteen-to-twenty-four age category will continue to remain at around 20 per cent of the population well into mid-century. Which means that millions more unemployed, high-energy and highly intelligent young people will be either expressing their dissatisfaction and destabilising society in their own countries, or looking for opportunities elsewhere. The resulting societal volatility in the poor countries with an over-supply of young people is further fuelled by the paucity of experienced, older and wiser leaders.

At the same time, the population pyramid of the richer countries will be turning itself upside down. An inevitable side-effect of slowing population growth rates is going through a period when old people outnumber the young. This is because during baby boom years, as happened in the United States right after World War II, lots of young people are added to the population. If they don't have babies in equally copious numbers, the older people end up outnumbering the children coming up the ranks behind them, with obvious societal impacts, not least of which is that as the baby boomers grow older, there are fewer and fewer younger relatives to care for them in their old age. In addition, the workforce of people in the young to middle-age categories becomes comparatively small, hampering society's ability to fund and staff programmes that give senior citizens the level of care and comfort they need. Such impacts can turn society upside down – for example, in Japan, more adult nappies are sold than baby nappies, a consequence of people in the fifteen-to-twenty-four age category making up only about 10 per cent of the demographic, compared to those over sixty-five, who comprise 23 per cent.

Remember, most of these population-growth impacts we've pointed out are a best-case scenario, which assumes that fertility rates will, within the next thirty years, fall to replacement value in all countries in which they are not already there. In this book, we're not even going to try to imagine just how bad things will get if we don't drop fertility rates to replacement level, fast – except to say, we suspect we'd really get to see what Ehrlich's Hell looks like. A key point to remember, though, is that no matter which of the population trajectories we actually follow – getting to replacement rate fast, half a child below replacement rate, half a child above replacement rate, or business as usual – we're *still* going to hit between nine and ten billion people by 2050. That's the reality we're stuck with in trying to make a viable future, and all the other issues we cover in this book are underpinned by it.

The trillion-dollar question, then, is whether it is actually possible for the human population to top out at no more than ten billion by 2050. The answer, fortunately, is a resounding yes. There are three ways to get there. One of them is a way nobody wants – some sort of global catastrophe that wipes out a large portion of the human population. We'll elaborate on the possibility of this in later chapters – things like pandemics, or war. But the bottom line is that a global catastrophe would be the most tragic sort of population control, filled with pain and loss, dystopia for most of us. There are better ways.

China hit on one solution: the one-child policy, which was officially announced in September 1980 in response to population growth that had been encouraged after a famine cost at least thirty million Chinese lives a generation earlier. The law imposed severe penalties in the form of fines, taxes, or even property loss, for families that exceeded their allotted single child, and rewarded families that stayed below the limit. Two generations later, the success of this approach in terms of limiting population growth is undeniable – China's population is poised to peak around 2030, after which demographic models indicate that it will fall quickly back at least to the level it was in the 1990s, about a 30 per cent decrease with respect to its peak population size. The social success is arguable. By the standards of most countries, injecting that amount of government control into the bedroom would at best be wildly unpopular, and would be viewed by many as downright draconian. It also introduced some real problems that have to be grappled with now and in the future, among them a disparity in the numbers of young men (too many) versus young women (too few), as a result of a cultural preference for boys which often led to infanticide for girl babies; the abandonment of unwanted children; and 'Little Emperor Syndrome', which refers to the fact that a generation of Chinese have grown up in the absence of siblings, with the result that many exhibit poor social skills, feel entitled, and are risk-averse. In addition, China is already experiencing the topsy-turvy population pyramid that other countries will soon be seeing, with simply too many old people to be cared for by the much fewer younger ones.

The third way to bring down birth rates rapidly is the one that has enjoyed the most widespread success, with the main social consequences being positive. It is, in fact, the one that has been employed in most places in the world that are now at or below replacement fertility rate. It's deceptively simple: make sure girls have access to decent education and job opportunities, and that contraception is readily available to those who want it. Time after time, this approach has resulted not only in bringing fertility rates under control, but in raising the standards of living for families and communities. Education is particularly important: the good things that correlate with educating girls and women not only include many fewer births, but also healthier mothers, better survival of infants and children, decreased risk of sexually transmitted diseases like HIV/AIDS, and much better earning power. The economic rewards alone are big: just one year of primary school tends to add 10 to 20 per cent to a woman's earning power later in life, and a secondary-school education gives her 15 to 25 per cent more. Which of course also means her family enjoys that much better quality of life. More than that, the country does too. Studies show that by empowering women through education, national economies benefit.

It was just such an approach that turned what is now one of the most densely populated countries in the world away from the brink of disaster. The tiny island nation of Mauritius, located about two thousand kilometres off the eastern coast of Africa, packs in more than six hundred people per square kilometre, a density one-third higher than India and four times higher than China. At about the same time that China was recognising its population-growth problem and instituting its one-child policy, Mauritius was recognising that its ballooning population was straining resources too. The local elimination of malaria, higher living standards and improved health care had brought down death rates, while birth rates continued to increase at a fast pace. Both countries integrated access to contraceptives into their health-care systems, but Mauritius emphasised education instead of laws that limited family size, including making school free by 1976, which made it much easier for families to choose between sending their sons or daughters out to work or continuing their education. But already by that time, as Ramola Ramtohul wrote in an article entitled 'Fractured Sisterhood:

The Historical Evolution of the Women's Movement in Mauritius', 'Mauritius had a generation of young women, especially among the upper classes, who had had access to quality education and thus had a different outlook on life' (*Afrika Zamani* 18 & 19:71–101, 2010–2011).

The result: a more than 60 per cent decline in fertility rate over the years 1965 to 1980, and a 75 per cent decline by 2010. Along with this came increasing prosperity for the country's people as a whole – from a low-income agricultural economy in 1968 to a diversified middle-income economy over the ensuing decades. In fact, for the past few years Mauritius has ranked first among Africa's countries (and forty-fifth worldwide) in terms of economic competitiveness, a measure that includes such things as infrastructure, education, financial market development, technology and market size.

That recipe for success is translatable to other countries that today stand where Mauritius did half a century ago, but it requires one more essential ingredient: tolerance for diversity of cultural traditions, and openness to new ways of doing things. Mauritians had those things built in through their history, with a succession of Portuguese, Dutch, French and British colonisers, who over the course of a few centuries melded with Africans (originally brought in as slaves), Indians (brought in as indentured servants when the slave trade was abolished) and Chinese settlers. Once colonial rule was removed, the resulting 'rainbow nation' included four ethnic and four major religious groups that had found ways to peacefully co-exist and work together to make things better. That kind of tolerance and cooperation will be absolutely essential if the Mauritius success story is to be replicated elsewhere; religious intolerance and ethnic rivalries end up being deal-breakers.

The drop in fertility rates in countries like China, Mauritius, India and others was unforeseen by Paul Ehrlich when he wrote *The Population Bomb*, and is one reason his prediction of widespread doom by the year 2000 did not come to pass. When he wrote the book, fertility rates in such countries were near six children per woman or higher; less than a decade later, the carrot or stick approach began lowering that precipitously, with the effect that by the year 2000, the average fertility rate in those countries had fallen to 2.5 or fewer children per woman. The lesson there is that it is very possible to bring population growth rates under control fast, especially when it is done with the carrots of education and economic betterment, in ways that make the majority of people happy and more productive.

The other very important thing that *The Population Bomb* underestimated was human innovation. The prediction of doom was strongly influenced by the food crisis that was looming in 1968 – people in poor countries had been dying of starvation on a massive scale over the previous few years. But with the recognition of world hunger as a problem, innovation and cross-nation co-operation kicked in, taking the form of the Green Revolution, which ramped up food production many times over in just two decades, and thereby staved off mass starvation for a billion or so people. Later, along came computers, the internet and mobile phone technology, which now make possible a global conversation about any world crisis, and harness what could be called a global brain – at last count more than six billion connected people – to formulate and implement feasible solutions. So we bought some time through the last bit of the twentieth century. What about now?

One more lesson comes out of the nearly four decades we've had since 1968 to observe how population growth and the human spirit actually work: despite the fact that things didn't crash by the end of the twentieth century, we are not out of the woods by any means. We now know with reasonable certainty that in just the next half a lifetime, some ten billion people will be on the planet, seething masses overwhelming the capacities of poor countries and banging at the doors of rich ones. As a result, cities will at least double in size, the old will outnumber the young in many communities, and many more places will see their social, political and economic systems put in a pressure cooker. Mind you, this is the best-case scenario – where we rapidly bring fertility rates down to replacement rate in all the nations where that is currently not the case. Even this optimistic scenario means that population growth is about to tip humanity into a future that will be as different from the present as the India we experienced in 2007 was from our home in the United States back then. Whether that future ends up looking like Ehrlich's Hell remains to be seen – it still could, if we make the wrong choices.

But one thing is for sure: sustaining at least the quality of life that the world provides to people today is not going to happen if we ignore how an extra three billion of us are going to impact the planet. It's not just our numbers we have to worry about – it's also what each of us needs and wants.

3

STUFF

Tony, near midnight, southern Colorado, around 1960

My heart was pounding just about as loud as his fist on the door. Bam! Bam! Bam! 'I want my money! I want my money!' Bam! Bam! Bam!

I was a little kid, maybe eight years old, eyes shut tight, hunkered down in our tiny house, a well-worn clapboard whose once-white paint had seen better days and was peeling here and there. Inside was hideous grey wallpaper with big maroon flowers in the cramped living room, a linoleum-floored kitchen with a chrome-legged, red-topped Formica table, one institutional-green bedroom for my parents, and a dingy pink room where I slept. One of the windows in that room had a prime view of the dirt alley where ragweed liked to grow, and the other opened right onto the slab-concrete front porch, which sat there like a pitiful stage in full view of one of the town's busiest streets. My bed was right next to the porch window, wide open that hot summer night, so the slamming door of a ratty pick-up truck less than twenty feet away had awoken me, followed by the angry stomping of feet up the two porch steps. At that point all that was standing between me and the drunk man pounding on our door was a flimsy curtain and a rusting screen. I fully expected his fist to come smashing through at any second. I lay there as still as I could, tried not to breathe too loud, and hoped for the best.

I had had a lot of practice in hoping for the best, because we were poor. I never got the full story on why that man was beating on our door in the middle of the night, but as near as I could work it out, he thought he was owed some money, and whether or not he was, we just didn't have any to give him. That year was a particularly bad one, I think – probably the same year when there was a month or two when we had to choose between getting our electricity or our gas shut off because we couldn't afford to pay for both, and when some meals came from hunting rabbits or doves on the outskirts of town.

The point being, I didn't have a lot of stuff when I was growing up. But I certainly knew a lot of kids who did. And like anyone who is forced to do without, I came to equate having nice stuff with having a better life. For whatever reason, that seems to be human nature, which is in large part why, fast-forward nearly fifty years, our family is now like millions of other middle-class families in industrialised nations. We have a decent house, with climate control and a nice irrigated yard, a couple of cars, computers, mobile phones, and what sometimes seems like an uncountable number of gadgets, the purchase of which makes us feel good, at least for a while. And, like most parents, we've done our best to make sure our children have all those things that we thought would make us happy when we were little. In a word, we've attained what a billion or so people consider normal.

Normal for places like the United States, the European Union and a few other small pockets throughout the world, anyway. Most of the human race now exists on less than $10 a day, and about a billion scrape by on less than $2 per day. Poor as we were by

American standards when I was growing up, I now know that even back when that guy was beating on our door, we were well off in comparison to most people in the world. And I'd wager that, just like me when I was young, the vast majority of those people are looking for that sense of accomplishment that comes from bettering their situation, and especially from working to make sure their kids have a better life. Happily, the opportunities for advancing the next generation are growing in many countries that harbour huge numbers of poor people, among them the most populous nations on Earth – places like India and China. Which means that, if human nature follows the same course in such places as it has in already-developed nations, in many, many more households over the next thirty years the presents will pile high as the old stuff is replaced with the newer models.

The emotional satisfaction that ever-growing pile will bring to billions is hard to deny, both in principle and in reality. Although material goods are certainly not the route to true happiness, in today's world, like it or not, they do in large measure help define social status, self-worth, and are often the currency with which to outwardly express affection, even love – diamonds are forever, so they say. And some material things – like our electronic communications network, planes, cars and so on – are in fact necessary to maintain the global connections that society now so depends upon.

All of which leads to a major conundrum, because the material stuff we value so much does not appear out of thin air. Ultimately, each and every thing we manufacture ends up eating a little bit of Planet Earth, and the pie is going fast. The best estimates, from a group called the Global Footprint Network, indicate that presently we are using up the planet at a pace that would require one and a half Earths to sustain us over the long term. Assuming no changes in how we do business, and taking into account the growing numbers of people in the world and the entry of more and more of them into better economic situations, we will require the equivalent of two Earths to sustain us by the year 2030, and three Earths by 2050. Actually, if everyone lived the lifestyle of the average American – that is to say, the lifestyle we live, and that many of you reading this book live – we'd need five Earths to keep us going. The problem, of course, is that there is only one Earth.

None of us are actively trying to trash the planet. We are simply enjoying the stuff we have, and in some cases actually need, in today's world. Mobile phones are a prime example. Most of the people in the world now carry around these electronic wonders, facilitating everything from the casual chat to getting water (as we mentioned in the first chapter), mobilising social movements in places like Thailand and the Middle East, and negotiating global crises. The fact that more than 6 billion mobile phone connections now link us is remarkable, in that it potentially connects most of the human race in a way that could be harnessed to solve global problems – a sort of global brain, if you will, where each phone is like a neuron that can transfer information from one part of society to the next.

But all those phones have to be produced out of raw materials, some of which you've probably never even heard of, but which are already in short supply. Take the ever-more ubiquitous smartphone as an example. Lots of people, us included, don't leave home without one of them, and it's not inaccurate to say there is a large sector of society that regard them as indispensable. No need to memorise, just Google it.

Just using one popular model as an example, as of March 2014, around half a billion had been produced and sold worldwide. Include all smartphones, and the number increases to more than 1.4 billion in use, a number that grew by 44 per cent in 2013, with many more poised to be manufactured over the coming years.

Mind you, there were no smartphones before 2007, so we're still in the early days. Even so, the world is starting to feel the impact, although all you feel immediately is a bit of pleasure as you heft that sleek new phone in your hand, and as you stroke from app to app on that wonderfully responsive touchscreen.

What you're actually stroking is rare earths. Producing that touchscreen requires somebody, somewhere, digging in a mine to extract minerals that will ultimately yield elements like yttrium, lanthanum, praseodymium, europium, gadolinium, terbium, dysprosium, cerium and neodymium. Rare-earth elements are not exactly rare, but are so named because there are few economically viable ore deposits that yield them, and they are found in only a few countries. For that reason, among others, world production of rare earths has shifted from country to country over the years, as one area gets mined out or as political and economic winds shift. India and Brazil used to be leading producers sixty years ago. Then the Mountain Pass mine in California took over as the top dog in the 1960s and 1980s. Today it's mostly all about China, which produces over 90 per cent of the rare earths necessary for manufacturing not only mobile phones, but also critical components in the motors and batteries for electric and hybrid cars, windmill turbines, and a variety of other things that are becoming increasingly important to society.

Which brings us back to tipping points, in two guises. The most obvious one is that any time a single country holds a monopoly on a needed commodity, problems can arise. In 2011, China produced a whopping 97 per cent of the rare-earth elements needed by the world. That has fallen to about 80 per cent since then, as mines in other countries came on line, but much of the ore from those mines ends up passing through China for processing anyway. This single-country bottleneck means we only have to look a couple of years down the road to see trouble. In 2010, world demand for rare-earth elements was about 136,100 tons, but global production was only 133,600 tons (remember, almost all from China). The 2,500-ton shortfall was covered by stocks already on hand from previous mining. By 2015, global demand is estimated to reach between 160,000 and 210,000 tons per year. Over the same time, China estimated that its internal demand would require 130,000 tons per year, which led to it restricting its exports, beginning in 2010. That caused some upheaval – it drove up prices for rare earths, meaning that United States and European manufacturers were forced to pay three times as much as their Chinese competitors, causing a dispute that landed at the World Trade Organization.

The outcome of that dispute aside (China lost, but as of 2014 was appealing), one simple fact remains. Within just the next two years, without a major recycling campaign, a lot more mines are going to have to be opened up to cover the anticipated shortfall of at least thirty thousand tons. While most experts agree that the reserves in the ground will probably meet demand for the next decade or two – it's uncertain after that – bringing a new mine on line and getting its products into the supply chain takes five to ten years, meaning that at least temporary shortfalls are already on the horizon. The political and economic ramifications include things like price spikes and trade wars. In the best case, you can think of such marked and political fluctuations as very rapid changes in global dynamics that are potentially reversible, much like the boiling-water-to-steam kind of tipping point described in Chapter 1. For instance, with rare earths, five to ten years down the road, prices and availability could stabilise for a while if more mines are able to be brought on line, but in the interim, a period of volatility could make for some rough going for society. In the worst case, control of a needed resource by a single country makes for a new world order – a tipping point that is essentially irreversible over human lifetimes.

Ramping up rare-earth production also brings us to a second kind of tipping point – adding all those new mines means that we inevitably destroy what was there beforehand, and often make the surrounding areas unfit places to live. One of the most infamous mines-gone-bad examples is China's Baotou district in the Gobi Desert of Inner Mongolia. Satellite images of the area bring to mind gigantic blobs of decaying grey-brown intestines splayed around waterways, and populated areas and waterways that show up as blood-red spatters and rivulets. (These remarkable NASA Earth Observatory Images can be viewed at http://earthobservatory.nasa. gov/IOTD/view.php?id=77723.) The intestine-blobs are open-pit mines, the largest of which are more than half a mile deep (a thousand metres) and cover more than eighteen square miles (forty-eight square kilometres). Some of the blood-red rivulets drain into and out of black-coloured ponds that hold the waste water and muck from the mines. The water isn't actually black (or blood-red) – that's just the satellite-image colour enhancement. The real water is in fact much more colourful – oranges, yellows, browns and greys – a Technicolor swirl that is typical of soups of toxic waste.

On the ground, the situation is every bit as bad as the satellite images suggest, according to reporters who have visited and interviewed residents. You can get an idea of the scale of the problem when you realise that processing one ton of rare earths yields about two thousand tons of toxic waste. As a result, in the Baotou area, newspaper accounts say that the well water, which people drank before they knew any better, 'looked fine, but it smelled really bad', as related by a local farmer, Wang Jianguo, in a *Guardian* news story by Jonathan Kaiman ('Rare Earth Mining in China: The Bleak Social and Environmental Costs', 20 March 2014). The reason for the bad smell was that the water was laced with carcinogens and other toxic substances. The article that reported Wang's words went on to say: 'In the 1990s, when China's rare earths production kicked into full gear, [Wang's] sheep died and his cabbage crops withered. Most of his neighbours have moved away. Seven have died of cancer. His teeth have grown yellow and crooked; they jut out at strange angles from blackened gums.' Some local sheep (those that survive) grow 'two rows of teeth, some so long that they couldn't close their mouths'.

Those kinds of examples are not confined to China by any means, nor are they confined to rare-earth mines – in the United States, for instance, just head west on Interstate 90 from Butte, Montana, towards Anaconda. In Butte you'll see the Berkeley Pit, the mile-long, half-mile-wide, third-of-a-mile-deep remnant of an open-pit copper mine. The Pit is now partially filled by a lake, which is actually a potent broth of arsenic, cadmium, zinc, copper and sulphuric acid. Keep driving west out of Butte and you'll begin to see stunted trees, then none at all, the result of soil contamination from noxious fumes and dangerous particulates that used to belch out of the copper smelters at Anaconda. Copper has not been mined in Butte or smelted at Anaconda for decades, yet a huge landscape, and its ability to support people and animals, and grow plants, has been changed forever.

We'll talk more about the tipping points triggered by environmental devastation in Chapter 7, but the key point here is simply this: keeping all those mobile phones rolling off the assembly lines, as we've done up to now, is taking an ever-growing toll on Planet Earth. The copper in your smartphone probably comes from Chile, the gold from Peru, the silver from Australia, and the platinum from South Africa. It could also have coltan from Africa. Each of those places, and many more, now has its own versions of Baotou or Butte, and the number of those tipped-to-devastation landscapes is growing by the day.

* * *

Mining the raw materials that go into the stuff we like is just the first part of the impact story. The next part is turning the raw materials into the final product and getting it to your doorstep. That takes, in a word, energy, in the form of electricity or heat to power various manufacturing processes, and petrol, diesel or jet fuel to transport components through all the places linked in a product's supply chain: for instance, the supply chain for smartphones can include about seventeen countries. All that energy means that the material goods we're so fond of contribute mightily to changing Earth's climate.

We'll say more about climate change and its part in the tipping-point recipe in Chapter 4. But for now, suffice to say that there is a tight bond between climate change and our current love affair with stuff, because every new item that is produced adds more greenhouse gases to the atmosphere. It's those greenhouse gases – primarily carbon dioxide but also nitrous oxide, methane and chlorofluorocarbons – that are essentially giving Earth a fever, causing not only more killer heatwaves, but also more droughts, floods, ocean acidification and so on. Greenhouse gases come from burning the fossil fuels we use to manufacture and transport all our material goods, a mode of energy production that people have exploited since the Industrial Revolution began some three centuries ago. And what that means in terms of manufacturing and transporting goods is that each and every thing you buy is part of the climate-change problem, as well as part of the raw materials problem.

The production and use of a typical smartphone over its life, for instance, adds somewhere between forty-five and seventy-five kilograms of carbon dioxide into the atmosphere. Let's use a middle-of-the-road estimate that averages out the differences between models, say sixty kilograms. Multiply that by half a billion of just one popular model sold since 2007, and you're up to about thirty million metric tons of CO_2. That by itself translates into just a tiny bit of greenhouse warming, a drop in the bucket really. But here's the issue: it's not only mobile phones that are part of the emissions problem, it's everything you buy. Even your basic plastic doll has a carbon footprint. A study by the California College of the Arts Design Strategy Program calculated, for example, that the production, packaging and delivery of a typical plastic doll – they used a Barbie doll – requires about 3.2 cups of oil. That means that every 210 dolls manufactured burn through about a barrel of oil, which emits about 0.43 metric tons of CO_2. Multiply that by tens of millions of dolls per year – for instance, at least 10.5 million Barbies are sold annually – and that means annual doll emissions amount to several tens of thousands of tons of CO_2. And taking into account that billions of plastic dolls have been sold over the past six decades, we're looking at a doll-carbon footprint well in excess of seven million metric tons. Calculating carbon footprints like this is useful in highlighting where they can be reduced for specific products.

Lego, for example, has recently collaborated with the World Wide Fund for Nature to reduce its carbon footprint at manufacturing plants from a hundred thousand to ninety thousand tons of CO_2 annually. But the majority of Lego's CO_2 footprint is from the supply chain, including material extraction, refinement and distribution. If the company could cut those emissions by 10 per cent, it would save the planet a whopping one hundred thousand tons, or the equivalent of removing twenty-eight thousand cars from the road. Do similar calculations for all the goods manufactured in 2014, and the number gets very big, accounting for a very significant chunk – more than 20 per cent – of the greenhouse-gas emission problem globally, and around 50 per cent for the United States, which leads the world in consuming stuff. As the rich man once said, a million here, a million there, and pretty soon you're talking real money. Or in our case, real climate change.

The bottom line here is that producing more and more of the stuff we want, in the manner we have been, not only marches us towards tipping points in resources, politics and economics, it also builds inexorably to a climate tipping point. This highlights a very important consideration when thinking about global tipping points: it's not just one trigger that we have to worry about. As we'll see, what can at first glance seem an isolated piece of the overall Earth and societal system – producing stuff, for example – is in fact intimately intertwined with many other parts. Therefore changes in one part of the system have the potential to trigger unexpected changes in other parts, multiplying both the likelihood of a global tipping point and the overall magnitude of the changes that would result.

Fixing the stuff problem is going to be one of the trickiest bits of setting the world on track towards a viable future. It requires, first, recognising and dealing with the reality that the world is now composed of the 'haves', those people lucky enough to be able to afford lots of stuff, and the 'have nots', those who have to make do with a whole lot less, but who see the path to social and emotional fulfilment as being able to afford lots of material things. The 'haves', of course, are those of us in developed countries – like the United States, Japan, the United Kingdom and most of the others in the European Union. We simply consume a whole lot more than our counterparts in most African countries, India, China and other such places.

One way to get a handle on the magnitude of that difference is to look at various measures of per capita consumption on a coun-try-by-country basis. While there is no magic 'consumption index', a correlate you can wrap your head around is how much oil, on average, each person in a country uses in a year, because your 'oil footprint' is determined not only by how much you drive or how you heat your house, but as we just mentioned, also from the oil used in producing or transporting pretty much every item you have, from the food on your table, to the table itself, to the jewellery you wear, to the clothes on your back, right down to your underwear. The more stuff you have, the larger your oil footprint.

Figures for per capita oil consumption by country are easy to derive from sources like the United States CIA World Factbook, and you may recall we mentioned the numbers for some countries in Chapter 1. Looking at a few more examples makes it clear that the disparities are tremendous. For example, the average person in the United States or Norway uses 110 times more oil in a year than the average Nepali, eight times more than the average person in China, about twice as much as in the United Kingdom or Germany, but only about a quarter as much as the average citizen in Singapore. Here is where the relationship between population size and consumption becomes important, though – a country's per capita consumption can be very low, but if that country has a lot of people, its overall contribution to the consumption footprint still comes out very high, and vice versa – lots of consumption by few people shoots a country to the top of the consumption problem.

That's exactly the reason that the United States, with only 314 million residents – around a quarter of China's or India's population, and less than two-thirds of the European Union's – is at the top of the consumption chart. Its total consumption (18.84 million barrels of oil per day, or twenty-two barrels per year per person) far outstrips much more populous regions in eating up the world's resources, like those that rank number two and three, respectively, the European Union and China. The EU goes through 12.8 million barrels per day for a population of 509 million people (9.2 barrels per person per year), with China earning its number three rank by having lots more people (1.3 billion), each of whom on average is burning less oil each day (9.8 million barrels daily, equating to 2.7 barrels per year per person). Japan holds down the number four spot (4.46 million barrels per day): though its population (127 million) is small by comparison with the top three consumers, its per capita consumption (12.8 barrels per person per year) is high (but still not as high as the United States). Like China, India makes it onto the top-five list not because of high per capita consumption – in fact, Indian consumption is almost pitifully low, at 0.2 barrels per person per year – but because the country is so populous (1.25 billion and growing). Singapore illustrates just the reverse: although it has only 5.3 million people, its huge per capita consumption of oil (80.7 barrels per year per person) kicks it all the way up to number seventeen on the world's top consumers list (1.38 million barrels per day).

Such accounting makes it pretty clear that if we are going to avoid tipping points triggered by the continual production and coveting of stuff, equalling out the disparities in consumption patterns as we go into the future is going to be essential. That's not going to be easy, human nature being what it is, with the haves wanting to hang on to what they've got and to get more, and the have-nots both wanting and, by any moral compass, deserving the opportunities to earn what they see the haves enjoying. It doesn't take a genius to see that if per capita consumption patterns in India, China, the Middle East and Africa were at United States levels – even today, with 'only' 7.3 billion people on Earth – the world would be, in a word, screwed. Not to mention the way things would go once the inevitable population growth described in the last chapter kicks in. The world would be one of political instability as nations made a grab for the last remaining resources, of economic instability as price wars and real wars flared up in response to limited raw materials and disrupted supply chains, and as many, many more Batous and Buttes spread out across the globe.

Avoiding those kinds of scenarios will require some shifts in how people think in three related areas. First, it's going to be necessary to bring per capita consumption down in those nations that are currently over-consuming, while at the same time allowing under-consuming countries to rise to comfortable levels. Second, the current myth that the only viable economic model is continued growth – i.e., producing and selling more stuff – is going to have to be replaced with reality: the only thing that is going to work for the planet is maintaining the economy at a comfortable, consistent level, rather than constant growth. And third, we're going to have to become much more efficient at designing products whose cradle-to-grave environmental footprint is effectively zero, and encouraging the reuse and refurbishment of products already made.

Is it even remotely realistic to think that humanity is capable of accomplishing these three things? The first two are not totally out of the question. The hope there lies in the increasingly globalised society in which we now live. Not the abstract global, but the real movement of people from country to country, culture to culture, that results in the immersion of more and more 'haves' in ways of life that are different from those in which they grew up. This move-ment around the globe is increasingly common as jobs, or simply the taste for adventure, thrust growing numbers of people – espe-cially those from developed countries, which are the chief drivers of the overconsumption problem – into living situations that cause them to question what they thought they needed. Sure, there's no place like home, but some of what you see in far-flung places cannot help but make you question just how much stuff you truly need to make you comfortable and happy. For various reasons, we've had the good fortune to spend considerable time in places where people consume a whole lot less than they do in the United States. We've lived for extended periods in Europe and South America, and our work has taken us into the major cities and back-country of places like Nepal, Costa Rica, India and China.

And here's what we've learned. First, no denying it, more money, more stuff, *can* buy you more happiness and satisfaction, but *only up to a certain point.* We've seen the slums and misery in various places in Africa, Asia and South America, the beggars in the street, and seen the sleet sweep through sprawling slums of blue plastic tarps strung with rope, or, for a 'lucky' few, corrugated tin nailed over scraps of wood. We guarantee you that we, just like the people living there, have absolutely no desire to live like that. What ultimately gets people out of that situation is having enough money to buy the food, housing, and eventually a few amenities, that unequivocally make their lives pleasanter and them happier.

But there's also no denying that once you acquire a certain amount of stuff, acquiring more does little to make you more comfortable or feel better about yourself. We know that first-hand by contrasting the life we led when we lived for a year in Santiago, Chile, with the life we live in California. Per capita consumption in Chile, at least as measured by the oil-consumption index, is about a third of what we were used to in California. In Santiago we scaled back to fit that norm. We lived with our two kids – at the time Emma was fifteen and Clara was twelve – in an apartment that would fit in a couple of rooms of our house in California. There was no central heating or air conditioning, but a small space heater took off enough of the chill in the winter, and we moved it from room to room with us. Chileans live with much less climate control inside their homes and offices than we do: Liz's office mate sat at his desk computer typing in fingerless gloves and an overcoat every cold day in the winter. We had no car, relying instead on public transport, or occasionally hitting the local rent-a-car company for road trips. The material goods we brought with us to Chile, and which suited us just fine for the year, fitted in one suitcase each. Yet, on a day-to-day basis, we never really noticed what we had left behind, and in many ways we were liberated by having less. By no means were we roughing it. Our eighth-floor, window-walled downtown apartment in Las Condes overlooked the gleaming skyscrapers and bustling streets of Santiago's financial district. Downsizing in the stuff department had no effect on our emotional well-being, because even the downsized version of our normal life was, well, excellent.

Our experience is by no means unique. There have been many studies that have tried to figure out the price-point where money and the stuff it buys no longer substantially increase happiness. That point is surprisingly low on a worldwide basis: per capita annual income of about $12,000. Of course, the price-point for basic happiness varies depending on what's considered normal where you live, and how exactly you define happiness. In industrialised nations, the price is much higher than the world average, and the cut-off differs depending on whether you are talking about emotional well-being (feeling good about yourself) or life satisfaction (feeling you've been successful in comparison to others). For the United States, the world's top-consuming nation (but only the fourteenth richest in terms of average per capita income), the money-to-emotional well-being curve plateaus at an income of about $75,000 per year (as of 2010). However, in terms of feeling 'successful' (in the United States anyway) – measuring your self-worth against others – money seems to keep on talking no matter how much you make.

That study was spearheaded by Nobel Prize-winning psychologist Daniel Kahneman, and it (and others) shows that the real issue for changing how much stuff we think we need is not so much what makes us feel good about ourselves (emotional well-being), because emotional well-being plateaus at a relatively low price-point in the money-versus-happiness relationship. The stuff problem is fuelled largely by thinking that once we hit the emotional well-being plateau, what will take us even deeper into Happy Land is buying the latest new car, new gadget, and in general having more stuff than the people around us. That, of course, just doesn't work – if you want to use money to buy happiness, the answer seems to lie not in buying more stuff, but in buying more experiences, and in spending more of the money you don't need to fulfil your basic necessities to help others. Those were among the findings of psychology professor Elizabeth Dunn, from the University of British Columbia, and Michael Norton, a professor of marketing at Harvard University, in their book *Happy Money: The New Science of Smarter Spending*. They found that buying stuff (once you have the basics), while not necessarily making you unhappy, does not make you any happier, whereas buying experiences – like going to a concert, or taking a trip – *does* in fact actually bring lasting joy. That certainly rings true for our family: those fun things we tend to talk about around the dinner table are invariably the things we did, not the things we bought.

In that simple truth lies a big chunk of the solution for bringing per capita consumption down. Once you've hit that basic comfort level with material goods, rather than buying more and more stuff, which won't ultimately make you any happier, if you must, buy more and more experiences, which ultimately will. That, in turn, can drive the global economy from one focused on maintaining itself (and growing) by producing more and more stuff, to one that provides more and more experiences, things that make people happier while at the same time trashing less of the planet. Clearly those markets already exist – everything from learning to knit or sail, to hiking and camping holidays, to wine tours, to just plain old reading a good book – all those things are out there already, and are making lots and lots of people happier by the day. Given the range of experiences on people's bucket lists, the opportunities are almost endless for clever entrepreneurs.

But what about the fact that many people's overall life satisfaction continues to increase, with income far beyond that at which emotional well-being levels off? That's the other fact that came out of Daniel Kahneman's work, and basically it comes down to asking yourself, 'How good am I compared to those around me?', and evaluating that by counting your things, seeing you have more than the person next to you, and saying, 'Hee hee hee, I'm better than you!' because of it. That competitive edge to human nature is not something we are ever going to get rid of, nor would we want to – although maybe we could tone it down a little – since ultimately competition results in some great achievements, even if they sometimes end up being the flip side of great disasters. Insofar as solving the stuff problem goes, then, the trick is not to try to get rid of the competition: it's to change the slogan on the T-shirt from '[S]He Who Dies with the Most Toys Wins' to '[S]He Who Dies with the Most Experiences Wins'.

Let's say humanity can pull off that trick, and do it within the next couple of decades. We're still faced with the looming reality that there are billions of people who need to climb higher to even get to the stuff-to-happiness plateau; that is, they really don't have the basic level of material goods they need to be happy. Almost certainly, over the next few decades a large proportion of those people will make that climb, and in a perfect world, all of them should. Which, as far as tipping points go, means that even assuming that attitude readjustments like substituting experiences for stuff in the quest for happiness come to pass, at least some natural resources, and possibly many, will become strained to the breaking point. Earlier we mentioned the Global Footprint Network, a group of scientists that audits the consumption rates of various global resource indicators like land, water and biodiversity. The basic method is to compare how fast a resource is being used up, versus how fast it's being replenished, and it is those kinds of comparisons that lead to assessments such as that one and a half Earths would be needed to sustain us at our present pace. Clearly, the using-it-up side of the equation is only going to get larger as more and more people acquire their basic allotment of material goods. Is there any way to balance that by increasing the replenishment side of the equation?

That may be possible, at least to some extent, through the tried and true mantra of reuse and recycle. The gains could be tremendous. For instance, returning to our smartphone example, one leading manufacturer estimates that the average lifespan of a new phone is about six years. Yet, how many of you who own smartphones still have the one you bought six years ago? If you live in the United States or the United Kingdom, probably just about none of you – the average turn-around time for mobile phones in those countries is about two years. In the United States alone, somewhere in the neighbourhood of three hundred million of the most popular brand of smartphone have been sold since 2007. A two-year turnover means that about two hundred million of those phones should be available for reuse. It's a no-brainer that simply passing them on down the line to the next consumer who would want them – like the billions of people who are still doing without the basics – would save all the raw materials it would take to produce two hundred million new phones. It's also a no-brainer that in order to make the kind of difference that is needed, the baby-step way in which we presently reuse and recycle is going to have to be scaled up dramatically. The global norm would have to reach the point where each and every one of us would regard tossing our used-up gadgets, paper, plastic and so on in the rubbish instead of in the recycling bin as on a par with, say, peeing on the kitchen floor.

Of course, after a time all products simply wear out. Today, when they reach that point it's often cheaper just to dump them into the landfill than to break them down into pieces and materials that could be used elsewhere. That cost–benefit ratio is bound to shift as critical materials get scarcer: given our technological expertise, there is no reason that it shouldn't be less expensive to mine raw materials out of, say, cast-off smartphones than it is to tear down a mountain. Especially when you consider that one ton of discarded phones would produce 324 times more gold, fourteen times more copper, and seven times more silver than a ton of ore at economically feasible hard-rock mines these days.

Right now, however, recycling things like electronics is usually a ship-it-to-the-third-world industry, and leaving aside the carbon costs of shipping, the environmental and labour laws in the third world are lax to non-existent. We hear horror stories of backyard smelters where mum, dad and the kids smash up computer monitors with sledgehammers, melt down motherboards with hand-held blowtorches, and soak components in open vats of sulphuric acid to recover lead, copper and gold. In Delhi, whole neighbourhoods are devoted to this toxic, deadly enterprise, a perfect study in the worst way to recycle. Clearly, industry is capable of developing better, more efficient ways to turn many kinds of e-wastes (and other wastes) back into raw materials needed to produce the next round of stuff, if we simply bring our human ingenuity and our technological prowess into play. Among the key challenges will be figuring out ways to recycle critical materials that now fall by the wayside. For example, whereas we already know how to retrieve various metals from scrap electronics, we have yet to invent the way to extract and reuse the rare-earth elements that are locked up in them.

The other means by which human ingenuity and technology can come to our rescue is by coming up with ways to more comprehensively track the environmental cost through the cradle-to-grave life-cycle of each of the many products that society now uses with such abandon. Already consumers find it useful to read lists of ingredients or warnings on product labels when deciding where to lay down their hard-earned money. Many of us like to know where our food comes from, and in the 1980s, national pride elevated the 'Made in USA' label into a money-making endeavour, even if it implied a less-than-quality product. Now that label connotes an increase in quality, valued in the States and elsewhere too. US consumers are more and more aware of lax labour and environmental laws in manufacturing, and are more likely to rebel against purchasing products from those countries with little concern for their workforce. As a result, large companies are modifying their reliance on 'sweatshops' because they know that, more than selling their product, they are selling an image.

In the same vein, having an 'environmental footprint' rating on every product would probably go a long way towards postponing, or in the best case even avoiding, stuff-triggered tipping points, at both the grassroots and the regulatory levels. At the grassroots level, most people, when given the choice between buying something that they know is ultimately harmful in the long run versus something more benign, go for the more benign choice. The result: bigger profits for the producers of environmentally friendly products. If you don't believe that, ask yourself why even oil companies are emphasising how environmentally friendly they are these days. BP promoted itself as 'Beyond Petroleum', and you can find just about any major company you care to name advertising what it's doing for the environment.

That's given rise to a whole new word in the advertising lexicon – 'greenwashing', which refers to a company casting itself and its products as environmentally friendly, even though they really are not. How is the consumer to figure out who's telling the truth? That's where regulatory agencies come in: actually tracking cradle-to-grave environmental footprints would make it clear who is merely greenwashing and whose environmental claims are based in fact. Environmental footprint ratings would also give regulatory agencies a way to reward producers of environmentally benign products, through providing various monetary incentives, while at the same time penalising, through taxation, environmentally destructive practices. Again, more profits for the good guys.

As greenwashing amply shows, words are one thing, and actions are another. A big reason people don't yet pay much attention to cradle-to-grave environmental costs is because our production of stuff has grown in such a helter-skelter way. A recent assessment of the state of the art in tracing supply chains, 'The Science of Sustainable Supply Chains' by Dara O'Rourke, put it this way: 'It is still almost impossible to trace the cotton in a popular shirt from the store back to the farms where it was grown … let alone to measure the full impacts and externalised costs of the apparel supply chain' (*Science* 344:1124–1127). That, in theory, can change, given our current technology and data-tracking capabilities, and a whole new science of product 'life-cycle assessment' is growing up around that premise. Life-cycle assessment basically looks at things like the entire supply chain that leads to a finished product, how the product is used, and how it is disposed of, assigning an environmental cost or benefit to each stage. Ideally, such analyses hold the key to actually rating the environmental footprint of each and every product. That will have to ramp up pretty darn fast, though, if it is going to make a big enough dent in our stuff problem to avoid stuff-triggered tipping points.

We're hoping that such efforts do ramp up adequately, and that humanity can kick its stuff addiction in time. It's possible, but only if people are willing to shift their attitudes about material things, and if technology comes to the rescue in the ways we've outlined in this chapter. The reality, though, is that it's going to be nip-and-tuck – it is so ingrained in such a large part of the world that *things* are the measure of success, and to some extent of happiness, that it's entirely plausible – many would say it's more likely than not – that as we roll through the next thirty years we really will be needing even more Earths than we need today in order to keep on keeping up with the Joneses. If that comes to pass, the world our children will live in when they are our age will be one that not only has at least ten billion people in it, as we saw in the previous chapter, but also one in which billions more people than today are scrambling for the newest toy at the expense of all else. Under those circumstances, the stuff-producing mill will begin to creak and groan as it runs short of critical materials and increasingly fouls the planetary nest, and more and more political and economic flash-bang grenades will be going off as nations jockey to control raw materials that are only available outside their borders.

Unsettling as that picture is, it wouldn't stop there if we combine increasing human population and increasing demand for more stuff, while still powering our manufacturing systems in the same old way we're used to, namely with fossil fuels. As we alluded to earlier, that combination queues up yet another tipping point, an overarching one that affects not only this or that limited resource, but the whole world and every living thing in it. All those greenhouse gases produced by manufacturing and using stuff are already causing a shift in Earth's climate that is more massive than any human being has ever experienced, in the entire history of our species. Let's see in the next chapter how that would play out, if we didn't change our ways.

4

STORMS

Liz, Yellowstone National Park, July 1988

I had never packed pearls and heels in my backpack before. By invitation, I was on my way to the exclusive Silver Tip Ranch, on the northern border of Yellowstone National Park, nicely squeezed in between the Absaroka-Beartooth Wilderness and the park. My hiking partners were Yellowstone's then-Superintendent Bob Barbee and my boss, John Varley, who was then the park's Chief of Research. We made the decision not to take the journey on horseback or by wagon so that we could enjoy the walk through one of the most spectacular of all of Yellowstone's landscapes. Slough Creek Valley is the only meandering stream in all of northern Yellowstone, and its wide, glacially carved bed sits just below the aptly named Cutoff Mountain. The creek is famous for its cutthroat trout, which are wilier than most in Yellowstone, but fishing there is about as perfect as it gets, especially upstream, since few anglers are willing to hike that far for a fish.

I was pretty excited to be headed to Silver Tip with Bob and John, two men I had long admired, and I considered myself lucky to be spending some quality back-country time with them. Bob endeavoured to use science to make decisions about park management, and John oversaw hundreds of park research projects. Both were smart, desperately loved Yellowstone and were committed to keeping it a national treasure. The philosophy of management, then and to some extent now, was a 'laissez-faire' approach, one honed from a 1964 conservation 'bible' known as the Leopold Report and further refined as new issues presented challenges through the ensuing decades. Both these men viewed themselves as stewards of the park, with the responsibility to preserve its special qualities, despite the heavy hand of people. The park research they condoned helped to inform them about how the Yellowstone ecosystem functioned. In their minds, they were entrusted with keeping the park accessible to the millions of visitors who travelled through it, while maintaining it as 'intact' as possible within its boundaries. This philosophy is what was challenged that summer.

As the horse-drawn wagon with supplies for the ranch passed us, the cowboy driver tipped his hat. He would have changed his clothes and quenched his thirst by the time we arrived at Silver Tip Ranch hours later. Our rendezvous at the ranch had been organised so that I could present the results of my ongoing research into the palaeoecology of Yellowstone, and the intended audience was a group of wealthy personal guests of the ranch who had helicoptered in for their vacation. Bob and John thought I might provide this group with a little 'local research' about the national park, in the hope of forging a partnership. My work focused on the past several thousand years of history of the Yellowstone ecosystem, which I reconstructed through excavating and studying fossil mammals, birds, amphibians and reptiles from caves in the region. My research, in a sense, created a moving picture of the present ecosystem back in time. Which animals were there before the park was established? Were they similar in composition to the animals there today? Were wolves present a thousand years ago? What about elk? Did Yellowstone's environments change significantly through this time, and if so, how did the animals respond? The data were clear and compelling: the present Yellowstone ecosystem has been in existence for millennia. Yellowstone has demonstrated resilience in the face of changing environments, and its animal community has remained pretty much the same. Fires have come and gone, many generations of elk have been born in the park, and wolves were top predators hundreds of years ago, as they are again today (they were reintroduced to Yellowstone in 1995). I aimed to tell that story at the ranch.

About midway through the fourteen-mile trek we stopped for a snack, and looked back to the south. There we saw an enormous grey cloud, concentrated on the horizon above the green conifers and against a deep blue sky. I couldn't quite believe that it was from fires started by lightning from the typical summer-afternoon thunderstorms. I had never seen anything like it before – it was what I imagined the mushroom cloud from a nuclear bombing might look like. But Bob assured me that it was. This was what would become known as the Clover Mist fire. Although there was also a big fire burning on the western boundary of the park (started by a cigarette from men cutting firewood), the Clover Mist was started by lightning – it turns out that the afternoon thunderstorms weren't producing much rain that year. Bob mentioned that he thought his job was about to get tough – that the 'Let It Burn' policy then in place might be a little challenging to defend with the apparent size of the fire whose cloud we were watching.

He had predicted his summer pretty accurately. Indeed, as it wore on he became not-fondly known by some outside the park as Superintendent 'Barbee-cue'. But I'm getting ahead of my story.

Our arrival at the ranch was like a scene from a movie. At the front door was a line of fishing waders, fly rods and reels ready for guests to grab and go, outbuildings (one of which was my cabin for the night) shaded by giant conifers, and Slough Creek, winding through a meadow thick with wildflowers. A woman at her water-colour easel waved. A man in a smoking jacket and leather slippers met us at the door and ushered us into the grand entry, replete with mounted heads of Rocky Mountain big game, where he told us of the history of the ranch and offered us a cocktail. This was no typical lodge. My talk that evening – given in the pearls and the heels – went well, and dinner was a formal affair at which one of the guests asked me if I was related to the 'Hemingway Hadleys'. That would be a 'no'.

After my talk it became clear that the guests had only a vague idea about what Yellowstone really was, or where they were in relation to the park's boundary. Unlike the typical park visitor, these guests, mostly from the east coast, weren't stalled on their way to Silver Tip by traffic jams in the park – instead, most of them came in by helicopter after flying their private jet to the nearest landing strip. There was a definite feeling of isolation and insulation at Silver Tip; Yellowstone was just some other place in some other world, even though the Silver Tip visitors were right next to the park. But that bubble of insulation was about to burst. By the time we were out of Silver Tip Ranch and home, the bustling business of summer in Yellowstone – usually all about bear jams, leisurely drives, wildlife, geysers and sublime views – had morphed into a media frenzy and daily headlines about the 'Fires of Yellowstone'. And Silver Tip Ranch, the century-old private enclave, was just as vulnerable to forests going up in smoke as anywhere else. Money couldn't buy protection in this new climate wilderness.

That summer I became a fire expert. I learned how relative humidity, wind direction and fuel load influenced fire. I became knowledgeable about hot spots, burned acreage, firebreaks, fire-storms, crown versus surface versus ground fires, per cent containment, and that fires have behaviours and names. Hundreds, then thousands, of firefighters came in from all over the country, and every morning the parking lot outside my office at Mammoth Hot Springs became a meeting area for the crews. Every day was either hot, windy and reasonably clear, or still, dark and smoky. I learned that the reprieve my lungs got on those windy days meant that the fire was expanding ferociously somewhere in the park, and the still days meant that the fire crew could assess the fire margins; but breathing hurt, and my eyes stung. I carried my walkie-talkie radio with me everywhere; all my plans were tentative. I studied fire perimeters and prepared for emergency changes of plan. My daily hike into my cave site became considerably shorter, because the river was so low that I could ford it – although even at that low stage it was waist-deep – which I had never been able to do before, except in winter when it was frozen. The air smelled like a smoky campfire in the morning, and by the end of the day a bandana across my face would come away blackened. Some evenings after my day of excavation, as the sun was setting I would drive to see the flames consume the trees along Specimen Ridge. As the summer progressed I watched the giant smoke clouds along the southern horizon billow and coalesce into a whole sky of clouds that expanded across the eastern, then northern horizons, surrounding my field area. I began to wear a government-issued bright-yellow shirt and ugly, ill-fitting green pants made of Nomex – a fire-retardant material that was ironically quite hot to wear – when I conducted my fieldwork, just in case fire flared.

Then came the day at the end of August when I was told to close down my field site. A team of firefighters came to help me evacuate with my gear and my fossils before I was trapped by the fires burning around us. At the same time, fire surrounded and then burned over Silver Tip Ranch – no lives or buildings were lost, but the firefighting resulted in many trees being cleared or burned, permanently changing the setting. Shortly after, another fire threatened my house at the northern border of the park. Terrified, I sprayed the roof with water while dodging large chunks of burning cinders as they fell. My car was packed with my most precious belongings: some family photos and the fossils from my excavations. By then I couldn't see a thing, because the smoke was so thick … but the next day the wind came from the north, the fire burned back onto itself, and rain and snow fell, effectively shutting down new fire expansion, doing in a day what two months of firefighting could not. My visit back to my field area the following summer showed how close the fires had come before the snow fell and the wind changed direction on 11 September 1988: scorched ground pockmarked the sagebrush grassland around my cave.

The surreal drive out of the park that September is imprinted in my mind. There were no visitors left, exhausted firefighters in their Nomex suits emerged randomly from the forests, the mid-afternoon sun was darkened by smoke, and my car had to be ushered through what looked like a war zone, with flaming trees across the road, charred speed-limit signs and no evidence of animal life.

In all, about 250 fires burned in the Yellowstone ecosystem that summer, almost all of which were started by lightning. Lightning strikes, not uncommon in the park, that year ignited a lush growth of grasses and forbs that had grown dense during the wet, warm spring, adding to the tinderbox of fuel built up by almost a century devoid of natural fire. The fires burned more than three thousand square kilometres, almost a third of the park. The efforts of over nine thousand firefighters did little to stop the scorching flames, with standard 'firebreaks' useless in firestorm conditions so intense that large pieces of burning wood flew across the Grand Canyon of the Yellowstone, igniting the other side.

Little did any of us know, as we lived through those 'Fires of '88', that in fact we were witnessing the American West fall over the edge of a climate-triggered tipping point. Over the last century, Earth's average temperature has risen about 0.8°C (about 1.4°F), with most of that change since 1950. That seems ever so slow as people reckon time, because it's only about a degree after all, and it's played out over an entire human lifetime. In Earth time, though, the temperature has been climbing at lightning speed. A little perspective is helpful here.

Earth time is reckoned in billions of years, not in centuries, and certainly not in the years or decades people are used to dealing with. To Earth, life itself is a newcomer: for more than half of the four and a half billion years it's been circling the sun, our planet was a big sterile rock, devoid of living things, and for more than 90 per cent of those billions of years, there was no life more complicated than single-celled algae and bacteria. It was not until about 540 million years ago – just the frosting in the many-layered cake of Earth history, but unimaginably long ago to us – that complex life began to dominate on the planet. Since then, organisms built of many different kinds of cells, each of which has its own special job in keeping the plant or animal alive, have become big players in the biosphere. Examples include everything from worms, to bugs, to sea urchins, to trees, to us, *Homo sapiens*. The first humans finally began to walk the planet somewhere around two hundred thousand years ago, so many generations back that we can't begin to fathom it, but that's less than the blink of an eye in Earth time.

And now, over only the last century – in Earth time, less than milliseconds – we've heated up the planet by dumping lots of greenhouse gases, especially carbon dioxide, methane and nitrous oxide, into the air. At our present pace we're poised to heat it more over the next few decades; the expectation under business-as-usual scenarios is somewhere between 4 and 7°C, on average. To most people's minds, that doesn't sound like much, but that's where the Earth time perspective comes in. The total amount Earth's average temperature has fluctuated over the approximately six hundred million years that complex life has been on the planet is only a little over 10°C. So, in just a few decades, we are set to shoot the temperature up by half or more of the total amount it has varied in the entire history of complex life. We're heading to a place, in terms of climate, that human beings have never experienced, and we're sprinting there at a pace that is ten or more times what the Earth considers a typical speed.

That much climate change, that fast, does not mean good things for people – it means the loss of millions of lives, hundreds of millions displaced from their homes, crop failures, forest fires, new diseases, and the extinction of species we need. These are not idle speculations – we've already seen the beginnings of these things, and the expectations of impacts to come are based on sound science that points to serious near-future risks, as reported in numerous recent books, thousands of scientific articles, and summary reports by expert groups such as the Intergovernmental Panel on Climate Change, the American Association of Arts and Sciences, the United States National Academy of Sciences, and the UK's Royal Society.

Climate-caused tipping points tend to sneak up on us, seemingly coming out of nowhere, and flip us into a new normal within just a few years. Those Yellowstone fires showed us that. They burned not only Yellowstone, but a vast swathe of land that included parts of the Rocky Mountain states of Wyoming, Idaho and Montana. What had been happening with climate change in that part of the world up to then was not noticed by most people. We're all used to yearly fluctuations – some cold years, some hot years, some wet years, some dry years – and if you look at temperature graphs from around 1970 into the early twenty-first century for the northern Rocky Mountains, where Yellowstone is located, such fluctuations are exactly what you see. But when you look more closely at those graphs, you see that around 1985 something unusual happened. Prior to that time, the highest average summer temperature never rose as high as 15°C (59°F). Beginning in 1985, it was as if a switch had been flipped: though the year-to-year fluctuations continued, no longer were mean summer temperatures of 15°C uncommon. In fact, those 1988 fires were preceded by three years of abnormally hot summers, each of them averaging 15°C or more. And ever since, the average summer has usually been a degree or more hotter than pre-1985 summers. Likewise, after 1985, more years saw the snow melt off early in the spring. The combination of hotter summers and earlier snow melt equates to drier forests as the summer progresses, which means that fires, caused either by lightning strikes or by careless people, are easier to start, and once they get going they burn hotter, and are harder to put out.

Increasing average temperatures beginning in 1985 were the lead-up to 1988, but nobody really noticed until everything exploded into flames, which happened once the forests had dried out to the point that their moisture content was about that of kiln-dried lumber. It was just like that boiling teapot – it doesn't look as if much is happening until it actually starts to boil, although of course the water is getting hotter and hotter all along. The difference between the forests and the teapot is that the forests never did the boiling-water equivalent of cooling down. That is to say, once that new fire-frequency state was triggered in 1988, that's the way it has stayed. Climate itself had crossed a threshold, as hotter summers became the new norm. As a result, ever since 1988, the frequency of Western wildfires and total acreage burned per year has remained about double, on average, what was normal prior to that year. In the early days it was all too easy to attribute that to fire suppression and the build-up of fuels that resulted from the land-management policies of the twentieth century. But once the studies were done, it became clear that the overall increase was more attributable to the other thing people had done: changing the climate.

After that, wildfires went, well, wild, and not only in wild places. In 2012 we happened to be driving south on Interstate 25, through a part of Colorado where we had lived in our younger days, when we saw plumes of smoke erupting from the forests just outside the idyllic town of Colorado Springs, nestled at the foot of Pikes Peak. Even from miles off in broad daylight, the orange flames were clearly visible. Within a few days that fire, dubbed the Waldo Canyon Fire, would grow to cover an area of more than twenty-four square miles, cause the evacuation of more than thirty thousand people from the town and surrounding suburbs, and would burn down 350 houses and kill two people. It was just one of many wildfires that broke out in Colorado that particularly dry year – at least fourteen of them major. Despite the many years we'd lived in Colorado – Tony grew up just south of Colorado Springs – we'd never seen a fire season there like 2012 was stacking up to be. The statistics bore out our subjective assessment; as Colorado Governor John Hickenlooper pointed out, the Waldo Canyon Fire alone was bigger than any there had ever been in the state before.

By 2012 the entire American West was noticing a similar increase in the number of fires, as were many other places in the world. In 2013, Australia declared a state of emergency in New South Wales when the Blue Mountains near Sydney went up in flames, destroying hundreds of homes, during an intense bushfire season that continued into 2014. While the highest levels of the Australian government claimed the fires were nothing out of the ordinary, the scientific evidence said otherwise: climate change in Australia has been producing more hot days per year and drying out the vegetation more, which has the net effect of increasing the length of the bushfire season and increasing the risk and intensity of fire even in what had always been fire-prone areas. Russia too was hard hit by wildfires in 2010 and 2012, again the result of record high summer temperatures that dried out forests and set up the ignition conditions for hundreds of individual fires that in 2010 blanketed Moscow in smoke, killed at least fifty people, and drove more than three thousand from their homes. The 2012 wildfires in Siberia burned for most of the summer, producing a blanket of smoke visible from space. In Portugal, wildfires raged in August 2010 and 2013. Ten years earlier, when Portugal parched during what was up until that time the hottest year on record globally, wildfires there killed eighteen people while torching an area about the size of Luxembourg. In Valparaíso, Chile, a 2014 wildfire thought to be the worst in the city's history killed fifteen people, caused the evacuation of thousands, left eleven thousand people homeless, and permanently changed the nature of the historic coastal city. Indeed, fires in South America have escalated to approximately five thousand per day, the sum of which results in smoke pollution across millions of square kilometres.

As we write this, in 2014, fires are sweeping across much of the boreal forest in the Northwest Territories of Canada, with smoke and ash going so high into the stratosphere that it is carried long distances, influencing air quality in the United States as well as the global climate, with ash detected as far away as Portugal. These boreal forest fires are unprecedented in their scope, exceeding the extent of burns known over the past ten thousand years. In our part of the world, the American West, the average fire season by 2014 was seventy-five days longer than it was in 1975, and our home state, California, is experiencing its worst drought in history. By late summer 2014 we had seen at least a thousand more fires than the average for the previous five years, and had already lost twenty-five thousand more acres than what the past average says should be normal. Flames had driven families from more than a thousand homes, and the costs of the damage had already surpassed $97 million. Particularly telling was that the first fire began on 1 January 2014, signalling that our state has crossed yet another threshold: no longer is there a 'fire season' and an off-season. Fires have become a year-round phenomenon. Wildfires, once recognised as local phenomena mostly controlled by precipitation, are a new global 'normal' mostly controlled by temperature.

Here's an interesting perspective. Some of us have lived through this state-shift in fire frequency, and we notice how much worse things have become. But if you were born after 1988 you'd assume that these bad fire years are normal. And you'd be right, because now they are. But the new normal that we suddenly tipped into around 1988 is not here to stay. Wildfire frequency and intensity are heading towards yet another precipice. We're already apt, in fact, to view the increases in wildfires we're now experiencing as the good old days. Models indicate that continued warming and increasing frequency of hot, dry weather in places like the American West, Australia, Russia, the Mediterranean, southern South America and other fire-prone areas is likely to heighten the probability of large fires and the damage they cause over the coming decades. Just what that means is illustrated by detailed studies that focus on the American West: in the Yellowstone and Colorado examples we mentioned above, by 2050 the area burned each August would be quadruple what we consider normal today. With the intensity, frequency and extent of the new 'fire-season' normal, the whole character of the forests will change forever – the scorched earth will be growing different kinds of plants than those we're used to today.

It's not just wildfires that climate change sends over tipping points. Gradually changing winter conditions have wreaked a different sort of havoc in the United States and Canada, in the same forests that are burning up in the summers. Those forests are predominantly conifers like pine, which have, throughout their history, provided a home for a beetle called, not surprisingly, the pine bark beetle. Prior to about 1990, winter temperatures in the Rockies were cold enough to kill a large number of the beetles each year, keeping their populations sufficiently low for both trees and beetles to stay happy – the beetles persisted, but not in numbers high enough to kill their host trees. As average winter temperatures gradually rose through the second half of the twentieth century, not much changed for the trees and the beetles until, finally, a critical threshold was crossed: that last fraction of a degree of temperature rise that meant that instead of most beetle larvae dying from the cold, most lived on to reproduce.

All of a sudden, instead of one small generation of beetles hatching out each year, there were two large generations. And that's when both the trees and people began to notice. The trees died, seemingly overnight. What used to be tens of millions of acres of mature green forest when we were growing up and when our kids were born, are now dead sticks reaching for the sky, from New Mexico all the way up the Rocky Mountain chain through Canada into Alaska. That's why, as you drive through that part of the world, in places you'll find that 60 to 80 per cent of the trees are dead. All that death happened in the course of a decade. It is crashing real-estate values in some areas, troubling the timber industry in others, and has turned large swathes of the Rocky Mountain landscape into an eyesore for the foreseeable future. The forests will never be the same, and it will be hundreds of years, at least, before the signs of such widespread death are healed by Mother Nature.

Yet another kind of climate-induced tipping point comes in the form of devastating floods and severe storms, which the world is already beginning to experience more often as a result of the overall warming of the atmosphere and the oceans that we have caused over the past several decades. We're talking about the kind of floods that covered a fifth of Pakistan in 2010, displacing twenty million people and killing two thousand. Or that caused waterfalls to pour into the New York subway system in 2012. Soon, people will find themselves considering such weather catastrophes as nothing out of the ordinary. Among the many problems that arise from heating up the planet, even a little, is that warmer oceans and a warmer atmosphere cause faster evaporation of water from oceans and land surfaces, which loads more water into the air. And since what goes up must come down, all that extra water in the atmosphere causes rainstorms that are more intense than usual to occur increasingly often. It's that sort of underlying physics that causes climate models to predict that by the end of this century, the one-in-twenty-year annual maximum daily precipitation amount is likely to become a one-in-five- to one-in-fifteen-year event in many places. Similarly, hurricanes are expected to get stronger.

What all this means is that what we now regard as 'unusual' extreme weather events – like the droughts that lead to wildfires, those terrible Pakistan floods, or the flooding of New York's subway – will no longer be unusual at all. If all this seems pretty far off in the future, well, it's not. In the United States, weather catastrophes (defined as those that cost more than $1 billion) have been on the increase since 1980, at the rate of about 5 per cent per year. Forty-four such calamities occurred in the years 2008 to 2012, twice as many as in any ten-year period of the late twentieth century. Twenty-five of them occurred in just the two years 2011 and 2012. The trend continued in 2013, which added seven more billion-dollar-plus extreme weather events.

It's pretty much the same story worldwide. The worst floods in centuries hit Europe and parts of Asia in 2013. In London the Thames Barrier, designed to keep floodwaters out of the city, has been closed much more frequently in recent years, particularly during the deluges of 2013 and 2014, than at any time since it was completed in 1982. Dangerous heatwaves that sometimes kill tens of thousands at a shot have become more frequent over the past decade in places as far apart as the United States, Europe, India and Australia. The Mediterranean and West Africa appear to be seeing more frequent severe droughts. While climate scientists are wary of saying that any single one of these extreme weather events is a direct result of human-caused climate change, put them all together and the pattern is just what the climate models predict should be happening – and will continue to happen, more and more.

Looked at from the perspective of tipping points, increases in the number of extreme weather events mean major metropolitan areas are moving into a new normal for how much damage they can expect from bad storms. And a new normal for how much money they have to spend to protect their residents from the worst effects of more frequent extreme weather, be it floods, winds or heat. Such infrastructure adaptation doesn't come cheap, even in cases when it can be done fast enough.

For coastal cities, besides the increase in the intensity of storms that a warmer climate brings, there is also the problem of rising sea level. How that works is easy to envisage: as the climate has been warming, the world's glaciers have been melting. All that water ends up in the oceans, which, when combined with the expansion of water that takes place as it warms, causes the sea level to rise. Already this has caused the oceans to come up about a fifth of a metre (a little over half a foot) since 1900. All well and good, if the sea walls that keep storm surges at bay are high enough. The problem is, increasingly they are not. The coastal infrastructure in place today was built to withstand storm surges of a sea at pre-1950 levels. As the sea level rises, those storm surges climb ever closer to the top of the sea walls. That gradual rise has little effect until that last fraction of an inch that finally makes it possible for waves to crash over the top of the barrier. That's why water surged into the New York subway tunnels, a tipping point of the most noticeable kind.

And it explains to a large extent why half of Europe was impacted by flooding in 2013, the result of intense storms acting in concert with the relatively small sea-level rise that has already taken place, and coastal development.

Such problems are destined to become the new normal for most coastal cities: by 2050, the best-case scenario is that sea level will have risen another six inches. Without improving infrastructure in time, that means not only flooding from storm surges in such cities as Shanghai, London, Miami, New York, New Orleans, Mumbai, Cairo, Amsterdam and Tokyo, but parts of those cities actually being under water.

This best-case scenario assumes that the world's glaciers will continue to melt gradually and slowly, and that greenhouse-gas emissions will increase more slowly in the coming few years than they have over the past couple of decades. A worse scenario, which assumes we will continue business as usual on greenhouse-gas emissions, but still counts on a gradual glacier melt, predicts that the sea level will rise over a foot (forty centimetres) by 2050. At that point, without improving coastal infrastructure, more than a hundred million people would be flooded out of their homes annually, and many of those would be forced to move permanently to higher ground. That, incidentally, is already happening: since 2009, thousands of Pacific Islanders have been forced to relocate as the Carteret Islands they called home have been swallowed by the rising seas. They are among the world's first climate refugees.

Looking at even worse scenarios, the assumption that sea-level rise will continue to proceed slowly and gradually is very possibly wrong. The wild cards are two mega-glaciers, the Greenland and the West Antarctic Ice Sheets, which right now lock up an awful lot of water. Melting the Greenland Ice Sheet alone would raise the sea level by four to six metres (about thirteen to twenty feet). Add thirteen feet to today's sea level and all of Shanghai would be under water, as would southern Florida and most other coastal cities. We know that a large rise in sea level happened about 125,000 years ago from melting ice – especially Greenland ice – so we know it can happen again.

We also know that big glaciers probably do not melt at a constant, gradual rate. Just like ice cubes in your drink, as long as they are big, they seem to melt slowly, but once they shrink to a certain size, they disappear pretty fast. Such sudden partial collapse is exactly what seems to have happened to the Greenland Ice Sheet when the sea level rose 125,000 years ago, and also when the seas rose four hundred thousand years ago. Melting the West Antarctic Ice Sheet would raise the sea level by ten to sixteen feet (three to five metres), and in fact its collapse is already under way. Luckily, the best estimates at this point are that total collapse will take two to five centuries, buying us adequate time to adapt; but, before you rest too easy on that point, bear in mind that a 2013 report by the US National Research Council, entitled *Abrupt Impacts of Climate Change: Anticipating Surprises* (National Academies Press, Washington DC), highlighted as a big unknown whether or not that collapse could be sooner.

More certain is another ice-related tipping point: the opening of a whole new ocean in the Arctic. The area and thickness of ice covering the Arctic Ocean in late summer has seen a dramatic reduction in the past couple of decades, at a much faster pace than scientists ever would have predicted twenty years ago. As a result, countries are now jockeying for position to take advantage of new shipping lanes that will soon open up, hoping to rule the northern seas. China, India, Italy, Japan, Singapore and South Korea have already petitioned for, and been granted, observer status in what used to be the more exclusive Arctic Council, made up of the nations that actually have an Arctic coastline: Canada, Denmark, Finland, Iceland, Norway, Russia, Sweden and the United States.

One of the reasons these other nations suddenly have an interest in the Arctic is because the opening of that ocean will mean the much quicker shipping of goods from one side of the world to the other. No longer will ships have to take the long southern route either through the Panama Canal or around the bottom of South America; it will be a quick shot through the Bering Strait.

The other reason goes back to what we discussed in the last chapter, our thirst for raw materials to produce the stuff we want: there are vast resources to be tapped in the Arctic. Ironically, fairly large reserves of coal, oil and gas, the drivers of the whole climate problem, will become economically feasible to extract as more ice disappears forever. Likewise, the rush will be on to mine nickel, copper, titanium, chromite, iron, manganese, gold, silver, platinum, molybdenum, aluminium, mercury, tin, phosphates, and even diamonds. Most of these resources are locked up not in the presently frozen shores of the more stable countries of the Arctic Council, but in Russia. It's not hard to see how a new world order could rapidly evolve once an Arctic land grab becomes possible with easier shipping access, which is likely to happen sooner rather than later. Even assuming that late-summer ice melt continues to increase at just its present pace – that is, no collapse as the sea ice thins more and more each year, which would accelerate things – the Arctic Ocean would be navigable in late summer by 2020, just six years from when we're writing this.

All this ice melting and water rising goes hand in hand with two invisible phenomena that lead to other kinds of ocean-based tipping points. It's not just the atmosphere that is getting warmer, it's the oceans too. Ocean temperatures have increased about a tenth of a degree Celsius (about two-tenths of a degree Fahrenheit) over the last century. It sounds like such a small amount, but the issue is that the ocean has long been a very stable temperature environment for the organisms that live there. As a result, even tiny changes can have big impacts, which we're already seeing. Coral reefs, which you can think of as the rainforests of the sea because so many species depend on them, are clearly feeling the heat. As with the land, an average increase in ocean temperature does not mean that the temperature increases by the same amount everywhere. Ocean temperatures in tropical and subtropical regions, where corals tend to live, have heated up much more than the world's average. In the so-called Coral Triangle, extending from the north coast of Australia up through Indonesia and the Philippines, which includes about a third of the world's coral reefs, ocean temperatures have been rising a tenth of a degree Celsius per decade, not per century. And it's not the average temperature that corals get concerned about; it's the extremes, as indicated by what happened in the Indian Ocean in 1998. Ocean temperature highs temporarily rose by only 0.5 to 1°C (0.8 to 1.9°F) above normal, but as a result, 80 per cent of all the corals in a region the size of the United States were bleached a deadly white, then 20 per cent of them died for good. The impacts hit Australia's world-famous Great Barrier Reef hard: the 1998 event, followed by another in 2002, ended up bleaching more than half of the reef system.

Now, throw ocean acidification, another result of climate change, on top of those temperature impacts. Recall that the ultimate cause of climate change is our emission of greenhouse gases, especially carbon dioxide, into the atmosphere. Carbon dioxide in the atmosphere seeps into the ocean where the water meets the air, and sets up a chemical reaction that has the ultimate effect of increasing the amount of carbonic acid in the water; that is, the ocean is getting more and more acid. We're already seeing that rise in acidity, and year by year it's getting worse. As far as corals and other marine creatures are concerned, this is bad news, because their metabolisms cannot cope with the levels of acidity the oceans are heading towards. Both experimental data and modelling indicate that combined warming and rising acidity are on track to kill most coral reefs on Earth by 2070, and many other species as well. Just the amount of ocean acidification that has already taken place has caused oyster and scallop farms in the Pacific Northwest region of North America to shut down, costing jobs in what were formerly burgeoning seafood enterprises. That is a disturbing harbinger of more widespread losses later this century, as shown by attempts to rear a variety of ocean creatures in tanks that mimic the ocean temperatures and chemistry that seem likely by the time our children's children are adults. Clams, snails, sea urchins, even fish – a broad swathe of marine life dies in those simulated oceans of the future.

If you don't spend a lot of time around the sea, all this may seem pretty esoteric to you, until you begin to realise that what we're talking about is not just the loss of lots of species you may never see, but a major hit to the world's capacity to produce food and jobs. In just a single country, Australia, the fishing and tourist industry dependent on the Great Barrier Reef contributes about £3.7 billion to the economy each year. If coral reefs disappear worldwide, it would cost the global economy around £20 billion annually, and result in the extinction of a quarter of all ocean life, which would eliminate about 10 per cent of the world's fisheries. That, in turn, would cause lots of people to go hungry, especially in poor, unstable countries: coral reefs provide more than half of the vital minerals and protein for more than four hundred million people who live in the poorest countries of Africa and South Asia. In the Coral Triangle alone, a hundred million people depend on the resources that coral reefs and associated coastal ecosystems yield.

* * *

Speaking of food – climate change will cause problems on land too. As we'll see in the next chapter, what we need in the coming years is more food, yet what are high-yield areas for major food crops like corn, wheat and rice today will no longer be so. Corn yields, for example, fall dramatically as the number of hot days in a growing season increases, especially in drought years, a climatic impact we are already seeing. In the hot, dry year of 2012, Midwestern United States farmers saw their yield reduced by up to 40 to 60 per cent. That sort of bad year will become more and more frequent given current trends of climate change. Studies by the world's leading food-security experts indicate that within fifty years, the average corn yield in the United States, now a major exporter of corn, will fall by 15 to 30 per cent. At the same time, rice-growing regions worldwide will suffer from rising sea levels and extreme weather, reducing yields by as much as 10 to 15 per cent, increasing prices by 32 to 37 per cent. All of this, mind you, at the same time as at least two billion more hungry mouths to feed will be added to the world.

These sorts of impacts – fires, floods, rising seas, new oceans, food security – have caused people you would normally expect to be climate sceptics to sit up and take notice: including big business and the military. Leading the charge on the business end is the insurance industry, a major economic player, especially in developed countries. In the United States, the insurance industry generates about $413 billion per year (as of 2012), accounting for about 2.5 per cent of GDP, providing 2.6 million jobs and investing $5.8 trillion in financial markets. Insurance companies' business, of course, is evaluating risk, so maybe it's no surprise that they take the risks of climate change very seriously, especially given the huge payouts they've had to make for all the weather-related disasters in recent years – like the compensation to insured parties for the unusually high number (thirty-two) of billion-dollar-plus fires, floods, hurricanes and so on that hit over the years 2011 to 2013. For just the Waldo Canyon Fire in Colorado, which we mentioned earlier, insurance companies ended up paying out around half a billion dollars for lost homes and property.

It's those kinds of losses that prompt such reports as one by Charles E. Boyle that appeared recently in the *Insurance Journal* (2 July 2014, 'UN, IIS, Willis Urge "Convergence of Communities" to Face Climate Change', http://www.insurancejournal.com/news/international/2014/07/02/333500.htm): 'While the re/insurance industry is justifiably concerned about excess and alternative capital, the digital revolution, cyber liability, reputational risks, increasing regulations and a host of others, the elephant in the room remains climate change. As global temperatures warm, well-known risks – floods, droughts, fires, windstorms, political disruption – are increasing and becoming more violent. Virtually no one in the re/insurance industry now questions the perils the changing climate poses.'

As a result, insurance companies are taking action to protect their bottom line. After the spate of Colorado wildfires they suddenly became much more cautious about writing fire policies, to the extent that many people have had their policies cancelled. The risks are now just too great for companies to gamble on your home in the woods not going up in smoke. And in parts of Florida, where rising sea levels are making floods more and more common, it's impossible to get flood insurance, which of course puts a damper on real-estate development. In the Chicago area, an insurance company took a previously unthinkable step, suing municipalities to avoid paying out for flood damage that occurred during a particularly severe deluge in April 2013. Its argument was that the municipal governments knew of the risks posed by climate change, and should have beefed up their infrastructure to handle increased storm drainage. The company subsequently dropped the suit, but the statement it issued in explanation was in fact a warning: 'We believe our lawsuit brought important issues to the attention of the respective cities and counties, and that our policyholders' interests will be protected by the local governments going forward' (as reported by Robert McCoppin, 'Insurance Company Drops Suits Over Chicago-Area Flooding', *Chicago Tribune*, 3 June 2014, http://www.chicagotribune.com/news/local/breaking/chi-chicago-flooding-insurance-lawsuit-20140603,0,6767298.story). The not-so-hidden message: if governments don't take climate change seriously and protect their constituents, don't expect a bailout from insurance companies.

Like the insurance industry, military leaders are also all too familiar with risk, and take a very pragmatic view in assessing it. That's why, to the climate naysayers who cite the uncertainty inherent in predicting the future to argue against taking climate change seriously, former US Army Chief of Staff Gordon Sullivan had this to say in a 2007 report: 'People are saying they want to be convinced, perfectly. They want to know the climate science projections with 100 per cent certainty. Well, we know a great deal, and even with that, there is still uncertainty. But the trend line is very clear. We never have 100 per cent certainty. We never have it. If you wait until you have 100 per cent certainty, something bad is going to happen on the battlefield. That's something we know' (The CNA Corporation, 2007, *National Security and the Threat of Climate Change*, p.10).

Sullivan is one of the high-level former military leaders who make up the Military Advisory Board of the CNA Corporation, a non-profit group that has long advised military, federal, state and local agencies on how to handle global-scale problems. The others on the board include General Paul Kern (ret.), former Commanding General of the Army Materiel Command; Brigadier General Gerald E. Galloway, Jr (ret.), former Dean of the United States Military Academy and Industrial College of the Armed Forces, National

Defense University; Vice Admiral Lee Gunn (ret.), former Inspector General of the Department of the Navy; Admiral Frank 'Skip' Bowman (ret.), former Director of the Naval Nuclear Propulsion Program and former Chief of Naval Personnel; General James Conway (ret.), former Commandant of the Marine Corps; Lieutenant General Ken Eickmann, USAF (ret.), former Commander, USAF Aeronautical Systems Center; Lieutenant General Larry Farrell, USAF (ret.), former Deputy Chief of Staff for Plans and Programs, Headquarters, USAF; General Don Hoffman, USAF (ret.), former Commander, USAF Materiel Command; General Ron Keys, USAF (ret.), former Commander, USAF Air Combat Command; Rear Admiral Neil Morisetti, British Royal Navy (ret.), former UK Foreign Secretary's Special Representative for Climate Change, former Commandant, UK Joint Services Command and Staff College; Vice Admiral Ann Rondeau, USN (ret.), former President, National Defense University, former Deputy Commander, US Transportation Command; Lieutenant General Keith Stalder, USMC (ret.), former Commanding General, US Marine Corps Forces, Pacific; Rear Admiral David W. Titley, USN (ret.), former Oceanographer of the Navy; General Charles 'Chuck' Wald, USAF (ret.), former Deputy Commander, US European Command; Lieutenant General Richard Zilmer, USMC (ret.), former Deputy Commandant for Manpower and Reserve Affairs, former Commanding General of Multi-National Force-West in Al Anbar Province, Iraq.

That's a long list of names and titles, but it's worth browsing through them to convince yourself of an important point: there is no doubting the military expertise, acumen, intelligence and practicality of this group of people. So it's hard not to take the conclusions they've issued in two recent reports seriously (the 2007 report mentioned above, and the 2014 update, CNA Military Advisory Board, 2014, *National Security and the Accelerating Risks of Climate Change*, The CNA Corporation). And their basic conclusion is this, from the 2014 report: 'We remain steadfast in our concern over the connection between climate change and national security.'

In describing the capacity of climate change to trigger national-security problems, the CNA coined the phrase 'threat multiplier'. The phrase expresses in two words what the rest of their two reports detail: that the combination of climate change, population growth and shifting resource availabilities and shortages result in a much bigger world problem than we'd anticipate from any single one of those impacts. The other two words that are apropos in that context are 'tipping point', as in tipping the world into a new normal for the number and intensity of military conflicts we might expect at any one time – that is, more wars. We'll explore how that all comes together in Chapter 9, but for now, suffice to say that the kinds of climate change we are currently experiencing seem destined to add lots of fuel to the fires of conflict.

Dire predictions indeed, giving rise to the all-important question: can we actually do anything to avoid increasing climate disasters? The answer is both simple and complex. The simple answer is that we know exactly how to avoid the biggest problems, and that is to convert our energy system from the present one, which is almost totally dependent on greenhouse-gas-belching fossil fuels, to one which is essentially greenhouse-gas neutral. In fact the technology to do that already largely exists, and what's more could be scaled up appropriately in about three decades if the needed economic incentives were put in place.

Our energy system actually consists of two largely distinct parts: the stationary system, which includes the power plants that generate electricity and allow us to heat and cool our homes, cook our food, and so on; and the transportation system, which powers our cars, trucks, planes and ships. Recent studies indicate that conversion of the present coal- and natural-gas-powered stationary system to a combination of solar, wind, wave, geothermal and hydro, with perhaps a touch of next-generation nuclear and newly developed carbon-capture systems thrown in, could, from a technological perspective, quite feasibly be achieved as early as 2030. Likewise, replacing the transportation sector with a combination of vehicles powered by electricity and by environmentally friendly biofuels, notably those produced from algae, is within our grasp.

What stands in the way, of course, is the popular and political resistance to changing our ways, and the lobbying efforts of industries that stand to lose a lot of money by a big energy changeover. And that is where the solution gets complicated. Part of the answer involves the development of the right economic incentives – things like carbon taxes, tax breaks for carbon-neutral industries that promote their rapid scaling up, and so on. It involves recognising that spending up-front, much as in the way we pay our insurance premiums, will be necessary to guard against the even higher costs we'll incur if we do nothing to guard against the future impacts of ongoing climate change.

All of that requires an acknowledgement by the general populace that the climate problem is real, and must be addressed, especially in developed countries. Such an acknowledgement is beginning to happen, but it is still an uphill battle. The other very important part of the solution is international cooperation, and cooperation across the political aisle, both of which have also proven difficult, to say the least. Nevertheless, equally big global problems have been successfully resolved in the past, some of which we list in Chapter 10. So doing what is needed to address the climate problem is not out of the question. What it will take is reducing greenhouse-gas emissions by around 5.2 per cent per year – 6 per cent per year in the G20 developed nations – each year from now until 2060. That is the best we can hope for, and that would probably keep the total rise of global temperature to around two degrees Celsius (3.6°F).

Even that best-case scenario, though, is hotter than *Homo sapiens* has ever seen, so it's hard to see how humans will not be facing many of the climate-triggered problems we've mentioned in this chapter. If we continue business as usual, which would warm the globe by as much as six degrees Celsius (over 11°F) by the end of the century – well, we really don't want to go there. Earth hasn't been that hot in sixty million years, and getting there in the next eighty-five years would pretty much guarantee all manner of disasters, with hundreds of millions of people fleeing from drowned cities and hot, poor equatorial areas, and fights to control the areas that climate change made more favourable, like countries in more pole-ward latitudes.

Given the pace at which the world is addressing climate change, that six-degree-hotter world is looking more and more like the one we're heading for. Two degrees or six degrees, though, combined with what we've seen in the last two chapters, the drumroll is beginning. Ehrlich's Hell could get *really* hot. Two or three billion more people on the planet. Increasing consumption. Climate change. Put those threats together, and the real problems start: problems that make the new normal for fire frequency we experienced in 1988 look downright insignificant by comparison. So let's move on to the next chapters and start thinking about how those three threats multiply into a tipping point that would impact even life's basics: food and water.

5

HUNGER

Liz, Tony, Emma and Clara, South Africa, August 2001

Lions had come through the camp last night. Their tracks were fresh. We noticed the big pawprints in the soft sand as soon as we threw open the flaps of our tent, the cold Kalahari air fresh on our faces, the dawn just breaking. Emma and Clara's tent was still zipped up tight, and we were very, very glad they had heeded our safari guides' remonstrations never, ever to leave it open at night, for any reason. As soon as they heard us, though, they came tumbling out, excited to see the lion tracks for themselves.

Just a few days before, we'd arrived in Africa for the very first time. As we stepped off the plane and crossed the tarmac, an orange winter sun was hanging low in the sky, sharpening our shadows and our feelings of romance and adventure. What had brought us there was a scientific meeting, but what really captivated our interest was the chance to see the last remnants of ecosystems that still had a more or less full complement of big mammals – elephants, rhinos, lions, cheetahs and more than a dozen different kinds of antelope. Everywhere else in the world, extinction, largely at the hands of humans, had wiped out nearly half the big-bodied mammals that were present when people first ran across them. So we'd arranged to join up with several colleagues on a mobile safari through part of the Kalahari Desert, hoping to learn a lot more about how those big animals survived. What we hadn't reckoned on was that we'd also end up learning a lot more about what the people who lived in southern Africa had to deal with day to day.

The week in the Kalahari was everything we'd hoped it would be, complete with a rare sighting of a caracal, a desert lynx, brought to everyone's attention by then nine-year-old Emma (it turned out she had the sharpest eyes of anyone, including our guides), and long bouts of simply basking in the sun watching the elephants, giraffes, kudu, gemsbok and other megafauna we had come to see just living their lives. In the evening we'd start with the almost obligatory gin-and-tonic sundowner, then move on to a tasty dinner with ample meat and vegetables spiced in traditional African style. After dark it would get chilly, and we'd huddle around the campfire, trading stories of the day under the Southern Cross.

It was all very idyllic, so returning to civilisation was a bit of a shock. As we left the Kalahari heading towards Sun City, the South African equivalent of Las Vegas, where our meeting was to be held, the two-rut roads that cut through wild country gradually gave way to graded gravel lanes, along which a few poor villages were scattered. Our convoy of Land Rovers, each packed to the gills with people, tents and assorted camping gear, was clipping along at a pretty good pace. We were bringing up the rear, trying to stay out of the thick clouds of dust being kicked up by the vehicles ahead, and watching out for the windshield-cracking chunks of forty-mile-per-hour gravel that are a fact of life on those roads. Despite the several car-lengths that separated us from the next Land Rover in line, fine dust was still seeping through every crack in our rattling four-wheel drive, coating everything inside, including our nostrils, with an ever-thickening layer of grit. Whenever one of us blew our nose it was road-brown sludge that came out. Still, it was easy to get a little hypnotised by the engine's roar and the rhythmic bouncing over the washboard surface, while absent-mindedly watching the scrubby vegetation for glimpses of birds and other wildlife that was exotic to us. It all made for some very heavy eyelids.

Our reverie was suddenly broken as a springbok darted out from the olive-green bushes blurring by on our right. Thump! Our driver slammed on the brakes a little too late, locking up the wheels and bringing us to a swerving, sliding halt, our own powdery dustcloud catching up to us and obscuring everything for a few seconds. There was no real damage to the Land Rover – the wrap-around tubular steel bumper was built for just such eventualities. The springbok, though, was very dead. Without much hesitation our African guides slung the limp body up on the roof and tied it down good and tight. A few hours later, when we stopped for the night, they skinned, gutted and butchered it, and we feasted on fresh springbok roasted over an open fire.

That was lesson number one: in these parts, food was not to be wasted. We didn't think about the implications too much at the time; it was all part of the adventure. It took lesson number two to really catch our attention.

The next day, the dirt turned to tarmac, and the roadside towns got bigger. We hit one of them just about lunchtime, and, anxious to keep going but giving in to the demands of our growling stomachs, we pulled in to a fast-food joint, a local version of Kentucky Fried Chicken. It was a far cry from the leisurely, peaceful lunch stops we'd taken in the desert. After some good-natured jibes among ourselves about how low we had sunk, and the weighty decisions about dark meat or light, mashed potatoes or coleslaw, Coke or iced tea, we went inside and gave our order.

As we were waiting for our food, we glanced outside and noticed a crowd of people milling about in tattered clothes, some with a hungry look in their eyes, but we weren't paying a lot of attention. We were too focused on sorting out who got which box of chicken as our orders started rolling out. It was hot and stuffy inside the restaurant, and over the past week we'd got into the habit of eating out under the sky, so once everybody was satisfied that they had what they'd ordered, we went outside and sat at the picnic tables. That's when we began to notice that the eyes of many of those people were focused not on us, but on what we were eating.

There was a fence around the picnic tables, a bit like chest-high prison bars painted tan, but it was not much of a barrier. As we ate, the onlookers grew in number, and some called out to us in a language we didn't understand. There were kids Emma and Clara's age, some younger, some older, and there were also weatherbeaten adults, all of them in some version of faded T-shirts and raggedy shorts decorated by dust patches the colour of the barren ground around that place. Some of them stood on the bottom fence-rail and leaned over, others kneeled down and reached through the bars with their matchstick arms, beseeching us for … what? In their eyes was hope, and in their body language a mix of desperation and resignation.

In our naïveté, we offered them a few coins, but they weren't all that interested. What they really wanted became all too gut-wrenchingly apparent when they grabbed greedily at our cast-off chicken bones.

That is the world of hunger, and that world is already here for around 850 million people. The good news is that, by some accounting procedures, the proportion of hungry people on the planet has gone down over the past twenty-five years (other accounting procedures suggest that hunger is on the increase, but we'll stick with the most optimistic interpretation here). In large parts of Asia and many Pacific islands, for instance, the number of undernourished people is estimated to have fallen by about 30 per cent since 1990, and in Latin America and the Caribbean by about 25 per cent.

The bad news is, one out of every eight people in the world still can't count on their next meal, and hunger has markedly increased in one of the world's growing trouble spots, Africa. At last count 239 million Africans, or one out of every four, were as hungry as those who were begging for our chicken bones, a 25 per cent increase since 1990. Also troubling is that the number of hungry people in developed nations has recently been increasing: in 2013 the count was sixteen million, up three million since 2004. That's going in exactly the wrong direction.

Given such statistics, you can't help asking the question: if we can't even feed everybody now, how in the world are we going to be able to feed the two or three billion more people destined to be on the planet by 2050? Especially seeing it's in the poorest places on Earth that most of those two or three billion are going to be added, and it's exactly those places that are suffering most right now.

That question is not all that different, of course, from the ones that came up in the early 1960s, when the world began to worry about the looming hunger crisis in India and Asia. Back then, it was a virtual certainty that if food production didn't increase dramatically, and fast, billions were destined to starve to death within a couple of decades. The response to that crisis was the remarkably fast revamping of agricultural practices, spearheaded by Norman Borlaug and his associates, that became known as the Green Revolution. Indeed, it was the Green Revolution that averted the descent into the hellish world that Paul and Anne Ehrlich had forecast in *The Population Bomb*. Problem solved.

Not quite, if we are to believe the chief architect of the Green Revolution. And there is every reason that we should. Norman

Borlaug was clearly a sharp and caring man, with lots of foresight. His hard work and innovations, pioneering spirit and genuine concern for humanity are credited with saving literally billions of lives, and for that he was awarded the Nobel Peace Prize in 1970, as well as the United States Congressional Gold Medal in 2006. We tend to remember him as the person who saved more lives than anyone in history, and to regard the Green Revolution as an exemplar of the near-invincibility of our species. What we tend to forget, though, is something that Borlaug knew all too well, and that he told us over and over, even in his Nobel Prize acceptance speech:

> The green revolution has won a *temporary* success in man's war against hunger and deprivation; it has given man a breathing space. If fully implemented, the revolution can provide sufficient food for sustenance during the next three decades. But the frightening power of human reproduction must also be curbed; *otherwise the success of the green revolution will be ephemeral only* [emphasis added]. [Quote from http://www.nobelprize.org/nobel_prizes/peace/ laureates/1970/borlaug-lecture.html.]

Alan Weisman pointed out the same thing in his recent book *Countdown* (Little, Brown & Co., 2013), and really hammered home the point that here we stand a few decades down the road, and what we face is exactly what Borlaug predicted. We did curb the 'frightening power of human reproduction' a little, through lowering birth rates in China, India and many developed countries, just enough to buy us four and a half decades of breathing space, rather than Borlaug's worst-case scenario of three. But today we're pretty much right back where Borlaug started, with a couple of very important differences that make our task even harder than his was.

Borlaug's problem was how to ramp up food production from feeding three billion people to feeding six billion. The problem we face today is magnified, because we're starting at seven billion people and heading towards ten billion. Furthermore, Borlaug didn't have to second-guess what the weather was going to be thirty years down the road – that is, he didn't have to worry about growing crops under a whole new climate. While carbon dioxide was silently building up in the atmosphere during the Green Revolution, it was only after 1980 that it reached the threshold necessary to trigger the rapid ramp-up in temperature and extreme-weather catastrophes that we are currently experiencing, and that will continue into the foreseeable future.

This makes the juggling act of how to produce the food we're going to need even more complex than it was at the beginning of the Green Revolution. Yet there is no doubt that we need to accomplish something every bit as dramatic – by 2050, credible projections suggest we are going to have to be producing around 70 per cent more food than we are today. As a result, the food security wonks are now talking about the Green Revolution 2.0, which in the jargon typical of scientific papers is abbreviated as GR 2.0.

A chief challenge for GR 2.0 is going to be Africa, given that most countries on that continent are already hotspots of hunger and poverty, and that by 2050 there will be twice as many people there, as we saw in Chapter 2. Africa's food problems today partly stem from the fact that the first Green Revolution never really arrived there. If you look at how much agricultural productivity of cereal crops increased on a nation-by-nation basis, for instance, over the period 1960 to 2010, you see yields increasing nearly threefold in the United States, western Europe, Brazil and India, but hardly at all in Africa. In a twisted sort of way, you could view that as a bright spot for the future, because it means that there are still huge gains to be made in food production in the very place where the hunger and population-growth problems are most dire. Right now Africa's agricultural productivity is only about 25 per cent of what it could be.

Complicating things, though, Africa is still plagued by many of the same issues that prevented the Green Revolution from happening there in the first place: relatively little infrastructure for agricultural research and extension programmes, few roads, little storage capacity, poverty that prevents small-plot farmers from buying expensive new seed stocks, lack of seed-distribution outlets, and a multitude of nations and tribes that make it difficult to put appropriate subsidies and price structures in place. On top of that, the chief crops on which the Green Revolution focused – maize (corn), wheat and rice – were not those that Africans were used to eating. Instead, African farming produced, and still produces, a multitude of so-called 'orphan crops', like sweet potato, cassava and millet, which are highly nutritious, but have not attracted much research that would improve their yields, because they are not big on the world market. Nor were the crop strains originally developed in the Green Revolution particularly resistant to the droughts that have been a given in Africa's past climate, and which are likely to intensify in the future. Modifications to Africa's landscapes by humans, and limited irrigation supply, also mean that much of the country is already facing desertification, a difficult tipping point to reverse.

All of these problems are now widely recognised in the agricultural community, and there are some signs of hope, as Prabhu L. Pingali of the Bill and Melinda Gates Foundation reported in the *Proceedings of the United States National Academy of Sciences* in 2012. During the first Green Revolution, the demand for intensification of agriculture in Africa was low, because land was relatively abundant. That situation has changed now, with the ratio of arable land versus people becoming more similar to what it was in Asia during the 1960s. Rather than relying on strains of maize, wheat and rice developed for Asian climates, new strains developed specifically for the rigours of Africa began to emerge in the 1980s, were in the ground in Malawi and Zimbabwe by 2000, and are now being grown in thirteen African countries. Some attention to increasing productivity of the orphan crops also began in the 1980s, with improvements in varieties of sorghum, millet and cassava. Such programmes have increased Africa's food production over the past couple of decades, but the present pace of improvement is not nearly enough. Already falling far short of feeding its people, Africa's food production is growing only half as fast as its population.

And now, throw in climate change. Africa is already prone to drought, and because of that, farming in many areas there has always been a risky business. That is all too well illustrated by stories such as what happened in the Sahel, the area south of the Sahara Desert, where farming and cattle-grazing seemed to work OK until a series of drought years hit, beginning in the last part of the twentieth century, at which point tens of millions of people starved and the landscape changed, seemingly permanently, into a barren desert. The prediction of such august research bodies as the Intergovernmental Panel on Climate Change (IPCC) and the World Bank is basically that those sorts of situations are only going to increase in Africa. An IPCC report that came out in 2007 projected that reductions in yields in some African countries could be as much as 50 per cent by 2020. A 2013 World Bank study warned that by 2030, 'droughts and heat will leave 40 per cent of the land now growing maize unable to support that crop, while rising temperatures could cause major loss of savanna grasslands, threatening pastoral livelihoods. By the 2050s, depending on the sub-region, the proportion of the population undernourished is projected to increase by 25 to 90 per cent compared to the present (htttp://www.worldbank.org/en/news/press-release/2013/06/19/

warmer-world-will-keep-millions-of-people-trapped-in-poverty-says-news-report).'

You don't have to look too hard to see how population growth, marginal food supply and drought, multiplied together, have already made a mess in parts of Africa. One of the most lawless places on the planet today is Somalia, located right next to Ethiopia, on the eastern horn of the continent.

Somalia roughly doubled its population from the 1970s to the 1990s. At the same time, the political situation was growing more and more fragile. The assassination of the president in 1969 put Major General Mohamed Siad Barre in power. He promptly got rid of the national assembly and political parties, suspended the constitution and established a revolutionary council that could rule by decree – that is, do pretty much anything it wanted. Incursions into disputed lands in Ethiopia sparked tribal conflicts and fluctuating international allegiances, first with the Soviet Union and then, when the Soviets sided with Ethiopia, with the United States and Saudi Arabia. As the population continued to grow, warring factions within Somalia clashed more and more. In 1991 Barre was ousted, and with two rival factions each recognising different leaders for the country, the result was full-on civil war. One effect of the conflict was to reduce agricultural output in what were already marginal lands from a climatic perspective.

And then the drought years hit. In 1987 and 1989 the rains failed in more than 50 per cent of the country, and in 1992, 90 per cent of the country dried out. What had been a bad situation for the fragile government in terms of feeding its population became impossible. A million and a half people were faced with imminent starvation when what few crops were growing withered, and masses of people headed for refugee camps in Ethiopia and Kenya. The international community responded by sending in food, but much of it was grabbed by the warlords and never made it to those who needed it

Hunger

most. At that point the United States military was sent in to help keep peace and distribute food, but that ultimately ended up in the October 1993 Black Hawk Down incident, which cost the lives of eighteen American soldiers and more than five hundred Somalis. That was bad, but more than two hundred thousand Somalis also died from starvation.

Ten years later, not much had changed, except that an additional four million people swelled the population even more, and the al-Qaeda-aligned terrorist group al-Shabaab was now in charge of large territories. Another drought hit over the years 2010–2012; rival groups continued to fight for power; and nearly 260,000 people starved to death. There were outcries that the international community could have done more sooner, but al-Shabaab prevented Western aid agencies from operating in regions it controlled, denying that there was any famine there at all. And anyway, nobody wanted another Black Hawk Down.

Somalia is admittedly an extreme case, given that its government had been so unstable for so many years before the droughts began to hit. But it's easy to find other examples of how the nexus between population growth, food and climate results in social upheaval. In the words of climate scientists James W.C. White and Richard Alley, writing in 2014 in a blog about what kinds of abrupt changes climate change can trigger:

Consider also the Arab Spring, beginning in 2010, which toppled governments and sparked protests and rebellions across the Mideast and North Africa. Many social stresses contributed, but a spike in food prices was rather clearly involved in triggering unrest. This run-up in food prices in turn had many causes, but one contributor was the drought and heatwave of 2010 in the Russian wheat regions. And that in turn was made worse and/or more likely by human-caused

117

global warming. It is far, far too glib to draw a straight line from slowly rising CO_2 to rapidly crumbling governments, but slow changes including those in climate did push the region across a threshold that triggered rapid, uncertain, and potentially costly changes. [Quote from http://consensus-foraction.stanford.edu/blog/what-to-expect-when-youre.html.]

What White and Alley did not mention was that Egypt and other countries in the region had also seen their populations increase by around a third in the two decades leading up to the uprising.

While Africa presents one of the scariest hunger scenarios, it illustrates the general problem that the whole world is facing: how can we feed at least two billion, very likely closer to three billion, more people when we can't even seem to adequately feed everyone on Earth presently? There are some obvious brick walls we run up against if the idea is simply to keep on doing things as we have up to now. The first of those is that we're already using about 38 per cent of Earth's land to grow our food, not counting ice-covered Greenland and Antarctica; counting all of the land, ice-covered or not, it's 33 per cent. Doing a little simple division, acres of land devoted to farms and pasturelands, divided by the seven billion people (plus or minus) now on Earth, comes out to about 1.7 acres of agricultural land presently needed to support each person. If we can't do any better than that in the future, that means that, with the 9.5 billion people forecast for 2050, we'd need to grow food on 50 per cent of presently ice-free land. Clearly that's a non-starter, because not all land is created equal, and we're already using all the best agricultural land, except for the maybe 5 per cent of the planet that holds the last remaining rainforests – which we wouldn't want to cut down for a variety of reasons, not least because doing so would guarantee the extinction of many, many species, as well as making the climate-change problem considerably worse, since such forests capture a lot of the carbon dioxide we dump into the atmosphere. And converting all the world's remaining rainforests to agriculture would account for only 5 per cent of the additional 12 per cent we'd need anyway. The remaining land that's available to try to raise food is in places like deserts, steep mountains, tundra – you really can't get the level of productivity needed in such places to make the effort worthwhile.

Luckily, in theory anyway, it seems possible to squeeze much more food out of the land presently under production by being much more efficient in how we farm – that is, by closing the so-called 'yield gap', which is the difference between what a given acre of land under cultivation could produce, versus what it is actually producing today. Much of the land under cultivation today in Africa, for example, could probably produce up to 75 per cent more food if it was switched to higher-yield crops with modern methods of fertilisation and irrigation. Closing such yield gaps worldwide for the world's top sixteen crops, by some estimates, would increase food production by 50 to 60 per cent, without taking over any more land for agriculture.

Actually accomplishing that would require increasing the infra-structure for agriculture in many poor parts of the world, switching from traditional crops to high-yield ones, developing appropriate crop strains and providing seed, and in many cases consolidating small farms into large, mainly monoculture operations. Fertilisation and irrigation are important parts of closing the yield gap, and both can introduce problems themselves. Over-fertilisation, which is more the rule than the exception, produces excess nitrogen runoff and pollutes waterways, which can lead to huge dead zones in the oceans. Irrigation of course requires water, which is becoming in such short supply in many regions that it promises to be the source of yet another tipping point, as we'll cover in the next chapter. So the studies that highlight the gains to be made by closing the yield gap also emphasise that doing so without environmental damage will require more careful, technologically advanced methods of applying fertiliser and water, and probably governmental controls and monitoring to ensure compliance with environmental standards.

Transforming the agricultural system in such a major way within three decades, especially in poor countries without adequate existing infrastructure and strong governments, will be no small feat; yet the fact that it actually occurred during the first Green Revolution suggests it is not out of the question. So perhaps the more pertinent question is: how are we *actually* doing so far? To succeed in doubling crop production by 2050, which is roughly what we need to do, would require increasing production by about 2.4 per cent per year. But since 1989 we've only been increasing production of our four main crops – maize, rice, wheat and soybeans – by less than half that amount (1.6, 1.0, 0.9 and 1.3 per cent respectively).

A second way to help make the food equation balance in the near future would be to eat less meat. That solution, however, is also bucking the trend of what's actually happening. Instead of eating less meat, the world is eating more each year. Globally, meat production has increased sixfold since 1950, because on average, per capita meat consumption has been going up and up, driven largely by the changing tastes of people who become more affluent. It turns out that if people can afford it, they tend to want meat in their diet. In China alone, the rise of more and more people into the middle class has spurred a growth in meat consumption from 3.8 kg per person in 1961 to about 55 kg per person in 2013. Producing this much meat actually subtracts from the overall amount of food that could be available to feed people, because much of the grain that could go directly into people's mouths is diverted towards feeding livestock. From a food-production perspective, it's much more efficient to harvest calories directly from plants than it is to feed those calories to livestock, then eat the livestock. That, of course, is because the livestock use up a good portion of the calories that the grain originally produced, which means the calories we then get from eating the livestock are essentially the leftovers. The dramatic increase in meat consumption over the decades translates to devoting about a quarter of all croplands to feeding our livestock, rather than directly feeding ourselves. If you count pastureland plus cropland, the proportion of agricultural land we use to feed our livestock goes up to 75 per cent. It's for that reason that cutting back on meat consumption would be a tremendous help to solving the food problem: if everybody were suddenly to become vegetarian, the amount of calories we produced that went into people's stomachs would increase by 50 per cent. An added benefit, as far as feedbacks that lead to climate-change tipping points goes, is that there would be fewer cows, goats and sheep producing methane gas, by farting, as they digest their food. Livestock farts are in fact a potent source of greenhouse gases, because methane is considerably more effective at trapping heat than is CO_2. Approximately 34 per cent of methane emissions are from agricultural animals and their waste.

Also bucking the trend of what's needed to feed the world is the amount of food that is wasted. In developed countries, we throw away about 40 per cent of the food we buy. In developing countries, people tend to eat pretty much everything on their plates, but the waste comes in earlier in the production process. A third to a half of the food that is grown never makes it to consumers, because it spoils or is otherwise ruined in the journey from farm to processing to storage to delivery. Obviously, overcoming this distribution problem requires coming up with more efficient ways to move food from where it's grown to where people are hungry.

So, although in theory we could handle the looming food crisis by a combination of implementing a Green Revolution 2.0 in Africa and other places where production is still low, eating less meat and wasting less food, in practice, all those things would take changing some ingrained human behaviour in fairly radical ways. And so far, it just doesn't seem to be happening at the pace it needs to in order to solve the problem.

And that leaves out the whole question of what climate change will do to the world food supply. The crops we presently rely on to feed most of the world – maize, wheat and rice – all have their optimum growing conditions, and the current strains we use most have been bred to grow best in the climatic conditions that characterised the second half of the twentieth century. But, as we saw in the previous chapter, we are virtually certain to see a world that is 2°C warmer in the next few decades, and we could see heating-up of 5°C or more within the century. That means there will be more summer days that are hot and effectively dry in our crop-growing regions. How would our current crop strains fare under such conditions?

Not very well, it turns out, according to an international group of researchers headed by A.J. Challinor from the University of Leeds. They analysed data from 1,700 published simulations that look at expected production of maize, wheat and rice in a warming world. Their results were published in the journal *Nature Climate Change* in 2014, and received quite a bit of press, for good reason. As you might expect, some regions look as if they will be winners, and some will be losers, but overall, without significant efforts to adapt farming to the changing climate, productivity falls in both tropical and temperate regions for all three crops. At 2°C (3.6°F) of warming, maize production in temperate regions decreases by about 2 per cent, and in tropical regions by about 7 per cent; at 5°C, the losses are close to 10 per cent in both regions. Wheat has even

122

greater problems: at 2°C, a 5 per cent reduction in both temperate and tropical places; at 5°C, the losses are 10 per cent and 40 per cent respectively. Rice seems to hold pretty steady up to 2°C warming, but any higher than that and yields reduce, dropping in both temperate (10 per cent) and tropical (5 per cent) regions by the time we hit 5°C of warming.

The same researchers also estimated the likely best we could hope for in the event that farmers adapted as fast as they could to the new climatic conditions. Under that scenario, and taking all crops into account, using adaptation strategies like adjusting the planting date, the amount and kind of fertiliser, irrigation, and using the optimum cultivar or crop strain, we may be lucky and see a slight increase in overall yield, somewhere between 7 and 15 per cent above the yields that would probably result from sticking with the way we're doing things now. Even so, with respect to yields we're presently getting, that would only gain us at most 5 per cent more maize and 10 per cent more wheat in temperate regions. That would be offset by up to 20 per cent losses in maize and wheat in tropical regions. So that's not even close to the 70 to 100 per cent increase overall that we would need to feed the world.

Another study, published in the same journal a month later by two Stanford University researchers, Frances Moore and David Lobell, zeroed in on Europe to anticipate what crop productivity might look like there in 2040 given 2°C of warming, a temperature rise to which our present trajectory is destined to take us by then. The news is not good. Yields of wheat are likely to drop more than 30 per cent, barley more than 20 per cent, and maize 10 per cent, without rapid adaptation of farming techniques and cultivars to climate change. With appropriate adaptation, the yield-loss would not be quite as much, but still close to 30 per cent for wheat, 15 per cent for barley, and just over 1 per cent for maize. Even those best-case adaptation scenarios are troubling when what really has to happen by 2040 to keep up with rising world population is a marked increase in food production, rather than a slight decrease.

The same general story holds for our major crops worldwide, which just don't seem to perform as well when the days get hot. Once temperatures exceed 30°C (86°F), for example, yields of both maize and wheat begin to decrease noticeably. For each day above 30°C, the final yield of maize falls by 1 per cent if the rains are optimal, and by 1.7 per cent if the heat is accompanied by drought. The worries here aren't far off in the future, as a recent study with the provocative title of 'Getting Caught with Our Plants Down: The Risks of Global Crop Yield Slowdown from Climate Trends in the Next Two Decades' highlighted (published in *Environmental Research Letters* 9, 2014). That work, by Lobell and his colleague Claudia Tebaldi from the US National Center for Atmospheric Research, pointed out that because of global warming, our chances of seeing a 10 per cent loss in yields of maize within the next twenty years have increased from one in two hundred to one in ten, and for a similar loss in wheat yield the chances are one in twenty. The chances of climate trends actually being large enough to *halve* yield trends over just a ten-year period are one in four for maize, and one in six for wheat. Lobell and Tebaldi point out that while a one in ten or one in twenty chance still sounds low, it is a real concern that the likelihood of these events coming to pass is now twenty times higher than it was before human-caused climate change kicked in. Given that millions of lives would be at stake, here's a good way to evaluate those odds: if the plane you were about to get on had a one in ten or one in twenty chance of crashing, would you still take the trip?

Most of the studies mentioned above deal primarily with increases in average temperature or precipitation, which affects crops of course, but which are not the only controls on how well they do. As any farmer knows, even more devastating can be unusual spells of heat or drought. As we saw in the previous chapter, it is exactly those sorts of events that global warming is likely to make more common, with potentially devastating effects. Imagine if the 2003 heatwave in Europe, which reduced wheat production up to 36 per cent in some countries, and resulted in agricultural losses to the tune of €13 billion, happened two or three years out of ten, instead of one. Or if the 2010 heatwave that crippled Russian wheat production and helped set off the Arab Spring uprising usually happened a few times per decade.

In that context it is worrying indeed that more and more studies are indicating that shocks to European wheat yields are going to become more normal within thirty years. One such study, published in *Nature Climate Change* in 2014, was by a group of researchers headed by Miroslav Trnka of the Czech Academy of Sciences. They were curious to see whether wheat-damaging weather was going to reduce yields more often if we keep on with business as usual for greenhouse-gas emissions. They looked at eleven weather conditions that affect wheat production adversely, and used climate models to estimate the probable increase in how often such conditions would occur in fourteen representative wheat-growing regions of Europe, ranging from Finland in the north, to Hungary in the east, to the United Kingdom in the west, to southern Spain and Italy in the south. The models showed that by the decades 2050–2070, the risk of the wheat crop in all areas getting hammered in any given year by at least one adverse weather event was likely to increase 30 per cent. In five of the regions (Sweden, Britain, Germany, Austria and Spain), the risk was likely to double. Adding to this alarm is that the nutritive quality of most of the crops that feed the world will decrease significantly under warmer conditions, adding even more burden to our food-production needs.

Put all this together, as the international relief group Oxfam has, and the world food crisis begins to look not only like a hunger problem, but also like a huge economic problem and a social uprising problem: 'New research commissioned for this [2011] report paints a grim picture of what a future of worsening climate change and increasing resource scarcity holds for hunger. It predicts international price rises of key staples in the region of 120 to 180 per cent by 2030. This will prove disastrous for food importing poor countries, and raises the prospect of a wholesale reversal in human development.' (Quote from *Growing a Better Future, Food Justice in a Resource-Constrained World*, Oxfam, 2011, http://www.oxfamamerica.org/static/media/files/Growing-a-better-future.pdf.)

All of this drives home the challenges we face with actually implementing a Green Revolution 2.0 that is, relatively speaking, as successful as the Green Revolution that Norman Borlaug spearheaded. We do have one potential arrow in our quiver that Borlaug did not, and that is the ability to genetically modify organisms, including crops. How genetically modified organisms (GMOs) will play into future food production is still a big unknown, but so far it does not look as if they will save us in time, if indeed they could save us at all. Some of the most reasoned discussions of this highly controversial topic come from noted food security researcher Jonathan Foley, who after a long stint as Director of the University of Minnesota's Institute of the Environment now heads the California Academy of Sciences in San Francisco. The upshot of his research is that while GMOs may indeed hold some potential for increasing food production, so far they have not. The reason is that 'GMO crops primarily in use today are feed corn (mostly for animal feed and ethanol), soybeans (mostly for animal feed), cotton and canola. But these aren't crops that feed the world's poor, or provide better nutrition to all. GMO efforts may have started off with good intentions to improve food security, but they ended up in crops that were better at improving profits ... the technology ... has so far been applied to the wrong parts of the food system to truly make a dent in global food security.' (Quote from 'GMOs, Silver Bullets and the Trap of Reductionist Thinking', *Ensia*, 25 February 2014, http://ensia.com/voices/gmos-silver-bullets-and-the-trap-of-reductionist-thinking/.)

Foley goes on to point out that in the United States, a hotspot of their use, GMOs have not markedly increased yields of maize or soybeans, primarily because of the way the crops have been modified: not for higher yield, but for pest resistance. The downside of this is that more and more pesticides are dumped on the crops, which works in the short run, but then the pests evolve to withstand the higher concentrations, which means more pesticides are applied, which becomes a losing battle – a never-ending race between genetic modification of the crops and evolution of the pests, with the net result that not much changes over the long run. On the other hand, GMOs have helped boost yields of canola in Canada, cotton in India, papayas in Hawaii, and show promise for combating adverse effects of citrus greening disease in United States orange orchards. But what still isn't happening with GMOs on a large scale is modifications that actually improve the basics of plant growth, like photosynthesis, or that help maintain yields in the face of the stresses that will be imposed by climate change.

Even if such modifications became the focus of stepped-up research, it's still not an overnight process to bring a GMO from the laboratory to your table. Just like the timetable for producing a new crop strain from traditional cross-breeding techniques, it takes at least a decade to go from that initial successful hybrid, through the several generations of plants needed to refine and build the seed stock, to marketing and distribution, and in the case of GMOs, through the enormous regulatory hurdles that still exist and that are not likely to go away any time soon. In fact, the tried and true methods of producing new crop strains that Borlaug used still seem to be as fast as, or faster than, developing a new GMO and bringing it on line. Which is worrying, given the decade or so turnaround time that is required, and the fact that we will need to have those new, higher-yielding crops growing in efficient, high-yield fields throughout the world in less than thirty years. And in the meantime, the wild relatives of crops still living in their native ecosystems are being eradicated, forever erasing the evolutionary advantages they might have had for more variable and harsher environmental conditions.

Perhaps by this time the basic message you are getting about the looming food crisis is pretty much the same one you got in previous chapters about population growth, overconsumption and climate change: that is, that there is a very real problem here. Another insight that should be emerging is that these are not problems that arise independently of each other; rather, each one multiplies the next. The third common thread running through this and the previous two chapters is that the problems are – in theory anyway – fixable, if we got busy today and started doing things in a different way. In the case of food, the clear, most efficient ways out are to minimise population growth; put the brakes on climate change; ramp up Green Revolution 2.0 through a focused scientific effort and international cooperation that includes governments, industry and philanthropic organisations; consume less meat; and waste less of the food we produce. If we did all those things, we'd probably come out OK. But we're not doing any of them to the full extent we need to.

And even if we do, there is another huge, related problem that we haven't yet mentioned, and that we're going to have to tackle. Water. After siphoning off all the water we need to produce our food and energy, there's going to be less and less to drink. In fact, our wells and rivers are already beginning to run dry.

6

THIRST

Liz, Tony, Emma and Clara, Escalante region, Utah, July 2008

Sitting around the campfire, life was good. We'd just watched the kind of nightfall you can only experience in the desert. The heat-shimmering sky had faded from blazing blue to cool violet; at the same time, the full moon began to peek above the red sandstone wall of the canyon. Gently, slowly, it rose higher, glowing silver and shining brighter as the sky continued to fade and a billion stars blinked on.

We were on our almost-annual pilgrimage to the desert canyon country. That's where we like to take a break, to regroup after spending too much time doing those everyday things that seem never to get done and to escape the worries of the world for a little while. Early that morning we'd filled a couple of water bottles each and set off to do one of our favourite things, exploring little-known side canyons just to see what we would see. We'd learned early on that taking enough water with us is paramount in that country – the gulches are dry, and the heat can be intense, parching you before you know it. Our border collie, smiling and panting, sniffed from shady spot to shady spot as we all walked up the dry riverbed, enjoying the silence, the absence of humanity, the smell of sage-brush and the occasional glimpse of a lizard skittering across a hot rock.

By late morning we spotted a good place for lunch – a rock shelter a little way up the canyon wall, with a flat floor and a big over-hang that kept the sun out most of the day. We knew it would be nice and cool in there, and we also knew, from past experience, that it was just the kind of place where Native Americans might have hung out a thousand years ago. Emma and Clara had heard often enough how, before they were born, we'd spent years exploring such places, sometimes in our past jobs as archaeologists or palae-ontologists, sometimes guiding students on back-country trips, and sometimes, as we were doing that day, for the pure fun of it. They also knew, from their own previous trips into the canyon country, that the cliffs below some of those promising rock shelters had shallow handholds and footholds notched into the rocks, carved by ancient cliff-dwellers who probably climbed up and down those steep slopes a lot easier than we did. And on past trips we'd all seen mud-mortared native flagstone walls well camouflaged in rock shelters that were so precariously nestled in cliff faces that the only way to get to them seemed to be with ropes and climbing gear.

We didn't need ropes and climbing gear that day, but when we scrambled up to our lunch spot we saw a familiar sight: the holes and piles of dirt that signalled that looters had already been there, as is the case for so many archaeological sites in the American West. As such archaeological vandals are wont to do, they had ille-gally dug up the sandy floor of the shallow cave, presumably in the hope of finding ancient baskets, arrowheads or other artefacts, but destroying the information that would have revealed important details of how the ancient inhabitants had lived and died. What the vandals left behind, though, was something they thought was just too common in those kinds of sites to be of any value: little corn-cobs, ancient maize, about the size of your finger.

It's amazing how common those corncobs are, not only where we were in Utah, but in many places throughout the so-called Four Corners region where Utah, Colorado, New Mexico and Arizona come together. These are deserts today, where you would no more think of putting in a cornfield than you would think of growing bananas; yet there are the corncobs, sure evidence that the corn-fields used to be there. On other sojourns into the canyon country we've found corn storage bins, with the cobs still in them, usually hidden high up on the canyon walls, built from the same rocks that form the cliffs, and chinked with mud that still has the handprints of the ancient builders. At many of those sites, as at that rock shel-ter where we were eating our lunch, there are *matates*, bowl-sized depressions in the bedrock where the corn was ground into flour by hand-held *manos*, oval-shaped rocks curved on one side to comfortably fit your two hands side by side, with the other side worn smooth and flattened by being rubbed across the rough sand-stone grinding surface of the *matates*.

There are also entire cities constructed in the cliffs, places like Mesa Verde in Colorado, with elaborate dwellings built into the canyon walls and large numbers of contemporary archaeological sites on the surrounding mesa tops, including large villages that must have been home to thousands of people. Delicate designs inscribed in the mud-plastered walls show that these people had time to pursue leisure and art. Elsewhere in the Four Corners region are contemporaneous roads that traverse hundreds of miles of deserts and canyons, further testament to the engineering and societal sophistication of those long-gone people.

These were the Ancestral Puebloans (or as they are sometimes known, the Anasazi), precursors of the Pueblo Native Americans who still live in the Four Corners area. From what they left behind, it is clear that the Ancestral Puebloans were farmers, their culture and survival depending on the corn they grew to support the tens of thousands of people who lived in what is now mostly a barren, though beautiful, landscape. Over the years, from the kinds of remains that we often run across on our desert back-country hikes, archaeologists have put together a fairly detailed picture of the Ancestral Puebloans' ancient culture. Their society flourished in the Four Corners for more than two thousand years. They first seem to show up around 1500 BC, and by AD 1200 their cornfields and homes dotted many mesas. But around that time they began building and moving into cliff dwellings – which are much more easily defended than mesa-top villages, and offer much more protection from the weather. And then, by AD 1300, they were gone, abandoning their castle-like cliff dwellings, baskets, stone tools, *manos*, *matates*, corn cribs and corncobs, which were subsequently mummified and preserved for the ages by the dry desert air. The entire sophisticated society essentially vanished from the Four Corners within the space of fifty years, maybe less.

Around the campfire that night, we speculated on what that exodus must have been like. It was quick, that's for sure, and they travelled light. When places like Mesa Verde were first discovered, there were baskets and other household goods just sitting there, as if the families had simply walked away one day, leaving everything they couldn't carry where it lay. We knew from human remains we'd seen in museums that things got tough for those people over just a few decades in the mid-1200s: skulls broken by stone axes, signs of cannibalism, broken limb bones. And that fitted with a move from the mesas into the cliffs – once you begin climbing up to those ancient cliff houses and food caches, as we'd done, you realise that you'd be an easy target for anybody who was sitting up above you with defence on their mind. We were trying to wrap our heads around why a farming society that had thrived for over a millennium would, in the space of just a single human lifetime, move down off the mesas into cliff-perched garrisons, attack each other, and finally, poof, everybody just up and leaves. What in the world could account for that?

Actually, we'd seen exactly what could account for it on our hike that day. Those tiny corncobs we'd found meant that cornfields were nearby when the Ancestral Puebloans lived in the shelter where we avoided the burning midday sun. Corn takes water to grow, lots of it. And all that slick-rock country is now bone dry. These people had run out of water.

Just as is happening around the world today.

That water shortage probably played a key role in the collapse of the Ancestral Puebloans' civilisation is based on a lot more evidence than our idle speculations around the campfire. The trees they used as crossbeams in their dwellings, as well as ancient wood from the broader region, tell a very detailed story about how water waxed and waned as their society fell apart. A tree chronicles its growth year-by-year by depositing annual, concentric rings around its trunk. In general, thicker rings indicate a good year for tree growth, which in the Four Corners region means more moisture; thinner rings indicate the bad, dry years. Dendrochronologists – scientists whose speciality is applying sophisticated statistical techniques to tease out the details of those tree-ring tales – have put together hundreds of tree-ring records that together tell the story of a twenty-one-year-long mega-drought that hit the region from AD 1276 to 1297.

The country the Ancestral Puebloans occupied, arid even in the best of times, has always been marginal for dryland farming, so the prolonged mega-drought was apparently enough to tip the corn-dependent society over the edge. Rivers, streams and springs began to dry up. Farms became smaller and moved to the ever-

shrinking pockets where water was still available, and the characteristic features of villages changed in ways that made it easier to
keep outsiders out. The environmental stress corresponded with
upheavals in religious and cultural traditions as well, as indicated
by the abandonment of architectural designs and artefacts inter-
preted by archaeologists as having religious underpinnings.
Modelling studies of potential corn growth under the drier conditions suggest that the Four Corners still could have grown enough
to maintain a much-reduced Ancestral Puebloan population, so
perhaps the drought could have been weathered had not societal
conflict also kicked in. It's not hard to imagine what caused the
societal conflict: the lack of water and consequent lack of food
meant everybody was fighting over ever-shrinking but essential
necessities for life.

After all, we're seeing the same thing now, like the drought-
induced food shortages that are causing problems in the Sudan
region and Somalia, as we mentioned in earlier chapters. And as we
are writing today, the tensions in the Gaza Strip, sieges in Iraq, and
even Ebola quarantines in Africa are all tipped in favour of those
who have access to food and water, and against those who don't.
You don't have to travel to those kinds of places to get uneasy about
today's situation. In the south-western United States, for example,
we've set up pretty much the same perfect storm for water problems that the Ancestral Puebloans experienced. People in places
like Los Angeles (California), Phoenix and Tucson (Arizona) and
Las Vegas (Nevada) live in the middle of deserts, so, just like the
Ancestral Puebloans, they've always been on the edge in terms of
having enough water to drink and grow crops. Also just like the
Ancestral Puebloans, they're beginning to see that the marginal
water supply they always considered normal is drying up, as what
may turn into a new, and very prolonged, mega-drought seems to
be settling in.

The problems these cities face are much, much bigger than what the Ancestral Puebloans faced. First off, there are many more lives at stake – tens of millions rather than tens of thousands. An arguably even more critical difference in terms of sparking water crises is that the Ancestral Puebloans, unlike big desert cities today, were only counting on the water that fell from the sky locally. Our current big desert cities have *never* seen enough local precipitation to water their huge populations. Instead, the water they depend upon originates hundreds or even thousands of miles away, and is routed to them via dams and pipelines. Even that is not always enough, so some cities augment the piped-in water by pumping from underground aquifers that can take hundreds or thousands of years to refill once they're drained. And draining they are.

Urban-dwellers aren't the only ones who depend on that water. The same sources are supplying the farmers and ranchers who are growing all the food those city folk need. And of course, farmers and municipalities in different states and even different countries claim shares of the same rivers and watersheds. In California, more than half the rivers are over-allocated for agricultural demand, and some drainages have been assigned between two and eight times the available water. This means that California, with all the agriculture that it produces, is operating at a severe water deficit. Somehow this has all seemed to work through the years, but mostly because additional water has come from elsewhere, like above-ground reservoirs or lakes, which are now almost empty.

Now what's catching up to people in the south-west country and beyond is rampant population growth combined with a critical accounting error that was locked in almost a century ago. The result of that error is that water allocations and urban development projections have always been based on what turns out to be an abnormally wet few years in the western United States. Here's what happened. The water on which cities through much of the desert south-west depend comes from the Colorado River drainage, and much of that from the Colorado River itself. The Colorado takes its name from the state in which it originates, but it actually receives its water from or flows through seven different states before crossing the border into Mexico, where it finally dumps into the Gulf of California. In the years leading up to 1922, states were fighting over who got what portion of the water, and to make a very long story short, in order to avoid future disagreements the Colorado River Compact was drawn up. The compact divided the Colorado River drainage into two more or less equal halves, and assigned a specified amount of water to each, thus simplifying some of the water-rights issues of the time.

But nothing is ever as simple as it seems. The people drawing up the compact had to specify the overall amount of water that normally flowed through the entire drainage in order to decide how much water each district was entitled to. They made their estimates based on the best data of the time, which wasn't much – but unbeknownst to them, the years leading up to 1922, over which they calculated the average yearly flow, were unusually wet. Therefore they promised each district about 10 per cent more water than was actually going to be available over the coming century, or than had probably been available on average prior to the wet years they happened to use as their standard. The outcome: urban planners thought they knew how much water they could count on in perpetuity, and they began to build their dams and cities accordingly.

A 10 per cent overestimate when it comes to water is quite a lot. As a result, after steady growth in the number of people drinking, washing, irrigating and flushing toilets, so much water was routinely taken from the Colorado drainage that the river was pretty much dried up by the time it hit the Mexican border. And then, in 1993, for the first time the amount of water that replenished the river from rain and snow was less than what was actually used. Reservoirs fell, then they rose a little from a few good years of increased moisture. Since 2003, however, use has consistently exceeded flow, and now giant bathtub rings that mark falling water levels in Lake Powell, Lake Mead and many other reservoirs seem more and more normal. Year by year the bathtub rings expand as the reservoirs drain. Now water levels are down to around half – even below half in some cases – of their normal levels, and are still falling. If those trends continue, Las Vegas will be out of water as early as 2020. In fact, by 2016 it will be crunch time, because that's when the waterline of Lake Mead will be just fourteen feet from falling below the intake pipe for 90 per cent of Las Vegas's water. It's for that reason that an $817 million project is under way to construct a new, lower elevation outlet from Lake Mead, so that even with the all-but-inevitable fall in lake level, water will continue to flow to the casinos; for a while, anyway.

Opening those new outlets is not likely to help much in the longer run. Water demand in the Colorado drainage is projected to exceed supply from now until the year 2060, which is as far ahead as the models look. Part of that projection comes from expectations of even less precipitation due to climate change, but much of it is because there are now simply too many people living in the Colorado River drainage for the water resources to support – even if those resources were typical of a pre-global-warming world.

Now, throw a mega-drought on top of that. Mega-droughts are unusually long stretches of unusually hot, dry years. As we write this, California is experiencing its worst drought in the history of weather records – it's been drying out for most of the twenty-first century – and most of the other western states have also been suffering abnormally dry conditions over the past thirteen years. Edward Cook, director of Columbia University's Tree Ring Laboratory, told a packed audience of scientists at the 2013

American Geophysical Union Meeting in San Francisco, 'There's no indication it'll be getting any better in the near term.' Mega-droughts are, incidentally, natural phenomena; you don't need human-triggered global warming to cause them, as the Ancestral Puebloans found out. But add in the impacts of today's human-caused climate change, and you almost certainly increase the odds of a mega-drought occurring.

In times of drought, humanity relies more heavily on sources of water other than what flows down rivers and accumulates in reservoirs – the underground water stored in aquifers, commonly known as well water or groundwater. The wells we dig and drill yield water because certain kinds of rock formations act as giant sponges. A large portion of the water that falls from the sky, either as rain or snow, ends up percolating down through the soil and flowing underground through porous and fractured rocks, until it hits an impermeable layer and pools up. Luckily for us, those underground storage reservoirs are vast, and within drillable distance of the surface. Actually, we rely on underground water even when there is no drought. Among the many river-poor cities that depend on aquifers to supply a major part of their water are Orlando, home of Disney World in Florida; and San Antonio and Houston in Texas. All three of those make the top-ten list for United States cities most likely to suffer water shortages in the next few years, according to a report issued in 2010 by the non-profit investment group Ceres. Incidentally, the other four cities we mentioned above – Los Angeles, Tucson, Phoenix and Las Vegas – also make the top ten, as do Atlanta, Georgia; Fort Worth, Texas; and the San Francisco Bay area, California.

The feedbacks between surface-water shortages and using up aquifers too fast are pretty obvious – if there isn't enough surface water, drill, baby, drill, and pump, baby, pump. But the problem is, aquifers take hundreds to thousands of years to fill up, and only tens of years to deplete. In 2014, the California aquifers began to be utilised even more intensively than usual, during a year when rain and snow were sparse and that turned out to be the hottest on record. By then, 60 per cent of the state's needs were being met by groundwater, which meant that the aquifers were (and are) being sucked down like draining a water glass through a straw. So much water is being pumped out that the Central Valley is actually sinking – decreasing in elevation at the rate of one foot per year, as farmers rely more on underground water in a desperate attempt to save their crops when their surface irrigation runs dry. Wells that used to be drilled to a depth of five hundred feet are now not hitting water until a thousand feet down, and drilling companies are so backed up with farmers clamouring for their services, at a price of $50,000 to $500,000 per well, that the wait is a year or more.

The aquifer-depletion problem is by no means confined to California. In many parts of the world, wells are basically drying up, or already have. Pleasant as a vacation on a Greek island can be, once you get to it, the only drinking water available is often from bottles that arrive the same way you did: by boat or plane. The fresh-water aquifers have been virtually exhausted. In many parts of Spain, groundwater levels are now falling fast as irrigation increases, leading to situations such as are now well documented in the Campo de Dalías region in the south. Intensive pumping of groundwater for irrigating crops – otherwise unable to grow in this arid region – has lowered the water table to the extent that saline water from the adjoining sea is now seeping into the aquifer, rendering the groundwater unusable for drinking or growing crops. Israel is struggling to provide drinking and irrigation water, as both of its aquifers – shared with Palestine – are going dry. China is over-pumping the aquifers of three of its key agricultural basins at a rate that, if it continues, would reduce grain yields so much that 120 million fewer Chinese people could be fed. In the state of Tamil

Nadu, southern India, with more than sixty-two million people, more than 95 per cent of small farmers' wells have already dried up. The list goes on and on: places like Saudi Arabia, Iran, Yemen, Syria, Egypt, Jordan, Pakistan, Baluchistan, Morocco and Mexico are also seeing the impacts of depleted groundwater.

Simple monitoring of well-water levels, by measuring how much deeper you have to dip or drill year-by-year to get to the water, makes it all too clear that aquifers are drying up worldwide. The other way to gauge what's going on underground, ironically, is by looking down from the sky, using information gathered by a satellite. The satellites that are used for this purpose are part of a NASA mission called GRACE, the acronym for Gravity Recovery and Climate Experiment. Basically, GRACE provides detailed measures of Earth's gravitational field, pretty much everywhere. The density of materials that make up Earth's crust exerts a large influence on the gravitational field, and water has a very different density from rock. By using that information, it becomes possible to watch underground aquifers ebb, flow and drain.

Which is what scientists who have been monitoring and analysing the GRACE data have been doing. What they have found is a bit startling, even to them. The overview is that groundwater aquifers have been depleted all over the world over the last decade, but we'll stick with the Colorado River Basin to give you a sense of the magnitude of the problem. From 2004 to 2013, the surface-water depletion – evidenced by those drying-up reservoirs we mentioned above – was paltry by comparison to what was depleted underground. Overall (surface plus aquifer), the water depletion over that time period was fifty-three million acre-feet, which is a tremendous amount: an acre-foot is the volume of water that would cover an acre of land one foot deep, or about what eight people in the US would use in a year. In all, the lost water amounted to about two Lake Meads (at twenty-eight million acre-feet, the largest surface-water reservoir in the United States) – about equal to submerging the entire United Kingdom under a foot of water. But here is what most startled the scientists: 77 per cent of the loss was from the aquifer, not from the reservoirs.

The Colorado River Basin is not an anomaly. For example, in seven years beginning with 2003, Turkey, Syria, Iraq and Iran, in the Tigris and Euphrates River drainage, saw their water reserves decline by a volume equivalent to the entire Dead Sea. Other major aquifers that are draining fast include those under the North China Plain, Australia's Canning Basin, north-western India, the Great Plains of the US, and parts of Brazil and Argentina, to name just a few. Similarly to our drilling into the fossil storage for oil, we are draining our fossil reserves of water. Many of these aquifers are filled with palaeowater that was initially charged during the last glacial period thousands of years ago.

Globally, aquifers are being drawn down so fast because, with so many of us in the world, we just need an awful lot of water. While people in some places may feel they have more water than they want, because of rainy days, floods or hurricanes, people elsewhere are continually parched. So, viewed worldwide, there is simply not enough fresh water falling out of the sky any more to slake the global thirst. It would be OK if it were only drinking water we needed, but what we need for drinking and other personal use is just a metaphorical drop in the bucket in the grander scheme – less than 10 per cent of all the water used. It's the other things we need water for that create the big problem. Here is where population growth, food, energy, climate change and demand for consumer goods intersect to drive the water crisis. The way these issues interact makes the point all too clearly that what accelerates our journey towards a global tipping point is not any single issue, but how they feed on one another to multiply the likelihood and magnitude of global crises.

For instance, we saw in the previous chapter that growing enough food using the methods that have prevailed for the past three decades is looking problematic. And that's without even considering the food–water nexus, which is important because agriculture is the thirstiest beast on the planet: globally it consumes a whopping 70 per cent of the fresh water we use. No wonder the ground is sinking beneath our feet as we pump all that water out of aquifers to make up for what's not falling from the sky. The problem here is not subtle: at some point, once those aquifers run dry, or get so depleted that it's too expensive to drill deep enough to tap them, the amount of food we can grow globally is going to cap out. And we will face shortages.

Exactly when that will happen is not yet possible to predict, because scientists don't have a decent handle on exactly how much water is held in all the world's major aquifers. But the kind of losses we've seen in just the past decade are troubling – the draw-downs observed in the Colorado River Basin, the Tigris-Euphrates drainage and others we mentioned earlier are clearly not sustainable for many decades. Some indication of when problems are likely to hit in major food-growing regions comes from a study of the High Plains Aquifer, which irrigates the prodigious agricultural output of the midwestern United States. Its conclusion: if no changes occur in the pumping rates, agricultural productivity in the region will peak in the 2020s, then rapidly decline, simply because the aquifer is running dry. The study, titled 'Tapping Unsustainable Groundwater Stores for Agricultural Production in the High Plains Aquifer of Kansas', was by a group of researchers led by David R. Steward at Kansas State University and published in the *Proceedings of the National Academy of Sciences* in 2013. It looked at a number of different scenarios for groundwater use in Kansas. Perhaps the most realistic scenario assumes that pumping rates, which are already decreasing as the water table falls lower and lower each year, will decrease by about 20 per cent over the next few decades. In that case, agricultural productivity peaks in 2040. Decreasing pumping by 40 per cent would buy a little more time, with productivity peaking in the 2070s. The bottom line here is that there is a hard limit to agricultural productivity, dictated by the amount of water presently stored in our aquifer water banks, that we will probably run up against by mid-century. That is bad news indeed for a world in which agricultural productivity has to continually increase over the next three decades to feed the additional billions of people that will inevitably occupy the planet by mid-century. Steward and his colleagues go on to point out that refilling those aquifers is not something that happens overnight: in the case of the High Plains Aquifer, replenishment would take in the order of five hundred to 1,300 years, and even then only if there is enough water coming down from the skies.

As water becomes scarcer in agricultural regions because of drought, drawing down of aquifers, or both, it sets up a conflict most of us don't think about too much – with the energy sector. Energy production too is a vast user of water, second only to agriculture in its needs. And the scarcer water gets for agriculture, the more energy is needed to move that water from one place to another. For example, 90 per cent of the electricity used on farms is to pump water for irrigation, and on a larger scale, pumping water from northern California to the crop-growing Central Valley in southern California is the state's single largest energy consumer.

Producing all that energy takes enormous quantities of water, most of it for cooling the power-plant machinery that generates the electricity that runs the pumps. In regions where hydro-electric power is important, it's also essential that reservoirs stay full enough to maintain adequate flows through the electricity-generating turbines. In fact, in terms of water withdrawn from the surface or aquifers, energy is even a little thirstier than agriculture: in the United States, 41 per cent of withdrawn water goes to energy production, and 39 per cent goes to agriculture (as of 2005).

To understand the problem here, it's necessary to digress just a little and talk about the difference between water *withdrawal* and water *consumption*. Water withdrawal is what we take out of rivers and aquifers, use for some purpose (like cooling a power plant), and can then, in theory at least, send down the line for some other use (like putting it back into a river for somebody to drink downstream). Water consumption, on the other hand, is what gets used and not returned – for example, when you drink a big glassful, that water is pretty much gone as far as using it for anything else goes.

Recall that agriculture *consumes* about 70 per cent of all the water we use on the planet; in the United States, agricultural consumption is even higher, about 85 per cent of consumed water. That's water that's taken away from any other use, which means that to satisfy society's demands in any given region – for both food and energy – there has to be enough water for agriculture to remove its huge share, while still leaving enough for the energy sector to generate the electricity that agriculture relies upon, not to mention keeping the lights on for the rest of us. In times of plenty, there is no problem. But when water starts to get scarce, as is presently the case in many arid yet populous parts of the world, an irresolvable conflict between growing food and generating adequate electricity can arise. That is exactly the problem that led to riots, burned trains and attacks on government officials in Pakistan in 2012, as we described in Chapter 1.

Now, throw climate change into the mix – generally hotter summers on the farm, as well as in the populous cities that pepper food-growing regions (see Chapter 5). Under such conditions, more electricity is required for irrigation (assuming the water is even available) and for keeping the air conditioners on. The vicious circle completes itself with the need for even more water – and more electricity – that is then needed to cool down the power-plant machinery.

And as population grows and more people move into higher economic classes, more electricity will be demanded as well as more food needed. It is these sorts of considerations that led the CNA, the think-tank that advises on national security concerns, and collaborating academic analysts to conclude: 'As demand increases, competition for limited water resources among the agricultural, industrial, municipal, and electric power sectors threatens to become acute in several global regions' (see Paul Faeth, CNA, and Benjamin K. Sovacool, 2014, Capturing Synergies Between Water Conservation and Carbon Dioxide Emissions in the Power Sector. CNA Corporation, p. 27. https://www.cna.org/sites/default/files/research/EWCEWNRecommendationsReportJuly2014FINAL.pdf). The bottom line is that by 2040 the world will face insurmountable water shortages, if things keep going as they have been.

Which means, just as was apparently the case with the Ancestral Puebloans, increased warfare will follow. You actually don't have to look into the future to see that happening. As we write this, the United States just bombed Iraq again. The tipping point for that decision was the takeover of the Mosul Dam – the main source of water and electricity generation for communities downstream – by the rebel Islamic State of Iraq and Syria. That put Islamic State in control of the water and electricity that the Kurds in Mosul and downstream need for survival, and sent tens of thousands of refugees into the mountains, where they have no access to water or food. The airstrikes were cast as a response to a humanitarian crisis, and have been accompanied by airdrops of water and food to the refugees, with good reason – as a CNN report by Holly Yan and Barbara Starr put it: 'Dozens of people, including sixty children, have died on the mountain, where the Yazidis [a Kurdish-speaking ethnic group] are battling extreme temperatures, hunger and thirst' (11 August 2014, http://www.cnn.com/2014/08/10/world/meast/iraq-crisis/). Things quickly began to spiral, though. Baghdad battened down the hatches with Iraqi troops and tanks, the Islamic State rebels continued on a killing rampage, and Britain and France promised to join the airdrops. Where it will end is still unknown, but where it began is all too clear: with a long history of ethnic rivalry in a water-limited land, and a recognition that whoever controls the water controls the region.

This latest war is only one of more than fifty water-related conflicts that have occurred in just the first fourteen years of the twenty-first century. The countries involved in the other skirmishes are spread far and wide: Afghanistan, Australia, Belgium, Bolivia, Burkina Faso, Canada, China, Colombia, Côte d'Ivoire, Ethiopia, the Gaza Strip, Ghana, India, Iraq, Israel, Italy, Jordan, Kazakhstan, Kenya, Kyrgyzstan, Lebanon, Macedonia, Mexico, Nepal, Pakistan, the Philippines, Somalia, South Africa, Sri Lanka, Sudan, Tibet, the United States, Uzbekistan and Yemen.

All this, mind you, in a world where we have considered water resources as more or less adequate. But in fact that's arguable, as becomes all too apparent if you simply Google the news for 'water shortage', as we just did. What came up are current water-related problems in Brazil, Bulgaria, Canada, Chile, the Gaza Strip, India, Iran, Iraq, Ireland, Jamaica, Mexico, Saudi Arabia, the United Arab Emirates and the United States (including California, Michigan, Nevada, Ohio and Utah). But this is just the tip of the iceberg. Globally, the water problem is so pervasive that it is not even news. Right now about 1.1 billion people – roughly one in every seven – lack adequate access to water. Many of them make do with only five litres a day, even though the minimum daily threshold is considered to be twenty litres.

Throw in increasing population and warming climate, and the number of people experiencing water stress is very likely to skyrocket – projections indicate that by 2025, the number of people short of water is going to increase to somewhere around three billion. That's more than one in every three people on Earth. Besides the breakdown in the water–food–energy nexus we highlighted above, and increased droughts in already arid lands, the looming problem includes what will happen to water supplies as mountain glaciers melt, which is already well under way throughout the world. More than one-third of the world's population, including in many parts of Central Asia, Latin America and South Asia, get much of their water from rivers supplied by upland glaciers. In Asia alone, reduced outflow from glaciers would be devastating: the Brahmaputra, Ganges, Indus, Irrawaddy, Mekong, Salween and Yangtze Rivers, all fed by glaciers in the Himalayas, provide water for over two billion people – more than one quarter of the planet's population. All of this points to water stress increasing over the next twenty years or so, and as we've witnessed in the past and present, with increased water stress comes fighting.

There is hope, of course, that the fulfilment of such dire predictions will not come to pass. Technology is likely to advance to the point that it could help in a rescue. As we've seen with fears about peak oil, new drilling technologies like hydraulic fracturing (fracking) seem to consistently come along, allowing recovery of underground reserves previously thought unreachable. But, of course, that comes at a higher economic cost than we are used to paying, and at much greater environmental risk. Out of necessity, people who can, will pay high prices. Even now, instead of discarding water from its oil wells, Chevron is selling it in California's drought-stricken Central Valley. Some techno-hopes sound good in theory, but are very unlikely to pan out on a massive scale – a case in point being the desalination of ocean water. Unfortunately, that requires so much energy that there seems no way we could ramp it up fast enough or economically enough; and even if we could, we would be left with massive piles of salt, which would turn into an environmental nightmare for the areas near the desalination plants. Desalination can be a solution for some places, though, and the building of small systems along coastal California is under way, inspired in part by success stories like the US Navy's reliance on fresh water produced from sea water for their sailors at sea.

Yet there are some technology fixes that would clearly help solve the water problem. States and nations already move water through pipes for hundreds of miles to get it from where it can be captured to where it is scarce, but as we discussed earlier, the energy conflicts – both in the amount of electricity needed and the amount of water required to cool the power-plant equipment that supplies the electricity – are prohibitive. The solution here is pretty much the same as that needed to address climate change: shifting to electricity generation that does not require much water, like solar and wind power. That would also help considerably in relieving the water-for-food versus water-for-energy tension.

Which brings us right back to the same kind of conclusions we've pointed out for the other big global issues. The real hope for averting the water crisis lies in humanity's ability to do some things we have not been doing so well in recent decades: recognising the crisis for what it is, and dealing with its root causes – too much population growth, and too much human-caused climate change. In the case of water, holding both population growth and climate change in check will be essential, so as not to increase the water deficit we're already experiencing. But actually reducing water-based conflicts will require the development of intra- and international water compacts, which are based on sound science and which recognise not only the rights people have to the water actually flowing through their land and stored in aquifers beneath their feet, but also the rights of those upstream and downstream. That is, in a word, sharing. And such sharing is not what many old, and old-fashioned, water policies adequately facilitate.

Whether there is real hope here is still up for grabs. Clearly, coming up with viable schemes to share water will be easier within nations than between them, but even so, considerable controversies seem to arise continually within national borders. For example, in 2014, Texas was suing New Mexico and Colorado for water, and Florida was suing Georgia. Both cases were under consideration by the United States Supreme Court. The problems magnify considerably when national borders are crossed, as in the case of the glacier-fed rivers in Asia listed above, and in the Nile drainage, which encompasses already politically fragile areas in North Africa, including Sudan, South Sudan and Egypt. Upstream, the Nile is also an essential water supply for Ethiopia and Uganda. While, in theory, a water-agreement scheme that involved coordinated management of the groundwater, dams and reservoirs sprinkled through all these countries would help stabilise regional water delivery, in reality there seems little chance of achieving that level of cooperation in the near future. As we write this, Egypt has demanded that Ethiopia halt construction on a dam across the Nile, threatening to protect the river's flow 'at any cost'.

Effective water treaties in coming decades may well also have to account for so-called virtual water transport – that is, water that is imported and exported in the form of water consumed by crops and industrial products. That accounting is already being developed, and illustrates the intricate water interdependencies that nations presently rely upon, usually without even thinking about it. Among the top net virtual water importers, in the form of crop, animal and industrial products are (in descending order) the United Kingdom, Germany, Italy, Mexico and Japan, which are getting their virtual water from the exporting nations of Brazil, Australia, the United States, Argentina and India. As water gets scarcer, virtual water is likely to figure more and more in international trade agreements. This is already being done at the national level, as evidenced by China's inclusion of virtual water in its plan for its enormous north–south Water Transfer Project, which has the goal of balancing water between the water-poor but agriculturally productive north and the water-rich but food-deficient south.

Truth be told, we're a little nervous about the water crisis. Maybe it's because of having spent so much time in the American southwest, and knowing what happened to the Ancestral Puebloans. Or maybe it's because of living in California, now parched and seeing the hottest year ever recorded, where the traffic-alert signs on the major highways are apt to flash 'Serious Drought. Help Save Water', where we're implored almost daily to use 20 per cent less water than we're accustomed to, where farmers are leaving their fields fallow because they can't irrigate them, and where whole cities have had their water allotment from reservoirs cut off. The mantra around here, referring to getting rid of lawns, is 'Brown is the new green.'

But there's also another uncomfortable rumble related to water that seems to be getting louder and louder. Even here in the United States, where we take clean water coming out of the tap for granted, two major cities have seen their tap water rendered undrinkable within the past year. A chemical used to process coal leaked into a West Virginia river and contaminated the water supply for the state's capital and largest city, Charleston. Then, in Toledo, Ohio, a toxic algae bloom wiped out the water supply for several days. And that's small potatoes compared to the tens of millions of people in developing countries whose only drinking water is contaminated with poisons like arsenic or harmful microbes. The bottom line is that besides an apparently shrinking supply, the water we have left to drink is increasingly contaminated with toxic wastes. Which, as it happens, are showing up not just in our water, but everywhere. So let's now turn our attention to pollution, and how that figures into the global tipping point.

7

TOXINS

Tony in Fes, Morocco, March 1996

I couldn't quite figure out which of my senses was being most assailed. I was in the Fes el Bali medina, one of the oldest market-places in the world. The noon prayer call had just echoed through the ancient alleyways, the eerie, disembodied tones of the muezzins (*'Allahu Akbar ... Ashadu ana la Ilaha ila Allah'*) overprinting, for a few minutes anyway, the rest of the cacophony. Bearded shop-keepers dressed in loose linen were imploring me to buy their goods, shouting out against the background chatter of thousands of simultaneous conversations. The clip-clop of a mule, packsaddle piled high with some sort of delivery, reverberated off the ancient stone buildings that walled the narrow passageways.

Jockeying shoulder to shoulder with the rest of the crowd on the cobblestone street, I was trying to keep my wits about me in this foreign land, but was distracted by the rows of fresh sheep's heads lined up at the butcher's stall on my right, arranged beneath a display of neatly-spaced animal bladders hanging from a rope that stretched above. The next stall over caught my eye, with stunning brass and copper candelabras, vases and jewellery, some expensive and some cheap. After a bit of haggling, I walked on with a couple of rings for our daughters. Leather jackets, belts, gorgeous handbags, piled one on top of another helter-skelter; Liz would love these, I thought. Across the way I caught the scent of the spice shops, bowls of orange and brown powders, and aromas of turmeric, cinnamon, cumin and cloves. Somewhere close by, a lamb tajine was simmering and coffee was brewing, making my mouth water. That quickly gave way to the perfume stall, where the spring air, now beginning to feel hot on my back as the sun reached deeper down into the ancient urban canyons, became an olfactory stew of floral and musky smells.

And then it was suddenly not so pleasant. As I climbed a stone staircase that was well worn from over a thousand years of use, the pleasant smells of down below gave way to something else – the stench of rotting meat. When I reached the rooftop and gazed down, I saw why. Actually, what I saw, as I wrote in my journal that day, was my version of hell.

It was a leather tannery, operating pretty much as it had for centuries past. Picture looking down on a city block, but instead of houses, visualise open cisterns tightly packed together, some looking like bathtubs carved into rock, others circular and larger, about two body-lengths in diameter. In each vat were stinking brews of pigeon guano, chromium and sulphuric acid, among other toxic ingredients. Animal hides, preserved in salt, lay around the edges. Those wonderful belts and handbags I saw earlier started out right here, and the putrid meat smell, now with a good dose of rotten egg and chemical undertones thrown in as I got closer, was the byproduct of treating the hides.

For a while I tried to imagine myself as one of those unlucky souls, barefoot and with toxic juices soaking their legs up to their thighs, balancing on the edge of the vats or stepping down into the muck after dragging the heavy hides over and dropping them in.

Then they'd macerate the soaked skins with long poles, and when that was done, lift them out, dripping and stinking, only to drop them into another nasty-looking pool of different-coloured vile mire.

I had ended up in Fes el Bali in a roundabout way. At the time I was attempting to facilitate international programmes between scientists who were concerned about the growing human impacts on mountain ecosystems, as part of my job directing a research centre at Montana State University in Bozeman, Montana, that focused on that issue. The day before, I had been working with colleagues at Al Akhawayn University in the town of Ifrane in the Middle Atlas mountains, about two hours away. They thought I should see Fes for a couple of reasons. One was because right near the medina is the world's oldest university, the University of al-Qarawiyyin, founded in AD 859, a source of great national pride and a must-see for any university professor like me, if the opportunity arises.

The other was because the medina itself had been designated a World Heritage Site, which really piqued my interest, since I had recently moderated UNESCO hearings to add Yellowstone National Park to the World Heritage list. Eventually, Yellowstone's addition was approved. The contrast between the two sites couldn't have been more stark: one of them among the world's oldest urban ecosystems, the other the world's oldest nature preserve. Captivating as those differences were, though, what struck me even more was a major similarity. Parts of both World Heritage Sites are suffering from the dumping of toxic wastes.

The effluents coming out of those tanneries at Fes el Bali, in fact, have pretty much killed everything in the Fes River, which runs right through the medina, and in other rivers downstream in the Sebbou drainage. A microbiologist showing me the region pointed out that the only signs of life in those waters are a few specialised bacteria. Not to mention that the contaminated rivers supply the city's water. In Yellowstone, the problems come from gold and silver mines that used to operate just outside the park borders. Ore-processing wastes that were long ago dumped at the north-eastern edge of the park contaminate what would otherwise be a pristine river inside the park's boundaries, stunting the riparian vegetation, reducing certain groups of aquatic life from what should be nineteen species to six, and elevating copper concentrations in the fish. A little farther afield, in scenic country near the south-east border of the park's buffer zone that, with the park, comprises the Greater Yellowstone Ecosystem, pollution from currently operating phosphate mines appears to be producing even more obvious, horrific impacts on trout: many are born with two heads.

Reflecting on the degradation of these World Heritage Sites from the toxic byproducts of humanity, it was hard not to wonder. Such places are, after all, the world's crown jewels. They have been judged by the international community to be among the most important places on the planet to preserve and cherish. If we're polluting them, is there any place on Earth we're not contaminating?

Years later, as Liz and I began to look more closely at the state of the world, it became apparent that there is a very simple, one-word answer to that question. And that answer is: no.

If you are anything like we used to be, you probably think of pollution as somebody else's problem. After all, you probably don't live near a tannery, mine dump, or any other point source of pollution (although you might be surprised if you did some checking). And even though you know such places exist, you might think that in the grand scheme of things, they're necessary evils and don't harm all that many people anyway. As soon as you dig into those suppositions a little more deeply, though, they begin to fall apart. For one thing, those point sources of pollution are amazingly widespread; for another, they impact hundreds of millions of people, causing illnesses, disability and death.

The direct human impacts of pollution are commonly measured as Disability-Adjusted Life Years, or DALYs, which express the number of years lost due to ill-health, disability or death. One DALY equates to losing one year of healthy life. To get a sense of just how bad the point-source pollution problem is these days, it's helpful to run through the list of the top ten polluting industries as identified in the 2012 report of one of the world's pollution watchdogs, the Blacksmith Institute. Number one on the list is lead-acid battery recycling. At some point you've probably got rid of your old car battery, so you contribute. Cottage industries that attend to this nasty task can be found in nearly every city in low- and middle-income countries. The cost in human suffering: 4.8 million DALYs. Lead poisoning from lead smelting ranks number two, at 2.6 million DALYs. Number three is mining and ore processing, like those mine dumps outside Yellowstone: 2.52 million DALYs. Tanneries like those in Fes rank fourth at 1.93 million DALYs. Industrial and municipal dumps, where your garbage ends up, come in as the fifth worst, costing 1.23 million DALYs. Number six: industrial sites, 1.06 million DALYs. Number seven: so-called artisanal gold mining, small-scale operations that end up poisoning more than fifteen million people, about 4.5 million of them women and six hundred thousand children, through direct contact with toxic mercury used to process the ore, costing over a million DALYs. Number eight: various kinds of product manufacturing, 786,000 DALYs. Number nine: chemical manufacturing, 765,000 DALYs. And holding down the number ten spot is dye manufacturing, at 430,000 DALYs. Add those together, and it's as if we're talking about the incomprehensible numbers that mark geological time; but we're not: it's more than seventeen million years of productive life lost. Seventeen million years.

Lucky me, you might be thinking, that none of those places are in my backyard. But you're not as lucky as you think, because it's not point-source pollution that is the biggest problem these days. More pernicious, both in its immediate impact and in the long term, is the stuff that spreads widely, a classic example being what we put into the air, which in most cities is increasingly hard to breathe. In fact, some of it – notably the black air that pours out of a rapidly growing number of smokestacks and exhaust pipes in China, can even be seen from space. Which is ironic, since it is often difficult for the residents of places like Beijing to see more than a few hundred yards, the smog is so thick. We got some inkling of what it's like to spend a winter under such conditions when we lived in Santiago, Chile, which is in much better shape than Beijing, Delhi, Karachi, Kabul, Doha, and a host of other highly populous cities, where hundreds of millions of people have to breathe air you can actually see. In Santiago, there were days when the grey haze was so thick we could barely see across the street when we looked out of our high-rise apartment window, and the irritants in the air led to sinus infections that went on for months. The respiratory ills we suffered were not uncommon: the hospitals were overflowing, as they usually are in winter, with over twenty thousand people suffering from similar complaints, and about seven hundred people in Santiago die of such illnesses each winter.

Ah, you may be saying, that's a developing country problem. Wrong again. Air pollution in London on certain days in 2014 was reported to be worse than that in Beijing by some measures. We now live in California, which has some of the strictest environmental laws in the world. Even so, when we drive from San Francisco to Los Angeles, we pass through Bakersfield and feel our eyes sting and our noses clog. For good reason: Bakersfield has the worst air in the nation in terms of particulates, and is just behind Los Angeles in harmful ozone, a result of industry, agriculture, power plants and unfortunate geography.

Los Angeles itself has long had a reputation for bad air, but in fact it has cleaned up its act tremendously over the past couple of decades, a result of stringent environmental regulations that enforced emissions limits on power plants, industry and vehicles. Vehicle emissions, for instance, have reduced by 99 per cent since the bad old days of LA smog in the 1960s and 1970s. As a result, compared to cities like Beijing and Santiago, Los Angeles's air is downright pristine: its average Air Quality Index typically measures between 50 and 60 (with higher numbers being bad), compared to Santiago's winter readings, which are usually above 100. Beijing's readings are almost always above 50, usually above 100, and not uncommonly exceed 200 or even 300. Nevertheless, the air of Los Angeles is still not what you'd call healthy, as the experience of one traveller shows. After a recent visit to the area, he emailed us with the following plea:

Our group of 25 people from Georgia recently visited LA for the Rose parade. We were on a 12-day bus excursion that arrived in Covina on Dec. 30th, for a 2-day stay. As a former smoker (quit 1 year), I suffer from slight COPD [chronic obstructive pulmonary disease], but was cleared by my doctor to visit, with adequate [ventilator] equipment for sleep. Upon arrival (4 p.m.), I collapsed with breathing difficulties, and was confined to my motel room for the evening. As breathing became more difficult, I required medical attention from Citrus Valley Medical Center and was advised to be admitted. Against medical advice from ER doctor, I decided to obtain portable oxygen therapy in the motel, and travel on to Las Vegas to cleaner air. Wrong. Upon arrival in Las Vegas, COPD worsened and hospitalization was required to maintain breathing and repair lungs from damage incurred in LA. After a 6-day stay in Desert Springs hospital, I was allowed (along with portable oxygen concentration) to fly home to Georgia. I later discovered that 2 other people had to leave the tour group and to get medical attention and fly home prematurely. A total of 6 visitors on this vacation have now sought medical attention for respiratory problems from this visit. I am retired with hopes of travel, but I am now limited for the next year to oxygen therapy when traveling until I have recovered from this visit. The state of California has a duty, obligation, and responsibility to warn visitors of hazardous conditions regarding health. I, along with 21 other people are soliciting the US Health and Human Services (Kathleen Sebelius) to require that travel companies post warnings for health risk associated with visiting areas such as LA, before booking travel. The monetary loss is insignificant compared to the loss of lifestyle and duration of life that I have to endure in the future. It is difficult to comprehend the long-term effects on the residents of your state due to this negligence. Don't abuse God's gift. Please become responsible stewards of your environment and take action.

This correspondent's appeal was to clean up a state that, as has already been mentioned, is recognised as having some of the toughest environmental standards around. His individual experience multiplies out by millions when you look at the problem on a global scale: in 2010, air pollution was causing up to six million premature deaths per year.

These are just the immediate costs. As we saw in Chapter 4, the long-term costs are even higher: it is in fact air pollution in the form of carbon dioxide, nitrous oxide, methane and chlorofluorocarbons, emitted primarily from burning fossil fuel, that causes the climate-change problem. Pollution from point sources like factories, mines and power plants, which we typically regard as somebody else's problem, scales up to contaminate the entire planet.

But air pollution is just the tip of the iceberg. We have, for instance, totally changed both the amount of the planet's nitrogen, and the way it cycles through the land, rivers, lakes and sea. Nitrogen is something all living things need, and it is extremely common in gas form – it makes up about 78 per cent of the atmosphere. The problem for living things, though, is that under natural conditions it is very hard to convert nitrogen-gas molecules into something that plants and animals can actually use. Historically, to meet the needs of plants for nitrogen, people used bat and bird guano (excrement) as fertiliser, but those sources ran out. Luckily for us, though, in the early part of the twentieth century some bright people figured out how to make more of the kind of nitrogen that living things need, in the form of chemical fertilisers that we have been liberally sprinkling on a large proportion of the planet's land ever since.

Making nitrogen fertiliser relies on a process that was discovered and refined by two German scientists, Fritz Haber and Carl Bosch; it's therefore called the Haber-Bosch process. The Haber-Bosch process became so important to the world that its inventors were awarded separate Nobel Prizes. Bosch's came in 1931; not long afterwards he was dismissed from his directorship of Germany's major chemical conglomerate for trying to discourage Adolf Hitler from going to war. Haber's Nobel Prize came earlier, in 1918. Ironically, that was right after he had put his chemical expertise to decidedly dastardly uses: during World War I he had the bright idea of using chlorine and mustard gas to incapacitate enemy troops, which was carried out to grim effect. Besides making fertiliser, he also had a not-so-widely-publicised motivation for producing reactive nitrogen: so it could be used in bombs. Later, it was Haber's invention of the highly poisonous cyanide-based Zyklon A that the Nazis eventually refined into Zyklon B, and pumped into extermination chambers to kill some eleven million people. So his contributions to the world have a bit of a mixed record, to put it mildly.

The Haber-Bosch process, though, was overall a good thing: it led to the feeding of billions more people than would otherwise have been possible. Basically, the process produces ammonia, which is a usable form of nitrogen for living organisms, by a chemical reaction that involves combining atmospheric dinitrogen with hydrogen and iron at high pressures and temperatures. In layman's language, that kind of ammonia-bound nitrogen is called fertiliser, which you can buy at your local garden or DIY centre. It was, in fact, the judicious addition of such fertilisers to fields that largely made the Green Revolution possible, which as we saw in Chapter 5 saved billions of lives.

The problem from a pollution perspective, though, is that we've added so much nitrogen to the world that it is getting into places it shouldn't, and having some very adverse impacts. Nitrogen oxide (NO_2) (a greenhouse gas) and ammonia (NH_3) in the atmosphere have increased fivefold since pre-industrial times. Rain and snow bring those molecules down from the air and deposit them in soils, lakes and rivers – such atmospheric deposition is now proceeding at a pace that is an order of magnitude greater than it was before people got into the act. On top of that, in many parts of the world, especially places like the United States and China, much more fertiliser than crops can use is applied to fields – it's just easier to throw on a whole bunch, rather than strictly control how much is applied. The extra nitrogen is picked up by rainwater or irrigation runoff and carried off by streams, then rivers, which in turn deliver it into lakes and the oceans.

Toxins

That extra nitrogen actually makes the waters more nutritious, which seems as if it should be a good thing, but one of the general principles that has emerged from ecological research is that the highest levels of biodiversity exist when you have not too few nutrients, not too many, but just the right amount. Adding nitrogen from excess fertiliser pushes ecosystems into the 'too many' end of the optimal nutrient balance, and when that happens, just a few species become overly prolific, pushing out everything else. In lakes and oceans, the species that get very happy with lots of nutrients are algae. So the water turns soupy green, an ugly and in some cases toxic condition that prevails for a little while, until something else happens. The algae are so prolific that they die in astronomical numbers, and their tiny bodies start to decompose. That decomposition takes oxygen, and with so many dead bodies needing to rot, virtually all of the oxygen is sucked out of the water. Which means nothing can live there – those places become dead zones.

Such dead zones are now widespread throughout the world's oceans, especially where major rivers flow into the sea. One dead zone in the Baltic Sea averages about nineteen thousand square miles annually, bigger than the entire country of Denmark. Another at the mouth of the Mississippi River, in the Gulf of Mexico, grows at times to seven thousand square miles, bigger than the entire state of Connecticut. There are now more than four hundred such dead zones known worldwide, up from forty-nine in the 1960s. They extend all along the east coast of the United States and in the seas off major population centres on the west coast, along much of the northern coastlines of Europe, and where major rivers in Africa, South America, Asia and Australia empty into the sea. The economic costs are colossal – in just one year, in one relatively small dead zone that covered about 365 square miles off the coast of New Jersey and New York in 1976, the losses for commercial fisheries and related businesses were more than $500 million.

Multiply that by all the fisheries in all the dead zones, and the figure becomes enormous, into the trillions of dollars. Not to mention the loss of food production that results – something that can ill be afforded in a world where we need to start producing more food, not less.

The dead-zone problem promises to get worse, not better, if we go into the future without implementing the agricultural and energy changes outlined in previous chapters. As do several other global-scale pollution problems.

Just a few more examples, to give you a sense of how pervasive our contamination of the planet has become. As summarised by sixteen of the world's leading environmental scientists, and endorsed by thousands more in the 2013 report *Scientific Consensus Statement on Maintaining Humanity's Life Support Systems in the 21st Century: Information for Policy Makers* (http://consensusforaction.stanford.edu/): 'Traces of pesticides and industrial pollutants are routinely found in samples of soil or tree bark from virtually any forest in the world, in the blubber of whales, in polar bear body tissues, in fish from most rivers and oceans, and in the umbilical cords of newborn babies.'

The key point of that section of the report, and many others like it, is that there is nowhere on Earth you can go now where you don't see evidence of the toxic substances that people produce. Eating too much fish in some places is hazardous, because you'll get mercury poisoning. Even polar bears in the middle of nowhere now have their tissues contaminated by mercury, which makes its way through the food chain to lodge in their tissues. No wonder, given that our waste has increased mercury deposition in the surface oceans 300 per cent relative to pre-industrial times. These toxic compounds concentrate in higher and higher percentages up the food chain, with levels peaking eventually in predators, including humans. Albatrosses, long-lived seabirds whose diets are exclusively fish, squid or krill, demonstrate 130 to 360 per cent higher concentrations of contaminants than they did just a decade ago. And in the albatrosses that feed off the Pacific coast of North America, the levels of polychlorinated biphenyls (PCBs) and mercury concentrations are a whopping 370 to 460 per cent higher than in those that feed further away from the California coastline. Concentrations of these toxins are highest in northern polar latitudes, because the input of circumpolar river systems that dump the wastes into the Arctic is combined there with nuances in airborne input due to global circulation patterns. Eskimos living traditional lifestyles now have elevated levels of cancer-causing PCBs and persistent organic pollutants (POPs), because the whales and other marine food they rely on are contaminated just from swimming around in the ocean. Some Inuit women in northern Canada and Greenland, who are virtually isolated from what we'd call civilisation, show levels of POPs higher than women in densely populated parts of the United States, and the levels of PCBs in their breast milk are five to ten times higher than in women who live in southern Canada. In some cases, the Inuit's breast milk (and body tissues) contains such high concentrations of nasty chemical residues that it could legitimately be classified as toxic waste.

POPs (including PCBs) are pernicious, because they pass through the placenta and cause lasting problems for developing babies, including learning difficulties and behavioural problems. Many POPs are endocrine disruptors, which have recently been recognised as being so pervasive in the environment that they may be changing the very way our children grow. Endocrine disruptors are classes of chemicals that cause reproductive, neurological and immune-system dysfunctions.

Endocrine disruptors manage to get into our systems in the most unlikely ways, via things you'd never suspect. Until recently, most baby bottles, reusable water bottles and food-storage containers were made from a kind of hard plastic called polycarbonate. The same kind of plastic was (and in some places, still is) pervasive in things like compact discs, the protective lining of tin cans, contact lenses and dental sealants. In 1998 a geneticist, Dr Patricia Hunt, then at Case Western Reserve University in Ohio (subsequently she moved to Washington State University in Pullman, Washington), was studying the ovaries of mice and noticed some strange results. Chromosomal abnormalities began showing up in unexpectedly high numbers in her control mice, leading to miscarriages and birth defects. She eventually traced the problem to elevated levels of a chemical called bisphenol A, more commonly known as BPA. The mice were getting the BPA from drinking water provided to them in, you guessed it, polycarbonate water bottles, from which the BPA was leaching. Subsequently, widespread testing for BPA was initiated in people throughout the United States, and lo and behold, it showed up in almost everyone – 93 per cent of people tested.

BPAs are technically a different class of endocrine disruptor from POPs; there are many different kinds. Other endocrine-disrupting pollutants are even more ubiquitous, especially those in pesticides like DDT, made notorious by the environmental damage detailed in Rachel Carson's *Silent Spring* in 1962. Even though DDT is outlawed in many countries, including the US, it is still produced in India, China and Korea, and continues to be used extensively in India and across Africa to kill mosquitoes and other insects. As with chemical fertilisers, pesticides and herbicides are seldom applied in just the right amount, so the excess percolates down into underground aquifers that often provide drinking water, and drains off into rivers, lakes and the ocean. Not to mention the residues that end up in the food you buy at the supermarket.

An example of a herbicide endocrine disruptor is atrazine, which has been a go-to product for farmers since 1958, and has been found in the water supplies of many communities in farm country. Atrazine has the interesting effect of inhibiting testosterone and inducing oestrogen production; that is, it suppresses the male sex hormone and increases the female sex hormone. That's important in the development of embryos and juveniles of many vertebrate animals, like you and me. As Tyrone Hayes at the University of California-Berkeley, one of the world's leading researchers on atrazine, puts it, the result of too much atrazine in an animal's system is chemical castration and feminisation. That is, boys end up looking and actually being like girls, to the extent that male fish and amphibians produce eggs and egg yolk, and in amphibians some males even grow ovaries. In human males, atrazine exposure is associated with decreased sperm and reduced fertility.

Endocrine disruptors are a part of our daily lives now; besides plastic products, herbicides and pesticides, they're found in our clothes and furniture (as flame retardants), various pharmaceuticals, detergents, toys and cosmetics. Their health effects are numerous, one of the most interesting being their impact on child development. Over the past half-century (the time in which the prevalence of endocrine disruptors in the environment has been increasing) girls have been getting their first periods and developing breasts and pubic hair earlier and earlier. First noticed in a landmark study reported in 1997, the trend is continuing. Reports of a follow-up study published in 2014 show that the average age for the beginning of breast development in a large sample of girls from the San Francisco area, Cincinnati and New York, was down to 8.8 years for African-Americans, 9.3 years in Latinas, and 9.7 years in Asian-American and Caucasian girls. The Caucasian girls showed the most dramatic shift, beginning puberty four months earlier than the 1997 cohort. And the proportion of African-American girls who begin to develop breasts at around six years old has tripled in the past fifteen years, to 18 per cent, while 38 per cent have done so by the age of eight, compared to 4 per cent of six-year-old Caucasian girls, and 21 per cent of eight-year-olds. For boys, it's just the opposite – exposure to endocrine disruptors has the effect of slowing down reproductive maturation. Other health problems caused by endocrine disruptors include lower fertility, more cases of endometriosis, some cancers, and increased incidences of obesity. The obesity link is doubly problematic, because increased obesity leads to more cases of heart disease and type II diabetes.

Endocrine disruptors are just one of a host of chemicals that find their way into unexpected places – not only into human bodies, but into the bodies of many different species. Even in what we like to think of as clean places. For example, in the bay that provides part of the spectacularly scenic backdrop to downtown Seattle, a relatively clean, environmentally aware city, here is the situation as reported in a local newspaper: 'Puget Sound a toxic stew, scientists say. Fireproof salmon, fish dosed with anti-depressants and shellfish tainted with amnesia-causing toxins can all be found' (Lisa Stiffler, *Seattle P-I*, 5 April 2006, http://www.seattlepi.com/local/article/Puget-Sound-a-toxic-stew-scientists-say-1200367.php). Killer whales in Puget Sound are thought to be the most PCB-contaminated mammals on the planet.

Where do all of these pollutants in ocean waters come from? Some come from industrial wastes, but a lot of them come from you, either directly, from dumping unused antidepressants and other drugs down the toilet, or indirectly, from the bodily waste that you also flush away. It turns out that those molecules survive even when they pass through waste-treatment plants (and in many places they never do, but end up flowing out of pipes that essentially connect toilets right to the nearest river, lake or ocean). And even at seemingly low concentrations they are able to do things like, oh, disturb the genes that control the brain function of shrimp, or cause fish to become less cautious, or make crayfish fight more.

Your sewage (combined with ours and everybody else's) turns out to be a huge problem, in fact – much bigger than simply making crayfish fight more. Sewage-treatment plants are literally bulging at the seams in many major cities, if they have adequate ones at all. And we're not just talking about developing countries. In 2009 several cities in the San Francisco Bay area – including that bastion of environmental awareness, Berkeley – were sued by the United States Environmental Protection Agency, California water officials and environmental groups for routinely allowing hundreds of millions of gallons of partially treated sewage to flow into the bay during heavy rainstorms. The problem is antiquated storm-drainage systems that can no longer handle the effluents from the growing California population, especially during storm surges. A settlement to upgrade the Bay Area systems was finally reached in 2014, and that kind of expensive situation is exactly what many major cities in developed countries are facing: for example, Victoria, Vancouver, New York, Venice and London, to name just a few. And in coastal cities the sewage-disposal problem will be exacerbated in future years by rising sea levels, as well as by population growth.

Sewage in developing countries is an even greater problem – there more than 90 per cent of human waste is dumped directly into the surroundings virtually untreated. As of 2011, the waste from approximately 2.6 billion people went directly onto the ground or into waterways; in India alone, half the population, equating to six hundred million people, have no access to toilets. In fact, there are fewer toilets in the world than there are mobile phones. The health problems from such lack of basic sanitation are enormous: they cause a child to die approximately every twenty seconds from complications of diarrhoea, typhoid, hepatitis, cholera or all sorts of other pathogens and infections. The children who survive often suffer permanent damage. In India, the long-term build-up of faecal germs in the environment – not malnutrition – has recently been identified as the cause of stunted growth in as many as sixty-one million children. That is what happens when you combine high population densities with raw sewage. The problem of untreated (to put it bluntly) human shit is so enormous – more than two hundred million tons of it each year – that the United Nations has all but thrown up its hands in despair, declaring its goal of halving the number of people who lack access to such basics of sanitation by 2015 to be out of reach.

How big are all these toxic problems on the global scale? Very big, it turns out. In 2010, health researchers estimated that the number of years (measured in DALYs, as we defined at the beginning of this chapter) lost due to environmental hazards is probably greater than the number lost to malaria, tuberculosis and HIV/AIDS combined. And over the next few decades the toxic-contamination problems promise to get worse if we simply keep on doing what we've been doing. If you think back to the kinds of examples we've given in this chapter, you'll have no trouble seeing that pollution of our world increases as a direct function of population growth and the resulting need to produce more stuff, burn more fossil fuels, grow more food, and siphon off more water.

So how do we change business as usual to stop polluting more as we grow to ten billion people? The glib answer is to say: consume less, pay attention to the environmental footprint of items you buy, get off fossil fuels, implement the agricultural solutions mentioned in previous chapters, and clean up the bad messes we've made in the past. And on that last front there is actually some good news in recent years. People really do seem to care enough to fix the mistakes of the past, at least in places they consider special enough. That's why clean-ups are under way, at impressive economic cost, at both of the World Heritage Sites mentioned at the beginning of this chapter. In 2013, Morocco's King Mohammed VI approved a

$39 million handicraft complex to replace the polluting tanneries and copper workings in Fes, and NGOs are pitching in sizeable sums to clean up the Fes and Sebbou Rivers. In the Yellowstone area, the state of Montana is spending $20 million to get rid of the old mine tailings that are polluting park waters, work that began in 2012. The Stockholm Convention in 2001 produced a treaty to reduce POPs worldwide. And in 2014 evangelical religious groups banded together to support the reduction of carbon pollution, an unexpected move given their usual affiliation with global-warming-bashing conservatives.

As far as fixing the global sewage problem goes, meeting that United Nations goal of providing basic sanitation facilities for the billions who lack them would go a long way – but that will take money and commitment. There are also some innovative and feasible, if a bit strange-sounding, approaches that are already working, even making money – like running buses on human faeces, and using the manure from animals to generate electricity. The former is already working in Norway, the latter on farms in the United States. Such solutions kill two birds with one stone, so to speak, by helping to solve the bodily-waste problem and cutting greenhouse-gas emissions at the same time. In addition, the field of green chemistry is advancing rapidly; entrepreneurs are looking for, and succeeding in finding, ways to produce a new generation of inherently safer, non-polluting chemicals for use in products the world clamours for. And, of course, it would be good to apply the precautionary principle to the release of new substances into the environment – demonstrating that they are safe before they are used, rather than waiting to see if problems develop a few years down the road, which is the way things have commonly been done up to now. That is going to require governments to get into the act with stricter regulations. And some very simple, essentially free measures can work to alleviate some of the toxins in human waste, too – an approach championed by Rita Colwell, the former director of the National Science Foundation and former President of the American Academy of Sciences, who has studied cholera for almost half a century. She proposed using saris – as worn by women in India – as a filter for drinking water in cholera-prone regions. Folded over four times, saris used as filters result in a reduction of cholera by 50 per cent.

But ramping up solutions quickly is of course far, far easier said than done, especially when special-interest groups that stand to lose a lot of money are lobbying against those solutions. Industries are not shy about rolling up their sleeves and fighting hard and dirty when it comes to regulating harmful products that are also big money-makers. Classic examples are the tobacco and fossil-fuel lobbies, both of which have underwritten disinformation campaigns and organised smear tactics against scientists who are discovering facts that the polluting companies don't like, as was so well documented in Naomi Oreskes and Erik M. Conway's recent book *Merchants of Doubt* (2011, Bloomsbury Press). The outcome is never certain, as illustrated by an ongoing battle over the use of a herbicide we mentioned earlier in this chapter, atrazine. Atrazine's role as an endocrine disruptor began receiving attention in the late 1990s, and soon thereafter it was banned in Europe. It is still used widely in the United States, however, but not without considerable controversy that pits big business against scientists, as related in detail by Rachel Aviv in the *New Yorker* magazine ('A Valuable Reputation', 10 February 2014). At stake are not only reputations – of both the researchers who study the health effects of atrazine and the companies that produce it – but also big profits for the companies. Sales of atrazine amount to at least $300 million per year in the United States alone.

That, as well as plain old inertia in not wanting to change, is what the world is up against in its attempts to make the planet a less, rather than more, toxic place as we head into the next couple of decades. Many people are fighting the good fight, but it's an uphill battle that may well get even tougher over the next few years, especially in stemming the tide of pesticides and pharmaceuticals that is such a big part of the pollution issue. Because as it turns out, there's yet another growing problem, to which our probable first reaction will be to spread more and more, rather than fewer and fewer, pesticides and drugs around the globe: there's a host of disease organisms that are on the move, and new ones are emerging. So, as if all the other difficulties we've covered aren't enough, we've got some global health problems to take seriously as well.

8

DISEASE

Liz, near the Panamanian border, Costa Rica, February 2013

Darkness descends rapidly near the equator, which makes the waiting easier, because that's why I am here – for the night. Our team – graduate students Hannah Frank and Chase Mendenhall, my colleague Gretchen Daily and a Costa Rican crew of expert naturalists – is here to trap bats. We are trying to time our hike so that we arrive just before nightfall in order to set up the nets and to avoid bushwhacking through steep terrain in the dark. Then we wait. The mist nets we use are almost as fine as human hair – very light, but strong. And in spite of being spectacular at finding their way around the thick forest understorey of a tropical rainforest, most bats can't avoid flying into these nets. Their delicate, wrinkly wings get caught, and we must carefully unwrap the net from their little bodies to take them out. We capture tens to hundreds of bats per night, and go from chilly, tired biologists to excited, exhausted ones, depending on how many we capture. We spend much of the night processing these strange-looking little animals, and then release them, unharmed, back into the darkness.

Handling bats is quite an experience. A photograph just doesn't do them justice: most are really tiny, very feisty and stunningly beautiful. You see intelligence in their eyes. Their wings, basically just tissue-covered hands, are surprisingly elastic, and their 'fingers' are as thin as toothpicks. They are surprisingly good at climbing, though, and that's what they try to do while we handle them. Their distinctive facial and ear projections, exquisitely evolved for 'seeing' by echolocating in the pitch black, help us identify which species they are. But identifications are tough in this part of the world, where the diversity is astounding – 110 species, over one-tenth of all the bat species in the world. So telling which is which takes a little time. No worries, though, because we take tissue samples that we will use to genetically corroborate our hands-on IDs once we return to the lab.

Tonight I hold the bats as Hannah takes a small blood sample and swabs inside their little mouths for a saliva sample, each swab stored in its own container. Most bats are pretty straightforward to sample, but the swabs in a vampire bat's mouth don't last long, since their tiny teeth are sharper than all the knives in my kitchen at home. We search the white canvas bags in which we temporarily hold the bats for faeces they may have let go in all the excitement, which gets put into a vial. Then we tweeze almost-too-small-to-see bat flies from each of the bats' wings and fur. It's fortunate for us, perhaps less so for the bat, that each one of them carries its own little ecosystem on its body: flies, some ticks, mites and various lice, and that each bat species hosts its own set of mostly unique bat flies and other bugs.

The bugs eat the blood of their bat host, who spends time grooming them off, sometimes alone and sometimes in social groups. If you're a bat, the primary social group is a mother and her pup. Usually, mothers give birth to one pup per year, and then the pup holds on for dear life as its mother performs her nightly aerobatics.

We caught several of these mother–offspring flying duos (the baby stays on its mother during our processing), shaking our heads in wonder that some pups were nearly as big as their mothers.

Bats roost during the day and, depending on the species, are more or less gregarious. Some species hang singly from branches or the bark of trees, not even touching each other. Some curl up in a leaf in smallish groups and stay there for a few days. The other extreme includes those species whose roosts are large caves containing millions of individuals. Most of these caves have been occupied for thousands of years. You can tell this by the amount of guano (bat faeces) at the bottom of the cave. It's a rich source of nutrients for many species, but it has an enormous bacterial load too. So you can imagine that one of the determinants of how many parasites and diseases particular bats carry is how long their roosts have been occupied, and by how many individuals.

Bats eat a variety of foods, too, and that makes them very important to people. Many eat fruit, some have diets of insects, and some specialise in nectar. Using Scotch tape, we take sticky samples from the faces of the nectar-eating bats so that another team can figure out which flowering plants the bats visited, by identifying the pollen stuck on the tape. In the process of feeding on nectar each night, these bats also pollinate the plants; in fact, some plants cannot reproduce without bat pollination. This is only one way that bats help out humanity; they actually perform all sorts of other helpful jobs as well. Part of Chase's dissertation is to determine just what those jobs are, both in the thick forests here and in the more human-modified areas, including coffee plantations, cow pastures and family farms, across this landscape. It's already clear that one very important service they perform is eating insects people tend not to like. Though bats are small, they can live a very long time – up to forty years in the wild. Put together small size, long lifespan and very slow reproductive rate, and the biological necessities mean that bats are voracious eaters. Insect-eating bats can in fact eat their weight in insects every night. Bat by bat, this adds up: the bat swarm from Braken Cave, Texas, has been estimated to eat two hundred tons of insects nightly. Working in the tropics makes us appreciate that. We shudder to think how many more insects there would be here without the appetites of the bats we're handling.

As the night progresses, we capture more and more species. Most are active early on in the night while the temperature is still warm, and only a few prefer the deep, chilly later hours. Handling the bats is slow going – we have several samples to take, and they are strong, squirmy little mammals with sharp teeth. It's tedious, but we have to be painstaking, working quickly so the bats don't get cold and lethargic. So our field crew is happy when the bat-visits to the nets decrease late in the night and we can pack up and head back to our field station. Climbing the slippery hill with just our headlamps is a bit disconcerting. Tree roots look huge, and the forest beyond our little path seems impenetrable; sudden movements in the dark are suspect, but luckily it is too chilly for most snakes. Sticky spiderwebs have been strung across our path in the past few hours, though, keeping us wondering just how many creepy-crawlies there are in this place.

Weeks later our team is back in our lab at Stanford, processing all these samples. For every night of work in the field, we end up with several weeks to months of work in the lab. Our goal is to understand how human modification of the tropical forest – a worldwide problem these days – influences the diversity of bats (and other species), the ecological services they provide, and, importantly, the diseases that bats carry and that humans may come into contact with. We have posed questions about which bat species should have the most parasites, and in turn, might harbour the most diseases.

As the months of lab work pass, we are surprised by the answers we find. We're using a bacterium called *Bartonella* as a kind of disease marker to help us predict potential pathways of all types of disease exchange between bats, their parasites, domesticated animals such as chickens, cows, cats and dogs, and humans. Instead of finding just a small percentage of bats with specific strains of *Bartonella*, we found that fully a third of those we caught had this bacterium in their blood, as did half the bat flies we sampled. Not only did we find an unexpectedly high number of infected bats and flies, it turns out that many of the strains of *Bartonella* in bats are identical to the ones that cause nasty diseases in humans – like endocarditis (an infection of the heart), cat-scratch fever, trench fever and sand-fly fever. *Bartonella* has also been implicated as a potential cause of unexplained illnesses worldwide in humans.

What this means is that we have found that in this peaceful, thriving tropical countryside there is a potential for release of diseases that we really have no idea about, being carried around by animals we can't do without.

Costa Rica is not an anomaly.

More than three-quarters of all the recently emerged infectious diseases have an animal origin. The current thinking is that these 'new' diseases are arising more frequently because we are increasing our penetration into formerly little-visited ecosystems and transforming them for our use. The diseases aren't really new, though. They come from pathogens that have a long history in natural ecosystems around the world, spread between vectors and hosts, sometimes to the detriment of the host, sometimes not.

What's new is that these pathogens are now infecting humans; and since we are not used to being infected, such diseases can cause all manner of health problems, even death, and they can spread like wildfire. Especially because there are so many more people on the planet now, and our numbers are ever growing. Simply by increasing the number of people that are exposed to animals, we increase the likelihood that some transfer of disease takes place. Today it is possible to travel from almost any part of the world to almost any other in a single plane ride.

As we write this chapter, what's happening with the deadly Ebola virus outbreak illustrates the dangers all too well. Ebola is a kind of 'worst nightmare' disease. It kills between 60 and 90 per cent of the people it infects, and victims literally pour virus-laden fluids from their bodies. They have fevers, intense headaches and pain in their joints, they have diarrhoea, they vomit, and in the latter stages of the infection some bleed internally and externally from their orifices and their eyes. This stage of the disease is when it is at its most contagious, when others come into contact with these secretions. Ebola is horrific because of the way it kills and because it is so highly contagious, so highly virulent, and there is no vaccine or cure. The only saving grace, if you want to call it that, is that it is transmitted solely through bodily fluids, rather than through the air. So far.

Ebola is named for the river in the Democratic Republic of the Congo near which it was first recognised in 1976. Since then, periodic outbreaks have emerged in Central Africa, but most peter out by themselves after affecting somewhere between a few people and a couple of hundred, or are stopped by within-country containment efforts. The 2014 version of Ebola was different, because unlike past outbreaks, it did not originate within a relatively distant, forested region, and it broke out at the crossroads between three countries instead of within the boundaries of one. It seems to have started with a two-year-old boy ('Patient Zero') in south-eastern Guinea, near the borders of Sierra Leone and Liberia. How this unfortunate child acquired Ebola is not known, but some contact with contamination by fruit bats is suspected, given what epidemiologists now think the animal vector is (see the spillover discussion below). However Patient Zero got the disease, it quickly spread to members of his close family; then, during the funeral for the boy's grandmother, mourners contracted it and took it back to their towns, distributed over several communities in the three countries, and spread the disease across the countryside, in hospitals, in the roads of villages, in the markets, and in buses, cars, trucks and planes.

At this point, nobody has any idea how many people are actually sick or have died, in part because locals are still actively hiding their illness, and their dead. Brave hospital workers have taken an inordinate share of the burden, but for their efforts they have been attacked by the families of the infected, because people fear that once an ill person goes to the hospital, they will not come home. Indeed, many think that their loved ones acquire Ebola from the hospitals or clinics. Some people, in a desperate attempt to ward off the disease, have turned to traditional healings and rituals, shunning the hospitals and health-care workers and their protective, but scary, hazmat suits, face shields and gloves.

This 2014 outbreak, at this writing, is still raging in western Africa, where it has infected an estimated eighteen thousand people, causing death to almost eight thousand of them. While the disease continues unabated in Sierra Leone and Liberia, interest and funding from Europe and the US have declined precipitously. But this particular outbreak of Ebola may never really stop. Courtesy of our connected, 'advanced' world, the disease has taken hold, and now, after months of reading about somebody else's problem – the infected, dying and dead people in remote lands – authorities are announcing that the disease is nowhere near contained. The very important reality now is that a single plane ride from the Central African nations where Ebola reigns can land a traveller in any one of thirty-five countries – and as we have already learned, just one more flight can get an ill passenger almost everywhere else. Because of that, the 2014 Ebola outbreak rapidly grew into an international health emergency. Infected passengers landed in other parts of Africa, the United States, Europe and the Middle East. International rules limiting travel out of the affected countries and particular areas within them, or defining 'cordons sanitaires' – areas from which no one can leave – were not the solution some had hoped for. These cordons are usually defended by the military, and they conjure up images of the Black Death of medieval times. They incite fear and panic within them, are difficult to manage, and actually limit the critical supplies of medicine, food and water needed to stem the disease. The last time such measures were used was in attempts to fight a typhus epidemic during World War I.

Such stories are destined to become more common, given the increasing spillover of new diseases from remote places and the fact that travel is a normal part of life nowadays, taking people and freight – and pathogens and disease – to and from the farthest reaches of our globe. In the future the number of trips will only increase, because more people from more places want to travel, and are gaining the means to do so. Two-thirds of the population of developing countries are projected to take a foreign trip by the year 2032, while in the developed world, per capita travel already exceeds one foreign trip per year. From 1970 to 2013 the number of airline passengers increased from about 310 million to over three billion, or a steady 1 per cent per year over more than forty years. The reality is, each trip a person takes increases the likelihood of transportation of a parasite, an infection in an animal, a plant or a human, and thus increases the probability of a novel emerging disease. Now, pretty much everybody is part of the emerging disease problem, which means we can no longer write it off as a third-world problem.

In fact, developed countries are actually the principal players in helping novel diseases to emerge and spill over into humans, because we are taking over more and more previously little-utilised land, especially in places where the disease load is heaviest. Those places, as we saw in our studies of disease load in the Costa Rican bats, happen to be in equatorial forests, places like the Amazon or remote Central Africa. These are not only the last vestiges of green wilderness on the planet, they are also the places where we are relentlessly cutting down trees for timber, or to make way for crops and cows, or to mine precious metals and minerals that are getting scarce elsewhere. As such habitats are coopted for human use they become less suitable for other species, resulting in population declines of native plants and animals, and concentration of the survivors in small pockets right next to where people live. Those species' parasites and pathogens also concentrate in the shrinking suitable habitats that remain, which in turn increases rates of infection and the probability that the resulting diseases may 'jump' to other species. Like us.

The tropics harbour the highest diversity of infectious diseases and parasites for a very good biological reason. Disease-causing organisms – bacteria, viruses, parasites, fungi – conform to the same controls on biological diversity that other species do: there are more species, with more genetic diversity, near the equator, and biodiversity declines towards the poles. In fact, the diseases of the temperate zones are actually nested subsets of those found in the tropics. This pattern of greater biological diversity near the equator is one of biology's most well-known patterns, and results from such controls as more effective solar energy in those regions, less variation in temperature, older ecosystems that have given evolution more time to create species, and simply more geographical area, available over longer geological time, for evolution to fill than in more temperate regions.

It's for that reason – that pathogens and parasites are doing just what you'd expect given the latitudinal gradient of biodiversity – that you can't just write off the prevalence of disease organisms in the tropics as being due to the fact that many low-income countries with poor health-care systems are clustered around the equator as well. Even when you control for economics, the tropics are still home to the most pathogens and parasites. There's no getting around the fact that the real problem is simply that the highest diversity of disease-causing organisms just happens to be in the same places where people are now penetrating and removing virgin forests or otherwise transforming the world's few remaining natural landscapes, bringing more people in contact with disease organisms they haven't had to worry about before. And given business as usual, that will only increase over the next couple of decades.

Just this ecological encroachment – let alone the multiplier of climate change, which we'll talk about a little later in this chapter – makes it highly likely that we'll see an increase in cases of infectious diseases we already know about, and the emergence of some new ones in places where we aren't used to seeing them. And the spillover of disease from one species to another will be a two-way street. Not only will humans be picking up more diseases from coming into closer contact with animals that we now live apart from, but other animals and plants, some of which people depend upon for food, shelter or cold hard cash, will be picking up more diseases from us.

Let's return to the tragedy of Ebola to see how the spillover effect works both ways. Ebola is a member of the family of filoviruses, lethal haemorrhagic fevers that infect humans and some wild mammals, including gorillas, chimpanzees, macaques and pigs. Of the five identified species of Ebola, three have been associated with disease in Africa, and the other two were found in the Philippines and China. The spillover from wild animals to humans sometimes occurs from handling dead infected animals from the forest, which happens frequently, because the hunting of 'bush meat' is still common practice among many African communities, for whom it supplies much of their necessary protein. Early on, it was thought that Ebola jumped from gorillas or other large animals to humans in exactly that way. But with more study, a gorilla reservoir for the disease made little sense. When gorillas get Ebola, they die at even higher percentages than humans do. A 2003 outbreak in the Democratic Republic of the Congo killed 114 people, but the same outbreak killed eight hundred western lowland gorillas in the same region, or two out of every three that lived there. By 2005, tens of thousands of gorillas in that area had succumbed in a catastrophic die-off that killed 90 per cent of the population, with a mortality rate of up to 97 per cent. The strong social connections within gorilla families – just like in human families – probably heightened infection rates, but mortality in the gorillas was much higher than in humans. Which meant it probably wasn't the gorillas that were harbouring the virus; they, like humans, were probably victims of the spillover from some other species.

That other species may well have been bats. We now suspect bats as likely sources of Ebola spillover because experimentally, when inoculated with a high Ebola viral load, they do not get ill. In addition, scientists have found genetically diverse strains of filoviruses (not yet Ebola, however) circulating within and between bat populations. These features of bats and Ebola are consistent with a long-term evolution of the virus, which would also be promoted by the extraordinarily large numbers of individual bats and bat species. If bats are the reservoir, the spillover to humans could occur from eating fruit contaminated by bats (with their saliva, urine or faeces), or from spending time in mines or caves frequented by bats. It's not hard to imagine gorillas eating contaminated fruit as well.

Nor is it hard to imagine gorillas catching the virus from humans, rather than the other way round. We know that tourists frequently infect mountain gorillas in Virunga National Park in Rwanda with respiratory diseases, as do the people who live in nearby communities. Not used to these human colds and flu, the gorillas get very sick, and some die. This is bad not only for the gorillas, but for the people who live around them, who depend on ecotourist dollars to fuel their economy. The present Ebola outbreak has already impacted tourism to Africa. Estimates so far this year suggest that safari bookings are down by 20 to 70 per cent, even in parts of the continent thousands of kilometres to the south and east of the outbreak in western Africa. The World Bank has estimated that losses to Africa will be three to four billion dollars, and if the virus spreads significantly beyond the borders of Sierra Leone, Guinea and Liberia, they could mount to $32 billion.

Another spillover example is HIV/AIDS, a disease that has emerged just in our lifetimes and that shows how bad things can actually get, and how fast. HIV/AIDS was first recognised in humans in 1981. Before that, you might have worried a little about contracting easily treatable sexually-transmitted diseases like gonorrhoea or syphilis, but you didn't have to worry too much about dying from making love. But that all changed almost overnight. As with Ebola, the species from which HIV/AIDS spilled over into humans was elusive for a long time, but it is now thought to be the result of people hunting chimpanzees in tropical Africa. Unlike Ebola, HIV/AIDS is probably the result of a single spillover event. Since that unfortunate day, over sixty million people have become infected with HIV/AIDS, and over twenty-five million have died. It is the second leading cause of death from communicable disease, after respiratory infections, in adults in developing countries, and by the year 2020 it is projected to be the cause of 40 per cent of all global infectious disease. Treatment costs now are in the tens of billions of dollars, and that doesn't account for the lost productivity of the working population. In sub-Saharan Africa the disease has devastated the age structure, so that half the population of those countries is now under the age of fifteen. Life expectancy there is fifty-six years (compared to Japan's eighty-four years, or Italy's and Australia's eighty-three), and we have almost certainly not even witnessed some of the most critical long-term effects of HIV/AIDS, which are not apparent until you look back in time. Among the things the world has lost in those places is the wisdom of the elders, the tempering hand needed for stable societies. So HIV/AIDS may well play a hand in stealing societal stability, as well as in stealing tens of millions of individual lives.

It may be tempting to say, well, let's just get rid of the animal vectors of these horrific diseases. But eliminating the sources of disease in the wild is not an option. Take for example bats, the suspected spillover source for Ebola and clearly harbouring the diseases we found out about in Costa Rica. Killing bats would just lead to a whole new set of problems, including the likelihood of actually increasing, not decreasing, pathogens and the unravelling of the beneficial services bats provide to us. As was pointed out at the beginning of this chapter, bats are vital members of the global ecosystem, which means they are vital to us. We mentioned that they pollinate plants – indeed, more than 450 economically significant plants including mangoes, peaches, avocados, wild bananas and agave, which is, incidentally, the source of tequila, depend on bat pollination. Bats also disperse the seeds of plants that produce food and medicine, and their guano has served as an exceptional fertiliser for over 150 years.

More to the point when it comes to infectious diseases, 70 per cent of the 1,100-plus bat species eat insects. A single individual can consume over a thousand mosquitoes in an hour. This 'ecosystem service' is critical, because mosquitoes – some three thousand species of them – spread their own version of disease carnage. And those are diseases we *really* have to fear. Mosquitoes transmit diseases that infect three hundred to five hundred million people each year, and kill more than a million – far more than the infections and deaths from Ebola since it was recognised in 1976. To put it in perspective, by December 2014, on average one person had died of Ebola for every seventy-eight thousand who succumbed to malaria. But that's not a statistic that usually makes the news.

Different species of mosquito carry different diseases. For example, *Aedes aegypti*, originally from Africa and now found in tropical and subtropical regions globally, carries yellow fever, dengue fever and chikungunya (we'll say more about this disease later). The mosquitoes responsible for carrying malaria, which results in over six hundred thousand deaths per year, are species in the genus *Anopheles*. These scientific names can sometimes be revealing: *Anopheles* is Greek for 'good-for-nothing', a sentiment you can probably sympathise with if you've ever been in heavy mosquito country. More than 450 species of *Anopheles* have been recognised, over a hundred of which can transmit human malaria, several of them being resident in northern temperate latitudes.

Malaria is a prolific killer. Historically, it was a big problem in China, India, the United States and Europe. In China and India, malarial fevers were written about thousands of years ago, and some accounts implicate malaria in the death of Alexander the Great. In Europe, malaria has waxed and waned over the past millennia. Some authorities suggest a particularly severe form of the sickness contributed to the fall of the Roman Empire in the fifth century AD, and malarial fevers ('the ague') were cited by Chaucer and Shakespeare during the fourteenth and sixteenth centuries respectively. European explorers and their slaves gave malaria to American indigenous populations when the infected intruders infected the resident *Anopheles* mosquitoes, which then infected the indigenous people. Many of those indigenous Americans succumbed to malaria and other diseases such as smallpox well before they were engaged in war by Europeans. Malaria had taken a strong hold in the United States by the mid-eighteenth century, and by 1870 it caused at least 14 per cent of all deaths, primarily in the south and east. And westward expansion brought malaria right along with it. By the middle of the nineteenth century, one in ten people worldwide could expect to die of the disease.

Such mosquito-borne diseases limited what people could do in many parts of the world for a long, long time, even slowing down the building of one of the world's most important economic routes, the Panama Canal. The canal today sees the passage of 70 per cent of all cargo imported to the United States and 5 per cent of all global seaborne trade, and the fees it generates earn almost $1 billion annually for Panama. The Canal Zone sits at the same latitude (8°N) as, and just two hundred miles east from, where we were trapping bats in Costa Rica, so the mosquito problems people were facing there a century ago resonate. During the early building phase around the turn of the twentieth century, the French lost over twenty thousand men, mainly to mosquito-borne diseases. So when the United States took over, it was regarded as an essential part of the mission to kill mosquitoes. Liz's grandmother, Anne McKell, gives some inkling of just what that involved. In 1917 Anne's father was on military assignment to the Panama Canal, which had opened in August 1914. Then a child of ten, Anne and her brother David spent a lot of time playing in the forest. And mosquito control was still on everybody's mind, as her later memoirs bring to life:

When Daddy had leisure he took us for walks down the peninsula. The beaches there were sand, and the color effects were beautiful. There were the ever-present palm trees, hanging orchids, birds and butterflies flashing back and forth. I still remember the terrible glare as we came out of the shady jungle. There were trails Daddy knew through the jungle. You couldn't see the sky, but the huge blue butterflies and others would fly, in contrast to the green of the jungle. Underneath was not so pleasant. There were large crabs with blue legs and a profusion of small red crabs with black legs. Sometimes one would be smashed and there would be a mass of black ants. Eventually the trails would emerge into intense sunlight with white beaches. The sky was usually a brilliant blue. Of course being in the tropics there could be heavy rain[storms], but for some reason I can't remember them, except for the sound, a roar, they made on the tin roof of our house ... It took constant vigilance, [but] the Americans had just finished conquering yellow fever. On our walks in the jungle we would find every puddle of water covered with black oil to kill the mosquito larvae. There would be natives with containers around their necks squirting the oil. If you found a mosquito in your house you were required to phone the dispensary and a man would come out, catch the mosquito alive and take it to the lab. Anyone who went out after dark had to take quinine.

Even so, well into the 1940s, hundreds of Americans were infected in the Canal Zone, and many died. The two world wars brought a renewed assault by the disease. During the First World War, about 80 per cent of the French army in Macedonia was hospitalised with malaria, and more than 160,000 British troops there were so sick from the disease that they were admitted to hospitals in the two years from 1916 to 1918, in contrast to approximately twenty-three thousand killed or wounded in battle in the same area during that time. In the Second World War, half a million US soldiers were stricken by the disease's debilitating high fevers, and over sixty thousand of them died. Malaria became so common that soldiers referred to the *Anopheles* mosquito as 'Ann' (we would be curious to know how Liz's grandmother felt about that). Later, thousands of American soldiers were infected in the jungles of Vietnam and brought the disease back home, reviving the nation's anti-malaria efforts. Just what a killer malaria actually was, and is, jumps out from a simple statistic: adding up all the wars the United States fought in the twentieth century, malaria killed more troops than were killed by bullets: the US military has called it 'Enemy Number One'.

All of which makes you realise why it was such a high priority to develop drugs to combat malaria, and to attempt to eradicate it inside US borders. That was finally accomplished by the heavy use of insecticides, primarily DDT, and in 1951 the US declared itself malaria-free. Similar measures resulted in the elimination of endemic malaria in Europe by 1975. Even so, thousands of malaria-infected travellers still enter the US and Europe every year, enabling malaria to re-infect resident mosquitoes. Up to now, aggressive mosquito control has prevented the re-establishment of the disease, but our future may well be very different.

Malaria and its vector, the mosquito, are poised to stage a comeback. Not only has our ability to control mosquitoes been hampered by their rapid evolution in just over a decade to resist insecticides, but our ability to combat the disease itself has been compromised by the rapid evolution of the parasite as well. Several of the malaria species that commonly infect humans in the Old World tropics have evolved resistance to antimalarial drugs, and the interaction, or cross-resistance, to one drug often confers resistance to another.

And then climate change comes into the mix. Mosquitoes are one of the disease vectors with the highest species diversity in the tropics: over two thousand identified mosquito species are found near the equator, dropping rapidly to below two hundred species by 50°N or 50°S. Besides malaria, tropical mosquitoes carry such debilitating diseases as West Nile virus, dengue fever, yellow fever and others. Given patterns of global climate change, the habitats for these disease-bearing mosquito species are spreading far and wide. In 1999, for example, West Nile virus first became established in New York, and proliferated there due to an unusually warm, dry spring and summer that probably concentrated mosquitoes and birds, which the disease also infects, around shrinking water sources. More and more mosquitoes bit and infected more and more birds, building up the frequency of the virus in the mosquito and bird populations. The same mosquitoes then bit people, and within six years the virus had infected people across the continent. To make matters worse, climate change is implicated in both the geographic and seasonal expansion of the virus. As we write this, our local newspapers are once again reporting that people are falling ill from West Nile virus in our California community, which now happens every summer – the disease first reached us just five years after it made its debut in New York.

Travelling in South Asia, Central America and tropical South America and Africa, we just accept mosquitoes as a daily threat. The rooms we sleep in have mosquito nets or plug-in lamps that emit chemicals nasty enough to kill the annoying little buzzers. Even on hot days we wear long sleeves, and we always use insect repellent. We keep our yellow fever shots up to date, but vaccines aren't available for malaria, so if we're in a place where it is rampant, sometimes we take prophylactic drugs – some of which have the known side-effect of literally driving you crazy. On returning home to California, we're always grateful that we don't have to take these precautions there – yet. But it's beginning to look as if sitting on the porch as the sun goes down will soon be a riskier way to spend the evening even in the United States.

Just how persistently these mosquito-borne viruses are knocking on the door is becoming all too evident, and not only West Nile virus. The march of mosquitoes out of the tropics, carrying the diseases they infect us with, is one more illustration of the potency of the interaction effects magnifying global problems. In this case it starts with people travelling more and more from one part of the globe to another, a byproduct of our interconnected global trade system. Business travellers and tourists visit tropical places and then return home, goods are shipped from tropical to temperate areas, and so on. Mosquitoes hitchhike in planes or shipping containers, or travellers who were infected in far-flung places bring the pathogens home, and the resident mosquitoes then pick up the parasites or viruses and pass them on. In the past this was less of a problem, because the climate in temperate regions wasn't right for the hitchhiking tropical mosquitoes. But, as we've seen with West Nile virus, that's no longer the case. As things have warmed up, the range of places those disease-carrying mosquitoes can be happy is increasing. Computer modelling of their climate-triggered range expansions show that they are likely to continue expanding into higher elevations and higher latitudes that will soon – or that already – have the temperature and precipitation required for them to thrive. All that's needed now is for new viruses to show up in those expanding mosquito populations, and then, just like West Nile virus, another new disease will be jumping into millions of people who have never been near the tropics.

Unfortunately, that scenario is already playing out with a crippling disease called chikungunya ('chi-kun-GOON-ya'), which in the Makonde language means 'that which bends up'. The disease's other name is break-bone fever, which sums up how bad it makes you feel. Chikungunya causes intense, crippling pain in those infected, for days, weeks – even the rest of their lives in some cases. There is no known treatment except painkillers. It is carried by the aggressive *Aedes* mosquitoes, two species of which are already resident in the United States: *Aedes aegypti*, of yellow fever and dengue fever fame, probably came during the slave trade, and again across the Pacific from Asia. Another species, the big, stripy Asian tiger mosquito *Aedes albopictus*, apparently caught a ride on a plane or in a shipping container and ended up settling in North America about 1985. It's also resident in Europe now.

Tiger mosquitoes are known to host twenty viruses that cause disease in humans, including dengue fever and West Nile virus – and also chikungunya. They are particularly dangerous disease vectors because, although they love living near and biting humans, they are cosmopolitan in their tastes. An individual mosquito will bite birds, other mammals and usually more than one person. So all that different blood, with all those different species' and individuals' parasites and diseases, gets nicely blended in the mosquito's digestive tract. And then the mosquito spits all that disease into you.

Once tiger mosquitoes arrived in North America, they quickly spread to twenty-five south-eastern and central states, helped along by the used-tyre trade; they are hardy, breeding in the tiniest pools of water, including dribbles that tend to persist in old tyres after rain, or that accumulate from the dew. Just recently, tiger mosquitoes have also made it to several counties in California, spreading from shipments of the popular houseplant 'lucky bamboo' from Asia, and they are thriving in their new homes – 'lucky' indeed. It seems only a matter of time before the species colonises most of North America, given the warming climate that will allow it to further expand its range out of its present strongholds. So the mosquito is ready; all that is required to make us miserable is for the chikungunya virus to become a persistent ingredient in its disease-vector spit-brew.

Which we are now seeing happen. In the winter of 2013–14 we had our first inkling of things to come. Headlines from the Caribbean started trickling in describing people suffering from chikungunya, which had never been seen there before. First documented in sixty-six people from the island of St Martin in December 2013, the disease was already infecting people in four other islands by January 2014. It spread like wildfire, jumping from island to island, and had infected more than a million people across the Americas by the end of the year.

The geographic spread of the 2014 chikungunya outbreak was extraordinary, facilitated perhaps by the involvement of at least two species of mosquito that could transmit the virus, and by the frequent travel of people between islands and mainland North and South America. By the end of 2014, chikungunya was resident in the Caribbean, Central America and several countries in South America. In the United States it has been diagnosed in more than five hundred travellers from the Caribbean, from all but four of the lower forty-eight states (as of 21 December 2014). Florida has documented several cases of locally acquired chikungunya, which means that some mosquitoes living there bit someone with the disease and became infected. Now they carry chikungunya, and can give it to anyone they bite. Which means that it is only a matter of time before most Americans will be faced with protecting themselves, day and night, against this debilitating disease that has just arrived, and others that both native and invading mosquitoes will be bringing in the future. That future, of course, is not only an American one – it's the same story globally.

So here we are, a century after Liz's grandmother was told, as she stepped around oil-filmed pools and reported mosquito sightings, that the US Army had 'conquered' yellow fever along the banks of the Panama Canal. But the real lesson of that narrative is that conquering disease is at best a short-lived victory. Yellow fever and malaria are still rampant in the tropics, and we're still fighting them. But now they're spreading, as are other diseases that weren't on the radar screen a century ago – like chikungunya and Ebola –

and killer diseases that didn't even exist in the human population back then, like HIV/AIDS. It's an evolutionary arms race out there, with disease-causing organisms and vectors evolving and moving as fast as we think we've found ways to guard against them.

That's always been the case, and always will be. What's different now, though, and what is sure to characterise our future as well, is three important contributors to the spread of disease. The first is billions more people in the world, which means the encroachment of more people into places where disease has always lived but people didn't – leading to increased spillover of new diseases for humans. The second is the already highly globalised world – more people travelling, and more goods being delivered from one side of the world to the other, which means that disease vectors and infections can spread at warp speed, compared to how they used to. And the third factor is climate change, which means disease vectors and diseases that are so abundant in equatorial regions will, more and more often, be able to thrive in northern and southern latitudes. All of that adds up to a heavier disease load in people. Which, if you recall the concept of Disability Adjusted Life Years (DALYs) from the previous chapter, results in millions more person-years lost to ill health, and mounting death tolls.

The take-home message here is that we're not going to avoid the emergence of new diseases and the spread of many we already know about – there is just no way to override the basic biology of the situation, given the global changes under way and the speed at which disease organisms and vectors evolve resistance to our best efforts to kill them. So the best way to deal with the future of disease is to be ready to act fast when emergencies flare up – that is, expect the unexpected. This means a hitherto unprecedented level of international cooperation to guard against both the underlying causes of diseases, and when disease takes hold, to prevent its spread to pandemic proportions.

A key strategy in guarding against outbreaks in the first place is to stop the encroachment of people into the few remaining tropical forests and other such highly biodiverse areas; that is, stop converting such areas to logging operations, cattle ranches, mining camps and palm-oil plantations. This, of course, would have multiple benefits over and above minimising disease spillover; these same areas are where two-thirds of all land-based species on Earth live, so destroying them would also doom most species on the planet to extinction. (Clearly the extinction issue is a huge one, but we don't dwell on it in this book because it has been well treated in two recent books: Elizabeth Kolbert's *The Sixth Extinction: An Unnatural History*, Holt, 2014; and Anthony D. Barnosky's *Dodging Extinction: Power, Food, Money and the Future of Life on Earth*, University of California Press, 2014.) Tropical and subtropical forests also remove an enormous amount of CO_2 from the atmosphere and absorb it for photosynthesis, so for every acre we cut down, the greenhouse-gas problem gets worse; in addition, rainforests make their own rain, so to speak, therefore destroying them also turns what are now wet regions into dry ones. The international driver of the spillover problem, as well as all of these related ones, is the global markets that make destroying highly biodiverse regions profitable in the short term. Those markets could be altered by trading in the dollar value of ecosystem services, like carbon sequestration or ecotourism, which in the long run can generate much more revenue than one-shot deals like logging, or even converting forest to farm.

Another hedge against spillover may well lie in international efforts, funded by NGOs and developed countries, to help communities in the midst of spillover regions replace the necessary protein they get from bush meat with domesticated sources, such as poultry. Efforts to do this have already been begun in some African locales, but they take time, because a switch from hunting to eating shop-bought food involves a big cultural shift. It also involves facilitating an economic system that provides access to jobs and money. The extent to which globalisation, with its byproduct of moving people and goods around the world, helps or becomes part of the spreading-disease problem in such cases remains to be seen.

For diseases we already know are going to be a problem, like Ebola and chikungunya, it's likely that vaccines or drugs to deal with the worst effects will eventually be discovered. In fact, vaccine trials for both are already under way. But, as we've seen with both diseases, vaccines just can't be developed fast enough to stop them from taking a firm hold and becoming essentially everlasting problems. So, the key is preventing the rapid spread from their centres of origin in the first place. That is much easier said than done, but a helpful first line of response may well be, in places of known outbreak – likely to be in tropical countries – to emplace strict health screening in airports and other transportation hubs, and strict quarantine procedures *before* people get on planes, which also requires assessing and increasing their efficacy. These wouldn't be popular with travellers or residents of infected areas, of course, and would involve a level of global bureaucracy that doesn't exist yet, but that may well be the kind of world we're looking at in the worst-case scenarios. Just how unpopular such necessities would be is illustrated all too well by a *New York Times* story on 20 August 2014: 'Liberia's halting efforts to contain the Ebola outbreak spreading across parts of West Africa quickly turned violent on Wednesday when angry young men hurled rocks and stormed barbed-wire barricades, trying to break out of a neighborhood here that had been cordoned off by the government' (Norimitsu Onishi, www. nytimes.com/2014/08/21/world/africa/ebola-outbreak-liberia-quarantine.html).

For diseases like mosquito-borne illnesses, it's all too tempting to attack the vectors as a first response. DDT worked extremely well for getting rid of the mosquitoes that cause malaria and yellow fever, for a while anyway, but as we saw in the previous chapter, it was not so great for almost everything else, causing all manner of environmental devastation. So the long-term solutions are probably going to lie in preventative measures: things like bug-repellant (not without its own health problems in some instances), long-sleeved shirts, sleeping under mosquito nets, and so on. These are relatively simple fixes, but they require a significant amount of international cooperation to educate people in high-occurrence regions, and also to provide the material things (like mosquito nets) that poor people need but can't afford. And, for diseases for which vaccines and drugs are available, it will require not only international cooperation, but also a significant monetary commitment to get the drugs to the people who need them. These days, both can be in short supply, as illustrated by the lack of access to HIV/AIDS medications in many parts of Africa and other poor regions in South-East Asia.

Putting the information in this chapter together with what we've written about in the previous ones, you may be getting the message that international cooperation figures in the future of global health in a big way, and is not only a necessary part of the solution for dealing with new and persistent diseases, but for dealing with all of the problems we've covered. Unfortunately, world cooperation has not been going so well lately. Which brings us to a final problem: war.

9

WAR

Liz, Rwanda, August 2012

Spending time with a gorilla family is an experience like no other I have ever had. They are enormous animals, and they are even larger than I expected once I am amidst them. When I gaze at them, their warm brown eyes look directly back at me, their stares penetrating. There is no doubt that 'someone' is in there. Our guide softly grunts to the silverback – he talks gorilla-speak, and can interpret the sounds the gorilla family makes – about food, about play, about us. I feel so safe, and I feel as if I am falling in love. That first day I was surrounded by several calm young ones and their mothers, a few younger males, and at least one very pregnant female. They were resting peacefully, females grooming females and the young ones wrestling. The silverback was lying down at the edge of the group with his head resting on his hand just like Rodin's *The Thinker*. As his eyes wandered over the group he watched a curious baby that ventured near me, reaching out to touch me. The babies ran in loops up the vines and down again, supervised by their mothers. They played just like human babies play, only they were much more agile in the trees. At the end they collapsed, exhausted, into their mothers' arms to be nursed.

I was reluctant to leave, because it felt so tranquil and protected and happy there. As I walked away I looked back, and saw that one of the gorillas had climbed a tall tree to watch us leave. I had no doubt about their intelligence, about the strength of their family bonds, about how gentle they were as parents – and about how powerful they could be if threatened.

But I was also moved by a sudden awareness that the silverback I had lain down next to had witnessed the genocide that had gripped this place only eighteen years before. He was most certainly alive then – his silver back and his size put his age at well over two decades – and judging by the signs of war that still marked his troop, he had probably seen people killing each other. He had almost certainly seen his black-backed brother maimed, now one-handed from being caught in a snare for bush meat. And like most humans in the country, that silverback had probably seen members of his family brutally killed during that terrible time: the gorillas were slaughtered just as wantonly as people, either for food or money, or out of blind anger. Somehow that knowledge, that this gorilla had had a front-row seat in witnessing man's inhumanity to man and beast, made me full of despair. He was so gentle, so powerful, and he was one of the very last remnants of his species.

I had been pensive about Rwanda and the plight of its gorillas even as we were bouncing up the rough road into the Virunga Mountains where they live. I was a faculty guide on a Stanford-sponsored travel-study trip, trying to make sense of all I was seeing, wondering what the other travellers were feeling. One thing we were feeling for sure was lucky – lucky that we had never experienced the horror of the Rwandan genocide directly, and lucky that we were able to see the gorillas at all. There are only 880 mountain gorillas left in the world, half of them here in the Virunga Mountains, hanging on by the skin of their teeth and by virtue of the ecotourism dollars they generate for the surrounding communities. A maximum of sixty-four people are allowed to visit the gorillas each day, with only eight per group. Day and night, rangers closely watch the few gorilla families that tourists are permitted to see. Most of the rangers, like our guides, are former poachers, so they know the country and the gorillas well. They all carry guns, and memories. Our driver, a man of about forty, told us all but one of his siblings had been killed during the genocide. He now works with the people who murdered his family.

At the end of the road, we began our hike up the mountain, first across farms and through tiny patches of cultivated land next to mud-brick houses covered with tin. Most of the people here have no running water or electricity, and the outhouses in the middle of the fields are mobile, so that human waste can fertilise the potatoes. Soon we crossed a rock wall, built to prevent the elephants and forest buffalo from the protected slopes of the volcanoes of the national park, our destination, from trampling the fields. Elephants are rare now, but the wall still marks the boundary between cultivated lands and the wild. Just eighteen years earlier, though, there had been no boundaries at all when the people went wild. During the genocide the park was a battlefield. It was land-mined, men with machetes and guns roamed it, and tens of thousands of refugees streamed through the forest, searching for a way out of the country, a hiding place, and food and water. Keeping gorillas alive was the last thing on their minds. Then, it was all they could do to keep themselves alive.

We had flown into Rwanda two days before, fresh out of the wide-open, peaceful Maasai Mara in Kenya, and although I was excited about spending time among the gorillas in Rwanda, I was apprehensive about where I had to go to see them. I remembered reading about the Rwandan genocide when it was happening; I was pregnant with our first child, Emma, at the time, and on the cusp of bringing a new life into the world, it seemed inconceivable that people could descend into such savagery. Reading about it was one thing, but going to where it had actually happened was something else entirely. Coming in for our landing at Kigali International Airport, we flew over the old palace of President Juvénal Habyarimana, which is now a testament to his violent death and the ensuing chaos. As his plane approached the runway on 6 April 1994 it was shot down, and he and eleven others died as it crashed into the palace we were flying over. Pieces of the wreckage are still there.

What followed was madness. Twenty per cent of the country's people were massacred in a few short months – a million souls. Another 40 per cent fled the country, running from the horrific things going on around them. The green countryside ran red with blood as neighbours dismembered neighbours. Killing gangs targeted women and children, and before death came repeated, brutal rapes and sexual mutilations of both men and women. Dogs roamed the streets and fed off human carcasses. The most difficult thing for me to understand is that murders were most rampant in the places where everyone knew everyone else, notably rural areas. I guess when you know everyone, it's easier to identify exactly who you want to kill. I still don't really understand how neighbours and families turned on each other overnight, how machetes made to conquer the forest ended up crushing a culture.

Before heading up the mountain to the gorillas, we had gone to the Kigali Genocide Memorial Centre, which records the horrors. It was hard to find words afterwards, difficult to even muster the energy to speak. Pieces of more than 250,000 dead people, all of whom had been interred in mass graves, are jumbled together there, stacks and stacks of skulls, ribs, leg bones, arm bones. The museum is a place of silence and reflection, and of pain. Photos of once-smiling people hang throughout, a poignant contrast to the recorded stories of survivors.

One of them was Eric. He was thirteen years old at the time. Here's what he remembers.

> In my search for a hideout, I found Jérôme, his legs cut off. I could not leave him in this state. I tried to lift up Jérôme so that we could leave together, but the car of the commune stopped near me. It was full of machetes and other instruments of death. I lay Jérôme down on the ground and ran because a man got out of the burgomaster's car to kill me. He finished Jérôme off. I saw this when I looked back to see if anyone had followed me. I will never forget the way Jérôme's face was filled with desperation. Whenever I think about it, I cry all day long.

It's easy to say that Rwanda is in the past, that such terrible events could never happen again, and that they could certainly never happen on a scale that would affect you and your loved ones. Yet those survivalists we mentioned in the first chapter are still stockpiling weapons, food and water, getting ready for the next descent into chaos. Just how well-founded might their fears be, given all the dangerous trends we've pointed out in past chapters?

It's worth taking a closer look at the lead-up to the Rwandan genocide to gain some perspective on that question. The specifics that lead up to every war are different, but the underlying pressures often show striking similarities: a history of cultural or religious differences among people living side by side; increasing numbers of people all wanting their share of something, either life's basics like food, water, fuel or jobs, or life's riches, like money, weapons or land; and the inability of the existing governments to make the situation any better. And in the lead-up to Rwanda, every one of these ingredients – grievance, need, greed, and lack of means to hold the bad things in check – was simmering in the cauldron.

The cultural rivalry was between the Tutsis and the Hutus. The short version of the massacre is that the majority Hutus annihilated about 70 per cent of the minority Tutsis in 1994. The resentments had built up over nearly a century. Colonialism played a role, as did religion, but the differences between the Tutsis and the Hutus were more about economics and class than about genetics, physical features, culture or heritage. Both groups share a Bantu origin. Tutsis were traditionally cattle herders, and Hutus farmers. Cattle being the currency of wealth in that part of Africa at the time (and still in many parts of Africa today), the Tutsis were regarded as the 'upper class', although Hutus could become Tutsis simply by acquiring enough cattle, at least prior to colonial occupation, first by Germany, then by Belgium. That social mobility largely came to a halt with Belgian rule, because of course the Belgians regarded themselves as the real upper class, and tended to favour those they regarded as the wealthier natives – the Tutsis – with appointments to government and other high-level positions. Hutus, who made up the majority of the population, basically became third-class citizens, which fostered simmering antipathies towards the Tutsis. As a result of the differences in religion and pressures from colonial rule, years of on-and-off social tension and violent skirmishes ensued. Thousands of Tutsis fled to neighbouring countries, enlisting the help of other refugees and locals in the training, education and support of rebel communities in exile. Hutus were killed, Tutsis were killed, and the grievances kept piling up.

At the same time, the population was skyrocketing, not only in Rwanda, but also in the neighbouring countries to which most of the Tutsis were fleeing: the Democratic Republic of the Congo (DRC), Uganda and Burundi. Between 1960 and 1990 the populations of Burundi and Uganda roughly doubled, and Rwanda's nearly tripled. This put severe strains on food supplies: by 1980, pretty much all of Rwanda's available agricultural land was being used, and although tiny, Rwanda became the most densely populated country in Africa. With the continued increase in population, the fields were hammered hard: crop rotation and fallow times were shortened, and the number of cattle per acre was increased. The result: depleted soil and diminished productivity. Another shortage was jobs – many young men had nothing productive to do, and to make matters worse, a quota system restricted Tutsi places in secondary schools, universities and the civil service to 9 per cent, which was the proportion of Tutsis in the population. That further fuelled the resentments between the two groups.

Further exacerbating the situation by the 1960s were widespread inefficiencies and corruption in the Hutu-dominated government, and continued attacks by Tutsi insurgents who often infiltrated from outside the country. In 1973 the instability at the top resulted in then-Defence Minister Major General Juvénal Habyarimana – a Hutu – overthrowing the elected president (also a Hutu), suspending the constitution and banning all political opposition. France also began to exert influence.

It was in this powder-keg that the genocide exploded. Rwanda had been in a civil war since 1990 or so. The minority Tutsis, who were then something like 15 per cent of the population, had been accorded some power-sharing by President Habyarimana, and a ceasefire agreement of joint governance led the majority Hutus to fear that the Tutsis were going to get too much power. At that point, the violent death of President Habyarimana catalysed ferocious anger and caused the madness to begin.

When Habyarimana's plane was shot down (who was actually responsible is still unclear), people were scrambling for food, for jobs, for basic health services and for power, and there was nothing but lawlessness to fill the power vacuum left by Habyarimana's death. The Hutus went wild and killed every Tutsi they could find. Tutsis killed Hutus. Another way to look at it is that Rwandans killed Rwandans.

Now, think about what's simmering today around the world. Start by substituting other names for Hutu and Tutsi. Like Jew and Arab. Or Russian and Ukrainian. Or Shia and Sunni. Or, on a broader scale, try Muslim and Christian. Or black versus white, Mexican versus American. There are no shortages of cultural, ethnic and religious differences these days.

The flashpoints for war, just as in Rwanda, will be places where deep-seated cultural or religious rivalries, high population growth from varying combinations of increasing births and immigration, shortages of things people need or want, and insecure governments intersect. As we've seen in all the previous chapters, there are already many such places, and there will be considerably more by 2050 – in fact, almost everywhere if we keep going as we have been.

National defence strategists know this all too well. Which is why they spend considerable time thinking about these things. Not only strategists in the countries where the flashpoints are actually likely to ignite, but also in the superpower nations, which are looking to what the future will hold for people within their borders as well as throughout the world. The United States, in particular, takes those war-producing intersections seriously, because, for better or for worse, it is the US that is typically the first responder when conflicts flare up, and the world expects it to be. Reasons aside – and sometimes the reason is to protect national interests, other times it's out of humanitarian considerations – the boots on the ground usually end up being military boots. As a result, at the top of the agenda for the leaders of the United States armed forces these days are most of the very issues we cover in this book: population growth, shortages of food, water, jobs and energy, and the rapidly changing climate.

We introduced the phrase 'threat multiplier' in Chapter 4, when we mentioned the CNA Corporation, the national defence think-tank with its headquarters right outside the Washington DC belt-way. It was actually the CNA that coined that phrase, in explaining how multiple threats came together to add up to more than the sum of their parts. Glance back to Chapter 4, where we listed the members of the CNA Military Advisory Board, just to remind yourself that this group involves commanders of all four branches of the armed forces: navy, army, air force and marines.

Reading their report, and talking to some of the hugely impres-sive military leaders and national defence strategists who collabo-rated in writing it, highlights an interesting cultural dichotomy for us – the divide between people concerned with global change and, shall we say, less liberal-leaning constituencies. It also highlights that the issues that divide those two communities are less real than is commonly perceived. Both of us come from families with strong military ties: Liz's brother flew helicopters for the army; her dad went through West Point and commanded troops in Vietnam, following in the footsteps of his grandfather, who battled across France during the First World War, seeing Germany from a hot-air balloon, and his father, who as a mobile hospital unit commander was on the front lines from Normandy to the Battle of the Bulge in the Second World War. Tony is named for an uncle killed on Iwo Jima in World War II, and his brother was a navy pilot whose son is presently a cadet at the Air Force Academy. Respect and deep love for one another notwithstanding, at family gatherings we find it best to be pretty careful. Conversations about environmental and population issues like those we write about in this book can all too easily go down the stereotypic path of the California touchy-feely science nerds versus the hard-core military realists. Yet here in a

2014 CNA report are hard-core military realists – commanders of every branch of the armed forces – worrying about the very issues we are, and mincing no words.

> As the world's population and living standards continue to grow, the projected climate impacts on the nexus of water, food, and energy security become more profound. Fresh water, food, and energy are inextricably linked, and the choices made over how these finite resources will be produced, distributed, and used will have increasing security implications.
>
> … the projected effects of climate change … are threat multipliers that will aggravate stressors abroad such as poverty, environmental degradation, political instability, and social tensions – conditions that can enable terrorist activity and other forms of violence.
>
> … The world has also become more politically complex and economically and financially interdependent. We believe it is no longer adequate to think of the projected climate impacts to any one region of the world in isolation. [CNA Military Advisory Board, *National Security and the Accelerating Risks of Climate Change*, May 2014, The CNA Corporation.]

That particular report focuses on the security risks of climate change, but makes clear that it is the threat multiplier effect that is the big worry: climate changes that exacerbate already looming shortages in food, water and energy within an overall context of rapidly growing populations, shifting political landscapes and unprecedented interconnectedness of countries. Stirring all of these things together in the same pot is what can boil over into war.

The report goes on to point out what is needed to avoid the worst-case scenarios: an end to what its authors call 'stovepipe thinking'. Stovepipe thinking includes compartmentalising seemingly different threats – population growth, resource shortages, climate change – rather than recognising and anticipating their interactions. Stovepipe thinking also includes focusing only on what goes on within national borders, rather than appreciating the global ramifications of local events. The Military Advisory Board draws this analogy:

> In the summer of 2001, it was, at least partly, stovepipes in the intelligence community and a failure of imagination by security analysts that made it possible for terrorists to use box cutters to hijack commercial planes and turn them into weapons targeting the World Trade Center and the Pentagon. Regarding these threats, the 9/11 Commission found 'The most important failure was one of imagination.' … Failure to think about how climate change might impact globally interrelated systems could be stovepipe thinking, while failure to consider how climate change might impact all elements of US National Power and security is a failure of imagination. [CNA Military Advisory Board, 2014.]

Bottom line: using the best information available from all sources, connecting the dots between interacting pieces, and using our considerable human intellect to imagine plausible outcomes, is going to be what keeps us out of trouble. Interspersed throughout this book we've connected the dots, as have others, for several recently past and present societal flare-ups: the 2012 riots in Pakistan (Chapter 1), crises in the Sudan region (Chapter 2), the Arab Spring uprising that began in 2010 and ended up deposing leaders in four countries by 2013 (Chapter 5), Somalia (Chapter 5),

Iraq (Chapter 6), and in this chapter, Rwanda. We've also presented a lot of information that makes it all too easy to use your imagination to see how the regional conflicts already under way will escalate as population continues to grow; as food, water and energy get even scarcer; as stovepipe thinking increases (in the sense of intense nationalism or only-my-way-is-the-right-way cultural or religious beliefs); as climate changes; and as governments become less secure in troubled parts of the world.

For instance, think about where the longstanding Israel–Palestine conflict could easily go. Fuelled by deeply entrenched cultural and religious differences, both sides have used women's wombs as one of the chief weapons in their arsenals, as pointed out by Alan Weisman in his book *Countdown* (Little, Brown & Co., 2013). As a result, population density in Palestine as of 2013 was about 734 people per square kilometre – nearly twice that of Rwanda when it exploded (and today). In the Gaza Strip, it's 4,661 people per square kilometre; even the more 'lightly' populated part of the country, the West Bank, crams in 481 people per square kilometre. In Israel it's around 370 people per square kilometre. Both countries have increased their populations by nearly 25 per cent over just the past two decades. By 2035, the Palestinian population is projected to increase by 60 per cent, the Israeli population by 40 per cent. Assuming the religious differences persist, which is a virtual certainty, the Jewish majority will no longer be decisive by 2035, when Jews will comprise about 53 per cent of the region's population.

Which means opposing factions and armies will be much more equal in terms of numbers. Especially in Palestine, the population pyramid is weighted by a large proportion of young people, unemployment is high and is likely to remain so, and competing factions fight for control of the government. Those things add up to a recipe for disaster on their own. Now take into account that all this is going on in a desert landscape. Water is already limiting. To grow food, Israel has diverted most of the Jordan River to irrigate the desert, with the usual problems of decreasing soil productivity as water evaporates leaving salts behind, and contaminating the water that returns to the river so that – again from Weisman's book – the place where Jesus purportedly bathed will now give you a rash, and if you drink the water, it will probably make you vomit.

And then comes climate change, which, for that part of the world, already water-stressed, is predicted to decrease water availability even more, and decrease food-growing capacity. Temperature is anticipated to rise about 0.3°C–0.5°C per decade (about 0.5°–1°F), precipitation to decrease overall but to fall as heavier, sometimes flooding storms, separated by longer droughts. Meaning, water issues aside, that more food will have to be purchased on the global market, which means economic hardship.

It also means more energy will be needed, both to pump water and to cool down buildings. Assuming the vast majority of the energy supplied to the region is from fossil fuels – which is likely, since that is the case now, and because Israel is just beginning to exploit newly-found natural gas reserves – more hot, still days will also mean more days when thick brown haze hangs in the air.

At the same time that the need for energy increases, energy costs for the region are likely to go up significantly, assuming no major changes in transforming the energy sector. Right now Israel controls almost all of the energy used in Palestine as well as its own, and the vast majority of that energy comes from fossil fuels purchased from outside the country. Even with further development of Israel's own natural gas fields, imports from other countries will remain necessary to fulfil much of the region's need for fossil fuels, especially considering how much adding tens of millions of people to the region will increase energy demands. As a result, more Israeli shekels will go to oil-producing countries instead of circulating through Israel and Palestine. More resentment will accrue if the increased costs of and demand for energy in the region also result in a reduction in the proportional allotments of Israeli-controlled energy to Palestine.

Overlaid on all these considerations, of course, is a long history of terrorism in the region in general, and emanating out of Palestine in particular. The seesaw of power within Palestine over the past decades, between Hamas, condemned as a terrorist group internationally, and Fatah, with roots in the Palestine Liberation Organization, is still shaky today. This has made it all too easy for radical factions to take matters in their own hands, in the form of suicide bombings and other random attacks on innocents to make political statements.

As they were in Rwanda, all the pieces are in place: animosities accumulated over generations, population growth, shrinking resources, a longstanding imbalance in the power structure that many people would like to see overturned, and factionalised government. To make it even more serious, the Israel–Palestine conflict also has some circumstances in place that were thankfully missing in the lead-up to the Rwandan genocide: nuclear capability, well-organised terrorist factions, and a setting in the midst of a broader region beset by similar problems. Bordering to the north is Lebanon, to the east are Jordan, Syria and Iraq. To the west and south are Egypt, Sudan and South Sudan, and next to Egypt is Libya. All of these countries are already showing signs of unrest, with factionalised populaces and precariously balanced governments. And, like Israel and Palestine, the changes coming down the road – population growth, and water, food and energy shortages exacerbated by climate change – are only going to make things worse if current trends continue.

It doesn't take a whole lot of imagination to see some very bad outcomes here. As a matter of fact, we pretty much laid one of them out for you in Chapter 1. Let's change the focal point from Egypt, where we started the war in Chapter 1, to the Israel–Palestine conflict. Here's one scenario. As the Palestinian population reaches critical mass to balance the numbers of Jews in the region, they demand more from Israel. Israel refuses, in part out of philosophical entrenchment, in part because it simply no longer has the resources to deal with so many people: the rains are less frequent, the soils are less productive, and the cost of oil, coal and natural gas has gone up as hundreds of millions more people – actually, over a billion more if we are talking about the year 2035 – worldwide are also demanding more energy in the global marketplace. One hot summer, nerves get frayed, resentments boil over, and Palestine steps up its terrorist attacks, killing many Jews in Jerusalem and Tel Aviv. Israel, in retaliation, unleashes destruction on the West Bank and the Gaza Strip.

Meanwhile, things are also tense in Egypt, Sudan, Lebanon, Jordan, Syria and Iraq. The same water, food and energy shortages that caused things to deteriorate in Israel and Palestine were also hitting hard throughout the Middle East. Islamic State was able to expand its influence through the 2020s, because the superpowers had been struggling to fulfil domestic expectations in a world where everything was getting scarcer, and had less will and fewer resources to engage in international support efforts. So, region-wide, the news of so many Muslims brutally killed in Palestine enrages Sunni and Shia alike, even in Jordan and Egypt, countries that have long been allies of Israel. It's the Sunni-dominated Islamic State that retaliates. Working with terrorist networks in Iran and Russia, it's been able to assemble a dirty nuclear bomb. Part of Jerusalem goes up in a brown mushroom cloud.

It's the last straw; Israel unleashes part of its nuclear arsenal on Islamic State strongholds in Syria and Iraq, and, having caught wind of Russia and Iran's involvement, also launches air strikes on

Tehran and the Chechnyan city of Grozny. Russia, incensed at the attack on its soil and in support of its oil-trading partner Iran, sends ground forces into Israel after first bombing it, and aims some of its warheads in the direction of Israel's ally, the United States. Russian troops and military aid also pour into Iran.

The United States, suddenly seeing a threat both from Russia and to the flow of oil from the Persian Gulf, aims its own warheads at Moscow and quickly works out agreements with Saudi Arabia and Kuwait, still its allies, to expand its military presence there, as well as re-invading Iraq to try to quell the Islamic State activity. The United States, Russia and the Middle East countries scramble into the Persian Gulf to gain control of the oil-shipping lanes. The European Union, caught geographically and philosophically in the middle, remembers the carnage of the Second World War, and tries to stay out of it, acting initially as a diplomacy broker. But still, France and Germany condemn Israel's bombings, straining relationships with the United States. In London, Paris, Amsterdam, Berlin, Vienna and Rome, suspicion and intolerance grow, as European-born residents and recent immigrants from the Arab nations take sides. The United Nations is conflicted, with some members coming down on the side of Israel and the United States, others arguing that the Arab nations and Russia are in the right.

Meanwhile, competing religious and philosophical factions take advantage of the situation in Saudi Arabia, Iraq, Syria, Yemen, Egypt, Libya, Sudan and South Sudan, and civil wars break out. The whole region descends into chaos. Because the populace is bottom-heavy with young people, child soldiers, bereft of experience and hope, roam the streets with automatic weapons and knives, looking out only for themselves. Terrorist groups move into the power vacuum, gaining many new recruits. Islamic State sympathisers, already sophisticated in their strategic approach, seize the opportunity to execute a coordinated attack they have been planning for years: all on the same day, bombs in the subways kill thousands in New York, Washington DC, San Francisco, London, Madrid and Rome.

Americans are incensed, and in a blind rage, many grab their guns and form vigilante groups that go after anyone who looks as if they could be Muslim – that is to say, pretty much anyone with dark hair and darker-than-white skin. In Europe, guns are harder to come by, so clubs and knives are the weapons of choice. Riots ensue, blood flows in the streets, social order breaks down, and the survivalists are in their element. Responding to strong public pressure, the United States government launches air strikes at the targets it believes responsible for fomenting the terrorist attacks: the Islamic State strongholds in several Middle East countries. The European Union jumps in, although there are splits within its ranks. The hits on the Middle East targets are shattering, killing many Russian troops in Iran as well as many Arab civilians there and in other countries. The Russian loss of life further polarises the two superpowers, which by now are poised for all-out nuclear war. The other nations of the world choose sides, based on which of the two superpowers they depend upon most for their economic well-being and such essentials as food and energy.

Meanwhile, China, yet another superpower, stays out of the fray and continues building inroads into places like resource-rich regions of Africa, South America and strategic parts of the Himalayan region. Its investments in infrastructure and business relationships in Central Africa – the DRC, Rwanda, Zambia, Zimbabwe, Angola, Burundi – are paying off. China has positioned itself well to benefit from the population explosion in Africa. With Chinese investment and technology, living standards in parts of Africa have increased just enough to provide buying power for many Chinese goods, bolstering China's economic growth. And Chinese, eager for new opportunity, have emigrated to Africa in droves, further staking their claim on resources there. Even so, the overall number of hungry people in Central Africa has increased since the beginning of the twenty-first century, leading to growing social unrest in that region too, so China has its own problems to manage. China by 2030 is less worried about the Middle East oil market than most, because, tired of the pollution that clouded its cities in the 20-teens, it has aggressively ramped up clean, renewable energy like solar and wind power, and has met its oil and gas needs by cutting deals with Mexico, Venezuela and Canada while phasing out dirty coal. Nevertheless, China knows it is just a matter of time before it has to come down on one side or other of the world conflict, because it needs natural gas from Russia, and also relies on imports of grain from the United States and its allies.

That's the kind of world we could be looking at within twenty years. Just how plausible is such a scenario? Pretty plausible, when you take into account what's already happening in the world. You can vary the specifics quite a bit and still come up with the same general story. Maybe the trigger point won't be Israel–Palestine. Maybe it will be Egypt and Ethiopia fighting to control the Nile. Or Pakistan and India making a grab for the dwindling water flowing out of the Himalayas as the glaciers finally disappear. Or maybe it will be climate refugees – or simply a steady stream of people in need of food, water or jobs surging across a national border because they can't get basic necessities in their country of origin, angering the longer-term residents by their different religions and their willingness to work for less pay. All of these dangerous scenarios, and many more, are already in the early stages of playing out today.

Need proof? Just look to places like Arizona, where vigilante groups have already formed in response to the influx of illegal immigrants surging across the Mexican–American border. Self-appointed gangs, often dressed in camouflage and sporting night-vision goggles, and always heavily armed, now roam the border region, stopping people they suspect of illegal immigration at gunpoint, raiding their homes and killing them. And as for the long-term views of superpowers today, while the United States is paying attention to and trying to mediate the flare-ups in Middle East hotspots, and Russia is making a grab for Ukraine, China is quietly and persistently investing in resource-rich places like Central Africa, South America and Nepal. In Rwanda, which has only five cars per thousand people – among the fewest in the world – wide highways built with Chinese funds stretch into the resource-rich DRC, which has untapped ores worth an estimated $24 trillion. In South America, China recently inked an oil deal with Venezuela, and is considering building a pipeline to carry Colombian crude to the Pacific coast. In Nepal, where much of the Himalayan water that quenches India and Pakistan's thirst originates, China gives the bordering Nepali villagers special ID cards so they can cross the border and buy from warehouses filled with Chinese goods. Access is via Chinese-funded roads that extend from the border and peter out a few miles inside Nepal, also providing a thoroughfare for illicit timber and other natural resources from otherwise inaccessible Himalayan mountain villages.

Wars in the future, of course, will not be anything new. Nice as it would be to live in a world where everybody loves and is kind to everyone else, that's just not the planet we live on, and seems never to have been. Even our genetic code tells us that early *Homo sapiens* first bred, and probably fought, with Neanderthals, before eventually wiping them off the face of the Earth. Since then, the conflicts have continued; it's been one fight after another, generally as more or less local skirmishes, but twice as all-out world war.

We're willing to accept the reality that some base level of conflict will be the normal condition for the human species for as long as the motives for war persist, which may well be forever, because those motives usually boil down to deep-seated cultural and religious beliefs, and the fear that by being open to other beliefs, you betray yourself and the ones you love. But the trick for keeping the future at least as good as today is to ensure that skirmishes do not increase in number, and that local flare-ups do not escalate into regional and global ones.

Which brings us back to the CNA's threat multipliers. Not liking someone for what they believe is hardly a justification for war, as long as you and that other person are both leading lives you consider comfortable. But when you need something that you think the other person is getting more than their fair share of, and especially if they are controlling the share you get, well, that's when not liking them can boil over into full-on combat. And if that something is essential to staying alive – like food, water, energy, or a roof over your head – it becomes all too easy to justify killing, especially if you are from a large group of have-nots, and war becomes inevitable.

It's not so much that running low on essential resources provides the motive for war – that's already there, at a much deeper, emotional level, rooted in longstanding beliefs that refuse to tolerate other beliefs. Running low on essential resources simply provides the perfect opportunity – the excuse, if you will – to act on the festering grudges that have built up over generations.

The trick then, insofar as keeping the future at least as good as today with respect to the frequency and intensity of war, is to limit the opportunities for conflicts to flare. Which translates to the same message we've been trying to convey throughout this book: minimising the threat multipliers of population growth, wasteful consumption and their downstream effects of climate change, fouling our nest, and shortages of food, water and energy. The scary thing is that we're not yet doing what's needed to minimise those threat multipliers; in fact, we're doing quite the opposite.

Again, straight out of the 2014 CNA report:

From today's baseline of 7.1 billion people, the world's population is expected to grow to more than 8 billion by 2025. The US National Intelligence Council assesses that by 2030, population growth and a burgeoning global middle class will result in a worldwide demand for 35 per cent more food and 50 per cent more energy. Rising temperatures across the middle latitudes of the world will increase the demand for water and energy. These growing demands will stress resources, constrain development, and increase competition among agriculture, energy production, and human sustenance. In light of projected climate change, stresses on the water–food–energy nexus are a mounting security concern across a growing segment of the world.

In the light of such assessments, are we destined to a future of more and more Rwanda-like atrocities? Will we tip into a new normal where rapes, lost loved ones, missing limbs, and dogs feeding on human carcasses become non-news, almost an everyday occurrence somewhere in the world? And out of fear of becoming involved, will we become ever more immune to these atrocities, and ever more isolationist in an attempt to keep control? Will the scars of today's war victims and returning veterans – so many permanently wounded by what they've seen, what's been done to them, and what they've done – become scars most of us are destined to suffer within our lifetimes? If we don't get a grip on the threat multipliers, and deal with them, the answer is almost certainly yes. The new normal for the world will be to tip into more and more horrific conflicts.

But maybe, just maybe, there's a way out. Because there actually is a better kind of tipping point that we still have a chance to experience, if we decide we want to.

10

END GAME?

Tony and Liz, NASA-Ames Research Center, Moffett Field, Mountain View, California, 26 May 2013

This was it. We had been basically flying by the seat of our pants for most of the past year. Now we were about to see if the landing would be smooth, or if we'd crash and burn. We were sitting in front of four hundred or so of Silicon Valley's finest, about to unveil an initiative we'd been devoting much of our lives to for months. Right there in the front row was the Governor of California, Jerry Brown. He'd be joining us on stage in just a few minutes, along with a few of our fellow scientists, to announce his take on what we'd been doing. Reporters and photographers crowded in, their tape recorders and big lenses poised for action, television cameras aimed and ready on their tripods.

It had all started almost three years earlier. Along with a group of our colleagues, we'd undertaken a scientific study that compared the state of the world today with how it had been about twelve thousand years ago, just before the planet tipped from the cold, glacial times it had been in for a hundred thousand years into the warmer, friendlier, interglacial time in which human civilisation as we know it advanced. What our team saw, as we pored over data for most of a year, was that the geological drivers of global change that had shoved the world from an ice age into the more hospitable planet on which we live today were immense. We'd seen that those past geological forces had lined up to push Earth over a tipping point – from a cold planet where much of the northern hemisphere was under a mile of ice, to a warmer place where people finally dispersed to every continent, the composition of plants and animals in any given place changed substantially, and half the world's big-bodied animals became extinct.

But the real revelation was that the forces that had pushed Earth over that previous tipping point were mild in comparison to the ways people are changing the planet today, both in terms of speed and strength. Which meant that Planet Earth is poised on the edge of another tipping point – one that we people are triggering, that we will feel in a big way, and that could take place in our lifetimes. We reported our findings in the journal *Nature* in June 2012, expecting it to be just another scientific study that fell by the wayside as the world went about its business. Instead, it had sent us here.

Tony: As I looked over the crowd, glad that my suit jacket was hiding my sweaty armpits and trying not to fidget, I thought about the wild ride of the last year. The news media had picked up on that *Nature* publication in a big way, and the next thing I knew I was getting hate emails – suggesting, for example, that I 'waste myself', and that my 'real master, Satan, has a special place in hell' for me – from people who seemed to take words like 'climate change' as a personal affront. That had certainly put a whole new perspective on doing science. An even more unexpected outcome, though, was that Governor Brown phoned one day, essentially a cold call that caught me by surprise when I was out on a run. He'd heard about the article, and wanted to know more about it. He also wondered why scientists weren't shouting it out from the rooftops if we really were heading for a planetary tipping point. That conversation made me realise that we scientists had just been talking to other scientists, when we really should be talking to the people who don't already know this stuff. And also, that dedicated world leaders were willing to listen. So a group of us wonky academics set out to communicate more clearly what we had learned, not only from the *Nature* study, but from thousands of other studies, about the chief environmental threats that had been published in scientific literature over the past several decades. Liz and I had lived and breathed this stuff late into many nights and through many weekends over the past year, and Emma and Clara were probably sick of hearing us talk about the state of the world over dinner. And here we were at last, trying to communicate what the scientific community knew, plainly yet accurately, to policymakers and business people in a very public way. I sure hoped I wouldn't screw it up.

Liz: I was sitting in the audience, proud that Tony, Emma and Clara were there too, but feeling a tad awkward in a purple dress and heels surrounded mostly by business suits. Not my typical scientific crowd, but I was really excited to be there. Next to me were a few of the other authors of the consensus statement, those we could round up at short notice: Paul and Anne Ehrlich, Rodolfo Dirzo and Steve Palumbi. I had brought with me an illustration that I had had mounted and framed – one that conveyed in picture form the message in the *Scientific Consensus Statement* we were about to deliver. I had been working with my technician Cheng 'Lily' Li, a talented young woman, as adept in the molecular lab as she is at art, to create a picture of the Earth on the edge of a cliff, about to tip from an idyllic utopia into a grey and dingy transformed landscape. The two most important features of the illustration (reproduced as the frontispiece to this book), which we intended to present to the

225

Governor, were that a person was holding the Earth back from its seemingly inevitable slide, and that in the background over the cliff was a gleaming cityscape, replete with trees and blue skies. That was the future we wanted to create, and that we believed was possible if enough time and energy were devoted to it.

For both of us, it clicked that we'd experienced a tipping point in our own lives since this had all started, going from academics who pretty much wanted simply to enjoy the doing and teaching of science, to feeling compelled to devote our time to communicating what we knew. And this was the perfect venue to be communicating what hard science said about the state of the world, because we were talking to people who were well equipped to take on the big challenges of the future. It was the 2013 SSV-WEST summit, an annual event put on by Sustainable Silicon Valley (SSV), a group that bills itself as a 'consortium of companies, governmental entities, academic and research institutions and non-profit organisations that work together to inspire collaboration, accelerate innovation, and encourage economic prosperity for a sustainable future'. The WEST part of the event's name is short for Water-Energy-Smart Technology. So besides Governor Brown, we were telling some of the world's most successful business people, innovators, venture capitalists and thought leaders why their talents were so desperately needed at this moment in history.

We watched as NASA's former chief scientist, Waleed Abdalati, showed graphs of temperatures rising through the decades and asked the audience, 'If this were a graph of stock performance, would you invest?' Yes, of course, they nodded. Then Jim Hansen, a well-known climate scientist who had headed the NASA Goddard Institute for Space Studies in New York, got up and explained why there is no time to waste in gearing up green-energy technologies if we are going to hold climate change to reasonable levels. Finally it was our turn. Our message was that, yes, climate change is a key challenge, but especially because it magnifies the impacts of the other major problems the world is facing – loss of biodiversity, using up so much of the land and sea, pollution, unchecked population growth, and our continual quest for more stuff. And that the interactions between these dangerous trends, and the ways in which they can rapidly multiply each other, is why Earth is now at a tipping point. Then the Governor gave his take: all of us need to get busy solving these problems, fast, or the world is going to be in big trouble.

At the end of the morning session we returned to the stage with Governor Brown, Paul and Anne Ehrlich, Steve Palumbi and Rodolfo Dirzo. We presented the Governor with the document we, along with ten other scientists from various institutions and countries, had spent so much time crafting over the past year. The *Scientific Consensus Statement on Maintaining Humanity's Life Support Systems in the 21st Century: Information for Policy Makers* was our response to Governor Brown's question about why scientists weren't shouting out the challenges from the rooftops. By that time the document had been endorsed by 522 of the world's leading global-change researchers, from forty-one countries around the world. Finally it was time to present him with the framed picture of Earth at the tipping point. The Governor pointed to the person holding up the planet and asked, 'Who's this little guy?' We all replied in unison, 'That's you.'

Governor Brown now has that picture hanging in his office in Sacramento, reminding him what one person, fearless and dedicated, can do. But we've since come to realise that the lone person in the picture in fact represents each and every one of us, buckling down to do all we can to make a better world. It looks insurmountable alone, but put us all together and we hit a good kind of tipping point – where a critical mass of the global society understands what Earth is up against, and wants to overcome the challenges.

At that point the end game changes – to one where people and the planet would thrive, rather than the one we've been heading towards.

Which end game we'll actually see is still up for grabs. As the previous chapters point out, the challenges humanity faces are enormous. If you are among the faint-hearted, a dose of depression may have set in after reading them, or a sinking feeling that since we're screwed anyway, let's just make the most of the time we've got left. We've been there too, in a place that almost anybody who begins to look at these problems in depth will find themselves. But what happened to us over the year leading up to the SSV-WEST summit began to give us some hope. Seemingly all of a sudden, people were caring about the big global issues that scientists had been documenting for years.

Which was a new thing for us. As researchers and university professors, we've been studying and teaching about these issues for more than three decades, as have many of our colleagues. And for most of those decades, the needle never seemed to move much. Oh sure, there were a few advances here and there – some lip service about population growth after Paul Ehrlich published *The Population Bomb* that he and Anne had worked on, and some real progress, for a while at least, on reducing some harmful pesticides after the publication of Rachel Carson's *Silent Spring* in 1962 – but for the most part the issues of climate change, extinctions, the destruction of non-human landscapes, pollution, population growth and overconsumption have been, for most people, just one big *blah*. And indeed, even for us, who studied and taught about these things for a living, it was all too easy to regard them as somebody else's problem.

That changed, though, as we immersed ourselves deeper and deeper into working first on the *Nature* paper and then on the

Scientific Consensus Statement. Somewhere along the line a light-bulb went on; it became all too evident that the things we were writing about weren't somebody else's problems, they were *every-body's* problems. Because no one was escaping the impacts, even if they thought they were. Us included.

If you strung together all of the things we have written about in the previous chapters into a science fiction novel about a species inexorably destroying its own life-support systems, you wouldn't believe it. It would be just too far-fetched. Yet nearly all of the things we've written about here have actually already happened, or are in the process of playing out right now. The reason we're seeing so many crises pop up one after the other – water shortages here, terrible storms there, a new disease outbreak that sets us scrambling, a humanitarian crisis in yet another place – are explained when you look at one of the key findings that came out of our *Nature* study. For the first time in our species' history, indeed in the entire planet's history, the Earth is being squeezed from the bottom up and from the top down simultaneously.

By 'from the bottom up' we mean that every building, farm or other new human construction takes away a little of what was there to support us before, even as it's adding something we may need in the short term. And the number of us just keeps growing, as is evident and made more tangible when you look at a global population counter, http://www.census.gov/popclock/. Add together all of what we've already done, and nearly half of the planet is different from what it was before we started – and more of it is transformed every day. Each one of those individual changes has downstream effects that add up to even bigger, separate impacts. Things like dead zones in the ocean, or too many greenhouse gases in the air. And those larger-scale manifestations of what we've done locally have in turn created a whole new set of global pressures that we, and all other species, have to react to and deal with: climate change, far more nitrogen than was normal in a pre-industrial world, endocrine disruptors everywhere, even in wilderness far from humans. Those global-scale pressures are what we mean by squeezing the planet from the top down.

We suspect it is the obvious impacts of those bottom-up plus top-down pressures – the things everyone is experiencing or hearing about on the news almost every day, like weird weather, water shortages, would-be immigrants pressing against national borders, a growing number of conflicts flaring up around the world – that made the results of our *Nature* article, among others, strike a chord with the public. That's what first made us think people were starting to take notice of the big challenges, and that they might, just might, be thinking it's time to do something about them.

That first ember of hope has been further kindled by what's happened with the *Scientific Consensus Statement*, and on a broader scale with other independent initiatives to effect the changes needed to address at least one of the big issues, climate change. For most of the past few decades we've rolled our eyes at the partisan bickering and the outright disbelief that people have anything to do with changing the planet's climate. Yet within the past year we've seen, at last, important action – action that is predicated on sound science. The presidents of the two biggest greenhouse-gas-emitting nations in the world, Barack Obama in the United States and Xi Jinping in China, have publicly recognised human-caused climate change as one of the world's most pressing problems, and both have taken actions, including a formal agreement between the two countries, to begin addressing it. Obama, hamstrung by a gridlocked Congress, convened a climate task force nevertheless, and has been aggressively pursuing actions that the US constitution grants the Executive Branch.

Meanwhile, other world leaders are breaking through political gridlock by developing workarounds at the supranational, national and subnational levels. The European Union, for example, has already set a target to reduce emissions overall by 20 per cent (compared to 1990 levels) by 2020, and Germany has gone all out, working to reduce its emissions by 40 per cent by 2020 and 80 per cent by 2050. In December 2014, delegates of nearly two hundred nations, heartened by the announcements that the US and China were acting to slow climate change, gathered in Lima, Peru, and came out with an agreement that each country would set limits to greenhouse-gas emissions within a year. At the subnational level, the state of California – significant because it is the world's seventh largest economy – has signed climate-change-mitigation and green-technology agreements with China, Canada and Mexico. The US Pacific states (collectively the world's fifth largest economy) signed a climate compact with British Columbia to decrease greenhouse-gas emissions and combat ocean acidification. And major cities like London, Manchester, Liverpool, Glasgow, Barcelona, Copenhagen, Hamburg, Rotterdam, Chicago, New York and San Francisco are planning how they can adapt to climate changes under way.

When lives are at stake, there is simply no room to put up with obstructionists. It's for that reason that the top leaders in the United States military publicly acknowledge that climate change is among the top threats to national security:

The national security risks of projected climate change are as serious as any challenges we have faced … We see more clearly now that while projected climate change should serve as a catalyst for change and cooperation, it can also be a catalyst for conflict. We are dismayed that discussions of climate change have become so polarizing and have receded from the arena of informed public discourse and debate. Political posturing and budgetary woes cannot be allowed to inhibit discussion and debate over what so many believe to be a salient national security concern for our nation. Each citizen must ask what he or she can do individually to mitigate climate change, and collectively what his or her local, state, and national leaders are doing to ensure that the world is sustained for future generations. Are your communities, businesses, and governments investing in the necessary resilience measures to lower the risks associated with climate change? In a world of high complex interdependence, how will climate change in the far corners of the world affect your life and those of your children and grandchildren? If the answers to any of these questions make you worried or uncomfortable, we urge you to become involved. Time and tide wait for no one. [*National Security and the Accelerating Risks of Climate Change*, CNA Military Advisory Board, May 2014.]

Money talks, too. Fossil-fuel magnates are building carbon taxes into their long-term business plans, and growth in the clean-energy sector is on a steep upward trend. On a larger scale, the CEOs of many of the biggest, most profitable corporations in the world have put together a long-term plan, Vision 2050, with decade-by-decade goals, that 'calls for a new agenda for business laying out a pathway to a world in which nine billion people can live well, and within the planet's resources, by mid-century' ('Vision 2050', World Business Council for Sustainable Development, http://www.wbcsd.org/vision2050.aspx).

Things are happening. What nobody knows yet, of course, is whether these moves in the right direction will continue, and critically important, whether they will accelerate fast enough. As we've seen in the previous chapters, the world has a very narrow window of time in which to change course. Basically we have to crank the rudder hard, starting pretty much now. If we do that, the bow will ever so slowly start to turn, and finally, in say around 2030, we'll be in line to chug full steam ahead towards a sustainable future. On the other hand, if we wait a decade or two to start cranking that rudder, it will be too late. We simply won't be able to turn Planet Earth fast enough to avoid a lot of unpleasantness. Very likely within our lifetimes, and certainly within our children's lifetimes, we'll see at first hand what a planetary tipping point looks like.

We get asked a lot what it would look like if the world went over the edge. A planetary tipping point is a vague notion at best, one that even many of our scientific colleagues have trouble wrapping their minds around. The gut reaction of most people is to envisage something like the Apocalypse – where the four horsemen of War, Famine, Pestilence and Death sweep through the world overnight. It's a tempting metaphor, but it's not the one the science we've done and seen would actually support. Well, not exactly anyway. Yes, as we've seen in previous chapters, there would indeed be elements of all four horsemen. But it's not the kind of change where one day things look rosy, and the next day the whole world has gone to hell and almost everybody and everything is dead.

Remember, from the first chapter, how tipping points actually work. What we're talking about is a change from the world we regard as normal today, to a new normal. The tipping point is when the 'normal' state crosses some critical threshold, at which point it *rapidly* shifts into a state that would previously have been considered unusual, and stays there – that's the 'new' normal. A key concept here is what is meant by the word 'rapid' – because 'rapid' in this context is relative to the amount of time the previous 'normal' state has existed. In ecological terms, the state we consider normal for the world today has actually been around, in some form, for about twelve thousand years. In societal terms it's more like a few centuries, starting with the Industrial Revolution. In either case, we're talking about a shift from the 'old normal' (the ecological and societal state we're used to) to a 'new normal' (where we'd end up after going over the tipping point) that takes place within a single human lifetime – say within thirty to fifty years. Maybe you think of that as gradual rather than sudden change, but in fact it's very sudden indeed, when compared to twelve thousand years, or even three hundred. And more to the point, it's something a single generation would have to cope with and adjust to. Born into one world, die in another. Just what would that adjustment to a new normal involve?

What we regard as normal today is actually a pretty high quality of life for a billion or so people, and, in more and more parts of the world, opportunities for those who are poor and suffering to improve their lot. We are used to seeing the human condition constantly improve, on average: longer lifespans, more material goods, more comfort, more opportunities for leisure. We are also used to a certain amount of human suffering: the billion or so people who are truly destitute, various humanitarian crises and wars flaring up at any given time, occasional droughts and floods, and, very rarely, disease outbreaks that for the most part we've been able to deal with. That is the normal state of the world, as far as most people are concerned, and we've been pretty complacent in assuming that's the way it's always going to be.

Going over a planetary tipping point, though, means that we will see a noticeable decrease in the good things in life, and a noticeable increase in the things we don't like. Will everybody die? No, of course not. Will upward trends in economic health and affordable essentials continue? No, those trends will flatten out, or start heading downwards. Access to clean water and adequate food? Hundreds of millions more people will want for these, rather than hundreds of millions more gaining them. Will we see a higher proportion of the world's population driven out of their homes by droughts, fires and flood? Absolutely. Humanitarian aid by developed nations? Less and less, as the resources of rich nations diminish. Will we see more local wars flaring up, driven largely by more people fighting for pieces of an ever-shrinking pie? You bet, maybe even world war. Will we have the ability to contain new diseases that are almost certain to appear? Probably not. Will people become complacent that this is just the way it is? They'll have no choice; there will be no going back.

That would be the new normal: a world that is simply not as rich, vibrant and good for human beings – or for most other species – as the world we live in today. Life would go on, but there would be a lot more losers than winners. And that would be our legacy to the future.

That's not just our own apocalyptic view; it's what ongoing trends and complex systems theory point to. We'd be remiss if we didn't call attention to criticisms of the whole idea of a planetary tipping point: some people, including some scientists, just don't think that tipping points – or in the scientific jargon, critical transitions – can happen at the scale of the whole planet. That ignores the fact that they've happened before, not just once, but many times: the glacial–interglacial transitions we've mentioned, for example, and things like mass extinctions, where some 75 per cent or more of known species die out in a geologically short time. Such things signal tipping points of the biggest kind, and are not out of line with the rate of biodiversity loss we're seeing currently.

The most thoughtful set of arguments against the concept of planetary-scale tipping points came out a year after our *Nature* study was published, in a paper that raised the question in its title: 'Does the Terrestrial Biosphere have Planetary Tipping Points?' in the journal *Trends in Ecology and Evolution* (abbreviated *TREE*), vol. 28, pp.396–401, 2013. It was published by a team of ecologists and geographers headed by Barry Brook from the University of

Adelaide in South Australia. Barry's a colleague – Tony has published a paper with him – so we thought long and hard about what they had to say.

Close reading of their arguments against planetary tipping points, though, reveals that even those critics agree that the dangerous trends we have covered have already changed, and are continuing to change, Planet Earth in dramatic ways. They are also quick to point out that there is no argument that tipping points are characteristic of biological changes from local to subcontinental scales, and that complex systems in particular change via tipping points. No one would disagree that ecosystems and their interaction with societies are complex systems of the most complex kind. That was clear enough in a companion paper in the same issue of *TREE*, this one by yet another international team of distinguished ecologists and theorists led by Terry Hughes from the Australian Research Council Centre of Excellence for Coral Reef Studies. In an article entitled 'Multiscale Regime Shifts and Planetary Boundaries', they wrote: 'The existence of thresholds and alternate states in many ecosystems at more local scales is not in doubt. Similarly, tipping points also occur in societies, in climate systems, and in coupled combinations of all three. At this stage in the evolution of the Earth, changes in society, ecosystems, and climate are intimately interconnected, and large-scale shifts in one become a driver of another' (pp.389–395).

But the Brook team took exception to the *planetary* tipping point concept because, in their words: 'Spatial heterogeneity in drivers and responses, and lack of strong continental interconnectivity, probably induce relatively smooth changes at the global scale, without an expectation of marked tipping patterns.' But as Hughes et al.'s article countered, the drivers-and-responses argument falls apart because it forgets that today there is mainly one ultimate driver, and that is humans.

End Game?

The lack-of-interconnectivity argument misses the important human component as well: these days all continents and all regional ecosystems are in fact intimately connected in a very direct way – by the billions of people who are physically moving back and forth across the planet, and by our global economy. Even in places where we don't set foot directly, we're still, pretty much simultaneously across the world, changing such basics for life as the atmosphere, the climate and biogeochemical cycles, resulting in, for example, unprecedented levels of nitrogen and mercury almost everywhere. Just think back to the examples we've pointed out in the previous chapters.

The third part of the Brook et al. contention – that the kind of change we'll see is more likely to be a smooth transition than an abrupt one – may just be a matter of perspective. Remember, we're talking about the changes that will play out in a human lifetime or two. To most people, especially if they're young, the passage of an entire human lifetime may seem very long. But compared to the twelve thousand years the ecosystems we're familiar with have been on Earth, or even the three hundred years since the Industrial Revolution, a human lifetime is short. So when it comes to recognising a planetary tipping point, passing through a critical transition that spreads out over several decades is still a rapid change relative to the length of time the conditions we've been taking for granted have persisted. And, in any case, as Hughes and his co-authors pointed out, it is a mistake to confuse 'the rate of change of a system, which may be fast and synchronous or slow and incremental, with the presence or absence of a tipping point. Crucially, a gradual ecological change through time can easily represent the lagged transient response of an ecosystem that has already passed a tipping point.' That is to say, a change can appear gradual, but can still push you over a tipping point once a critical threshold is passed – like gradually warming up an ice cube until it's warmer than the melting point, at which point it becomes inevitable that ice is going to turn to water, even though it may take a little longer for the cube to melt entirely.

This brings up another key question, which we get asked a lot: how do we know it's not too late? Have we already gone so far that, just like that ice cube that's sitting at room temperature, the tipping point is already past, in which case, there's nothing we can do to avoid bad scenarios?

We used to waffle a bit when we were asked that question, because it's undeniable that the changes we've seen since our grandparents' time have been more pronounced than those that have taken place over any two previous human generations. Clearly we already live in a different world today. But here's the important point: things have continued to get better in the world over the past couple of generations. On balance, the positive things that humans have done have outweighed the negative ones. The tipping point we're talking about is when the balance shifts, so the negative impacts outweigh the positive ones.

Which is exactly what seems inevitable if our present pace of climate change, extinctions, ecosystem loss, pollution and population growth continues. That's the new normal we're talking about. But, in theory at least, it's still possible to hold the balance of positive versus negative to what it is today, or even shift it more to the positive side. That's why it's not too late. There are things we can actually do to make the end game the one we want, rather than the one we mistakenly fall into.

We've talked in previous chapters about ways to turn around each of the dangerous trends. Just to recap, here's the broad brush.

Overpopulation: Educate women and provide economic opportunities and access to health care.

End Game?

Overconsumption: Spend money on experiences rather than things – which makes you happier anyway; design products with low environmental footprints in mind; and ramp up recycling/reuse efficiency worldwide.

Climate change: Replace fossil fuels with carbon-neutral energy sources.

Food: Increase efficiency in agriculture using environmentally sound methods; eat less meat; waste less food; improve food storage and distribution systems.

Water: International water compacts; waste less; contaminate less; more efficient agriculture; shift to wind and solar energy generation.

Pollution: Provide basic sanitation services to billions lacking them; convert waste products to energy; utilise 'green chemistry' in new product development; more closely regulate and monitor the use of herbicides, pesticides and antibiotics.

Disease: Keep track of vectors as they move across borders and through transportation systems; anticipate disease from the tropics; try to hold deforestation to an absolute minimum. And don't kill the bats – they are more significant ecosystem providers than they are disease distributors.

War: Hold population growth and climate change to lower levels; ensure adequate food, water, basic health services and education worldwide.

Something you might have noticed in reading through that list is that, while each problem has specific actions that are unique to it (for example, weaning ourselves from fossil fuels to fix climate change, or providing economic and educational opportunities for women to bring down birth rates), there is one common theme that runs through all the solutions.

And that is, there is no such thing as local any more. Every community on Earth is now connected to communities up the road and on the other side of the world through what we buy, what we eat, what we drink, how we make a living, and how we have fun. If you don't believe that, ask a Kansas farmer what would happen to his income if he couldn't export his wheat. Or take a look at the labels on the clothes you're wearing. Or where the apples you're eating in winter came from. There's no getting around it – we're all connected through a network of global trade, transportation and communication so vast that none of us can live the lifestyle we've become accustomed to without it.

This interconnectedness also means that there is now no nation on Earth that can support itself solely on what it produces within its borders. Even the superpowers like the United States bring in essential goods: for instance, after oil, America's next largest imports are machines, engines and pumps. No longer are they American-made. We import them from China, France, Japan, Germany, the UK, Spain and Brazil. America's favourite beer, the Budweiser that millions knock back on Super Bowl Sunday, is owned by a mega-brewing conglomerate based in Belgium and Brazil. China relies on other countries to supply raw materials for the electronic components it produces, and for electrical and other machinery, oil, medical equipment and cars. Although serious tensions exist between Japan and China, they are consistently among each other's top three trading partners. The United Kingdom imports about 40 per cent of its food, and

Japan imports the majority of its food: 60 per cent. The list goes on and on.

And, of course, all of the problems that are pushing us towards a planetary tipping point, just like that interconnectedness that keeps our societies ticking today, cut across national boundaries as if they weren't even there. Which means that in formulating solutions, we have to do the same. Avoiding a planetary tipping point is going to require getting a critical mass of people in the world to look past cultural differences – because that's all that really separates nations nowadays – and acknowledge that the same things that are threatening you are threatening me.

Attaining that critical mass would be the good kind of tipping point – a social tipping point that sends the world rolling towards increasingly positive changes, rather than the current acceleration of negative ones. A social push, person by person, is the only way that will be achieved. It's all well and good that we know the science behind world problems, and that international and intranational cooperation is starting to happen from the top down, as evidenced by the examples mentioned above. Basing our actions on sound science and top-down governmental action is absolutely essential to providing the required incentives and opportunities for social change. But ultimately, as we've seen from what's pushing us towards the bad kind of planetary tipping point, top-down action is driven from the bottom up. And you, us, and everybody else are what's at the bottom – we're each of us that little person fighting to keep the world from running over us.

Such bottom-up agreement – a critical mass of people deciding that a world problem is important enough for us to cross cultural and national boundaries and get the job done – is what mobilised the solutions to past global problems that were every bit as complicated as those we're dealing with today. Consensus in world opinion pushed global leaders – in government, industry and non-profit organisations – to get down to business and accomplish the Green Revolution, which saved billions of people from starving; to develop the Montreal Protocol, which reversed the dangerous expansion of the ozone hole; to provide the means to rebuild Europe and Japan after the devastation of World War II; and to come to agreement on nuclear disarmament. Within nations, too, attaining a critical mass of public opinion is what it takes to turn bad societal norms to good ones – for example, in the United States, the banning of the harmful pesticide DDT after its health effects became apparent, and the eventual abolition of slavery, even though that went against what most white people thought was economically advantageous. Abolishing slavery, however, took civil war to accomplish – the type of terrible transition that can be the inevitable outcome of people digging in their heels too deeply for personal gain. It's clearly much better to take the route of reason at the outset.

But what exactly is that route? How do we get to the good kind of tipping point marked by billions of people clamouring to fix the global problems we have covered in this book? Or, to phrase it another way, how does each and every one of us actually become the person keeping the world from going over the cliff in that tipping-point illustration we gave to California's Governor Brown? This is the point at which you may be rolling your eyes and thinking, 'OK, now they're going to tell us to change our lightbulbs, buy a hybrid car, recycle, stop eating so much meat, and use condoms.' Sure, you can do those things, and they'll help. There are whole books and websites devoted to giving you a checklist of such lifestyle tweaks that actually do make a difference. But before you ever get there, there are two simple steps that are even more important: embrace the present reality, and communicate the future.

By *embrace*, we're not talking about holding hands on Earth Day, though there's nothing wrong with that either. We're talking about embracing the very real need to deal with the global challenges we have covered in this book. Climate change, very real limits to food and water, increasing pollution and likelihood of epidemic disease, social conflicts – all these are already happening, and will only get worse with increasing numbers of people on Earth and with increasing overconsumption. Whether or not you believe in the idea of a planetary tipping point, it's virtually certain that if nothing changes the trajectory of these dangerous trends we've been following the past few decades, by mid-century the world will be a less pleasant place to live. And that the only way out of the mess is to recognise that the whole world is connected these days, and that leveraging common interests, rather than emphasising national and cultural borders, is the way of the future. Embracing those ideas, and what they mean for you and your family, is the first step to taking action. Once you do that, you will have reached your own personal tipping point, where you want to advocate and contribute to actions to solve these serious global problems.

The second step, critically important, is to *communicate*. Acknowledging the seriousness of the problems yourself is not enough. You need to talk to your friends and family about the issues we cover in this book, and give them your perspective on why they are important, because the only thing that is going to shift the planet away from the bad end game we're headed for and towards the good one is big, big numbers of people wanting to do so. The messages to communicate are what the problems are and how essential it is to address them, starting now; that we have the technological wherewithal to solve them; and that all that is standing in our way are cultural and political boundaries, a stovepipe mentality that keeps us from working together across the political aisle and across the world. And, of course, you need to communicate these things to your leaders at local, national and international levels. You do that by who you decide to put in government, and when you buy things, by where you decide to spend your money. World leaders, both in government and in business, have no choice but to respond to what their constituents or their customers demand of them, when those demands get loud enough.

The reason you can't leave the communication to someone else is because you are the one that people in your social circle are going to trust. All the words in the world don't mean a thing if people have convinced themselves that those speaking them are not trustworthy – and usually the people outside your social circle, whatever their credentials, are going to be deemed less trustworthy than you. People are diverse, with different upbringings, cultural connections and motives for doing what they do. So while a religious group, for example, might find it compelling to deal with climate change or environmental contamination out of moral considerations, the CEO of a major company might more readily respond if he sees it's good for the bottom line. And the right brain/ left brain thing is very important too: the way an artist spreads the word is going to be very different from the way a scientist, engineer or economist normally would. That's where you make the difference – by using your individual perspective to educate your own social group about the crossroads the planet now finds itself at.

That effort will probably be more successful than you think. True, some of the people you run across are going to be dead set against everything we've said in this book, while others are going to be already on board. Neither group will be very willing to change their minds. But don't worry too much about that, because the statistical reality is that most people you know won't have thought too much about these things, so they won't have a strong opinion on them one way or the other. If you want the numbers, they probably work out as about 20 per cent who have decided global environmental issues aren't worth worrying about, about 20 per cent who already want to see them fixed, and then the majority – about 60 per cent – who have not yet formed an opinion.

That breakdown comes from studies that look at attitudes that cut across cultural groups and sort people into three different categories, as explained by Liz's colleague at Stanford, Eric Lambin, whose research focuses on how humans interact with their environment. As he points out in his book *The Ecology of Happiness* (University of Chicago Press, 2009), about 20 per cent of us are 'altruists', who feel a strong obligation to work for the common good. Another 20 per cent are 'free riders', who look out for their own self-interests with little regard for the impacts on others. And then there are most of us, the 60 per cent who are 'conditional cooperators', a reasonable bunch whose opinions can be swayed back and forth, as logic and their needs dictate. Not to say that free riders can't be swayed to an action when it seems in their best interests, but it's really that undecided 60 per cent who hold our future in their hands, and those are the people to really target in your social group. With every one of them who decides they want to avoid tipping Planet Earth for the worse, we move closer to a tipping point for the better.

In the end, that's how we each hold humanity's future in our hands: by interacting, by who we touch, and how we touch them. As we finish this book, we're still uncertain where all the human interactions that are going on today are going to take the world, though we've been watching that future unfold in a big way over the years.

Over five decades, these global pressures have become all too real for us, both from our travels and from our perspective as scientists who study environmental change for a living. In our journey through life we've seen, up close and personal, the human suffering, the poverty, hunger, thirst and loss of life that are all too common today. And in being on the front lines of research into environmental tipping points, we see the writing on the wall: the bad things that will certainly get worse if we don't deal with the problems we've highlighted in this book.

We also know now how personal tipping points work. We've grown from young scientists mostly concerned with finding out how the natural world works, to wanting to make the world we love even better for our two daughters. Over the past twenty years we've seen them grow from babes in arms to young adults, and go over their own tipping points, from depending on us for pretty much everything to heading off on their own world adventures. Now Emma is back from stints in France, Spain and Latin America, and Clara is studying in London. Neither aim to become scientists; both want to become global communicators. Their eyes are bright, there are smiles on their faces, and they're looking forward to what comes next, as are the many, many young people our professions so happily bring us in contact with. Their generation's vision and hope of the future is vibrant cities, joyful, healthy friends and families, and nature they can enjoy. That, and the glimmers of change that we've seen from world leaders over the past couple of years, plus the incredible power of human innovation and ability to fix past global problems, gives us hope.

So there you have it. What our heads tell us, and what our hearts desire. At the end of it all, though, reality has to prevail. The world really is poised to roll in one of two different directions. One direction leads us right over an environmental tipping point that is exemplified by the machete-fight world with which we opened this book. The other direction leads to the bright future that our children want, and that we all want. Ending up at that future requires building communication bridges, and enhancing our global awareness, to the point that a critical mass of the global society and world leaders recognises our current environmental problems as real, and begins fixing them before it's too late. If we can get to that kind of tipping point we're in good shape, because we've already got much of the technology we need, and people are incredibly clever when they're motivated.

Back here in the present, though, we know it could go either way, and that the world is running out of time. Our heads tell us, wait too long, and we're just going to have to make do with the bad end game we're given. But our hearts are desperately rooting for the other outcome, the one where the positive things in our world grow, and the bad things diminish. In the final analysis, our heads and hearts come together to tell us that the end game we will actually see depends not on the path we take alone, but on the path that each of you decides to take as well.

ACKNOWLEDGEMENTS

Many, many people have helped us as we progressed through the years and coalesced the material we've written about here, starting with those important teachers and mentors long ago. For showing us the scientific ropes, providing opportunities and being role models in various facets of our professional lives, we extend heartfelt thanks to: Guy Abramo, Gretchen Daily, Mary Dawson, Rodolfo Dirzo, Anne Ehrlich, Paul Ehrlich, Chris Field, Don Grayson, Seymour Hakim, Frances Lefcort, Estella Leopold, J. David Love, Malcolm C. McKenna, V. Standish Mallory, Hal Mooney, Joanna Mountain, Jim Patton, Anita Pearson, Oliver Pearson, Dmitri Petrov, Uma Ramakrishnan, John Rensberger, Steve Schneider, Paul Shankman, John Varley, David Wake, Marvalee Wake and William A. Watts.

We have also had the pleasure of working with many fine colleagues on the research that resulted in the publication 'Approaching a State-Shift in the Biosphere' (*Nature* 486:52–56), which stimulated us to delve deeply into the concepts of tipping points, complex systems, and what they mean for Earth's future. That study would not have come to fruition without our amazingly smart, creative, diverse and diligent co-authors, who attacked the weighty questions from their respective areas of expertise: ecology, network and complex systems theory, palaeontology, population biology and conservation biology. We gratefully acknowledge their essential role in the scientific work and for being a great group to work with, the combination of which made working on that project so enjoyable for us. These wonderful people are: Jordi Bascompte, Eric Berlow, Jim Brown, Mikael Fortelius, Wayne Getz, Rosemary Gillespie, John Harte, Alan Hastings, Justin Kitzes, Pablo Marquet, Charles Marshall, Neo Martinez, Nicholas Matzke, David Mindell, Arne Mooers, Eloy Revilla, Peter Roopnarine, Adam Smith, Geerat Vermeij and Jack Williams.

Likewise, we have been enriched by our collaboration with the exceptionally talented group of global-change scientists who co-authored the *Scientific Consensus Statement on Maintaining Humanity's Life Support Systems in the 21st Century: Information for Policy Makers* (http://consensusforaction.stanford.edu/). We thank you all for the groundbreaking work you do on bringing environmental issues to the forefront of the world's attention, and for the critical roles you played in making the *Scientific Consensus Statement* a reality. And, perhaps mostly, for being so easy (and fun!) to work with. In alphabetical order: James H. Brown, Gretchen Daily, Rodolfo Dirzo, Anne Ehrlich, Paul Ehrlich, Jussi Eronen, Mikael Fortelius, Estella Leopold, Hal Mooney, John Peterson Myers, Roz Naylor, Steve Palumbi, Nils Christian Stenseth and Marvalee Wake. And we thank the thousands of scientists and others who have endorsed that document.

Liz is thankful to the Leopold Leadership Program, and particularly to the 2011 cohort for the examples of 'fearless and charming' environmental leaders they continue to exemplify. They are: Joe Arvai, Elena Bennett, Liz Canuel, Greg Characklis, Leah Gerber, Jessica Hellmann, Andy Hoffman, Tracey Holloway, Hope Jahren, Marco Janssen, Raghu Murtugudde, Lincoln Pratson, Ted Schuur,

Acknowledgements

Marty Smith, Valeria Souza, Jake VanderZanden, Jack Williams, Elizabeth Wilson and Dawn Wright. We both appreciate the brainstorming opportunity, and the enthusiastic suggestions, we had at the ALLP all-cohort reunion in 2012.

On a broader scale, there are many, many researchers whose work we have drawn on in developing our ideas – more than a hundred whose articles we have read and whose work we admire. Some of you we know, some of you we've never met, but we admire all of you for your cutting-edge efforts to understand how global changes really work, past and present. For readers who want to delve more deeply into the science behind tipping points and the related idea of planetary boundaries, we found articles by Stephen R. Carpenter, Timothy Lenton, Johan Rockström, Marten Scheffer and Will Steffen especially helpful. Googling these names and looking at the list of articles that come up will lead you to many other scientists who are doing excellent work on environmental tipping points and related concepts.

We owe special thanks to California's Governor Jerry Brown and his staff for reaching out to us to learn more about the science behind global-change issues, and for their work on the world stage to solve the problems we cover in this book. Among those in the Governor's office whose effectiveness, talent and affability we've had the pleasure of experiencing over the past year are Ken Alex, Cliff Rechtschaffen, Evan Westrup and Randall Winston.

We are also extremely grateful to our agents, Luigi Bonomi and George Lucas; this book would not have happened without their efforts. Also essential have been the capable staffs at HarperCollins in London (Arabella Pike, Joseph Zigmond, Robert Lacey) and Thomas Dunne/St Martin's Press (Marcia Markland) in New York. Paul Ehrlich kindly read a draft of the book and made helpful suggestions. We thank Cheng 'Lily' Li for her work on the tipping-point illustration and permission to reproduce it.

Heyward Robinson and Marianne Grossman were instrumental in organising the 2013 SSV-WEST Summit, and we thank them for inviting us to release the *Scientific Consensus Statement* there. Joseph (Mike) Horton generously provided useful information.

The institutions we work at – University of California at Berkeley for Tony, and Stanford University for Liz – have afforded us the opportunities to pursue adventures as an integral part of our jobs. How cool is that? The many fine faculty members we've had the pleasure of interacting with at both institutions, and especially our wonderful students, have been a constant source of inspiration. Both of us are hugely encouraged by the knowledge that members of our labs, past, present and future, will continue to work for a better world.

At the University of California at Berkeley, we gratefully acknowledge the support of the Berkeley Initiative for Global Change Biology, which sponsored the workshop that led to the *Nature* article (listed above) that revealed such wide public interest in the concept of planetary tipping points. Tony also acknowledges UC Berkeley's Department of Integrative Biology, the Museum of Paleontology and the Museum of Vertebrate Zoology, all of which actively promote intellectual interactions that in turn help foster new ideas. Barnosky Lab members, past and present, you rock!

Liz is grateful to have her colleagues in the Department of Biology, especially those working on Ecology and Evolution, who set some pretty high bars of scientific outreach. Liz is completely smitten with her lab. Over the years they continue to inspire her with their intelligence, wit and work ethic. What an amazing group they have been, and continue to be. Thank you to Melissa Kemp, Luke Frishkoff, Katie Solari, Hannah Frank, Jeremy Hsu, Alexis Mychajliw, Chase Mendenhall and Danny Karp.

Both of us also thank the Stanford Travel-Study Program, which generously invited Liz to be the faculty leader on many trips around

252

the world, providing us with the opportunity to visit places we might not normally go, some of which we mention in this book. Many of the travellers on these trips are leaders in their own fields, all are curious and engaged, and their stimulating questions and discussions have helped us to articulate the issues we've written about here. The opportunity to teach Stanford 'lifelong learners' is an enormous privilege.

We also appreciate the critical support of the United States National Science Foundation, which over the past thirty years has contributed funding to almost all of the discrete research projects that ultimately helped us in coming to the conclusions we do in this book.

Finally, there are the people who really made us understand how important it is to guide the planet's future, and who themselves have given us so many of life's adventures: our daughters Emma and Clara. Thanks, you two, for sharing what has been an incredible journey so far. There's more to come for all of us!

INDEX

Index

Index

Index